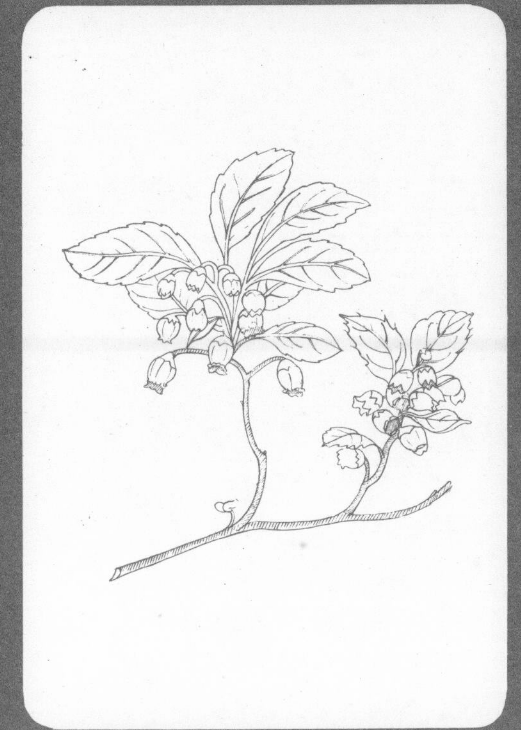

Wintergreen

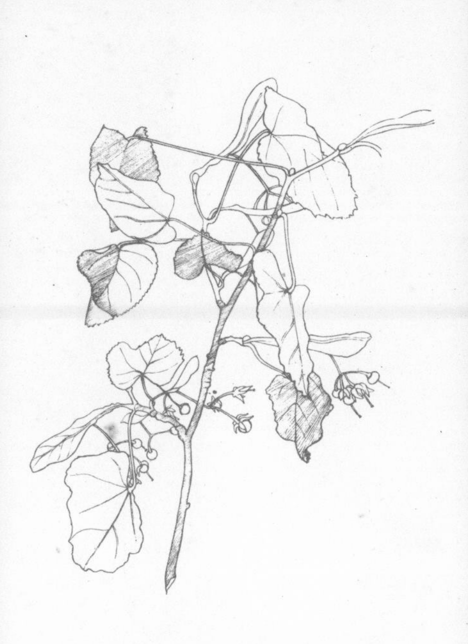

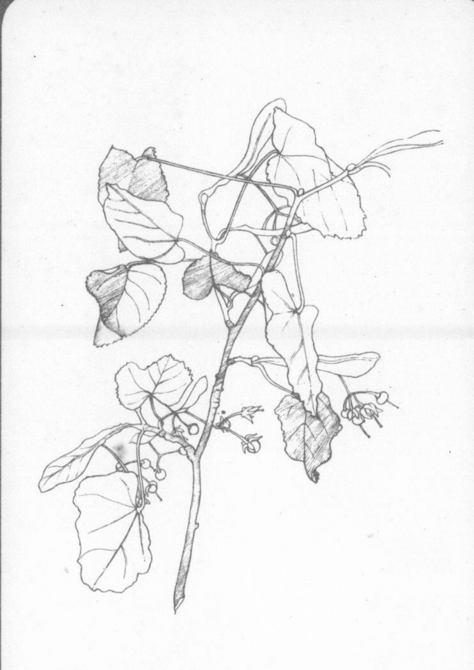

Lime

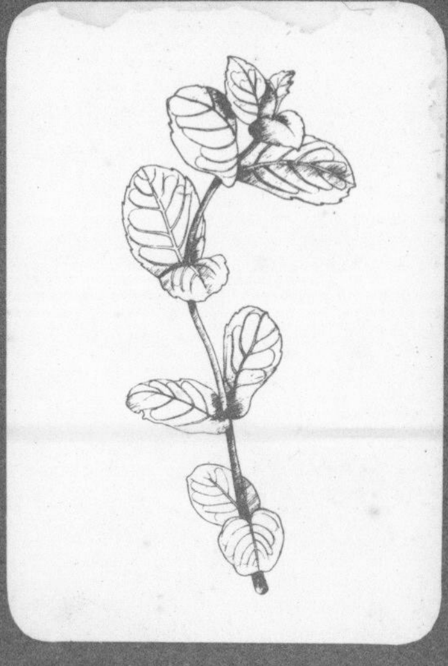

Mint

Witch Hazel

Tarragon

Sunflower

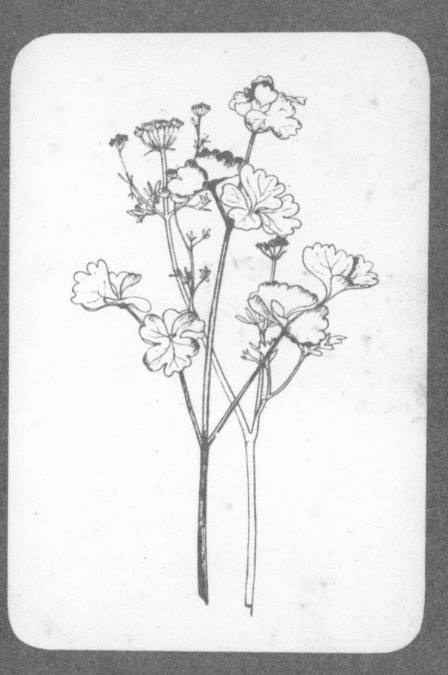

Parsley

The Complete Book of Herbs

Drawings by Edward Russell

The Complete Book of Herbs

KAY N. SANECKI

Macdonald : London

ISBN: 0 356 04701 6

First published in Great Britain in 1974 by
Macdonald and Jane's,
Macdonald and Company (Publishers) Limited,
St. Giles House,
49/50 Poland Street,
London W1A 2LG

Designed and produced by Walter Parrish International Limited,
London

Printed and bound in Spain by Roner S.A., Madrid
Dep. Legal: S.S. 590 - 74

Contents

Color Plates

Acknowledgements

It is to all previous writers on the subject of herbs, and to the recorders of tradition that my main gratitude is directed. Theirs was the knowledge that has provided some of the happiest of my browsing hours and theirs the authority on which I have depended. This present work could not have been accomplished without the co-operation and generosity of Mrs. Gertrude B. Foster, Falls Village, Connecticut, who gave so readily of her knowledge of American plants and practices and engaged with me in a spate of trans-Atlantic correspondence. Especial thanks are due to Edward Russell for his co-operation and infectious attention to detail in the preparation of the illustrations: a task in which he communicated his pleasure. Also to the Committee of Management, Worshipful Company of Apothecaries and to Mr. W. G. MacKenzie, the then Curator of the Chelsea Physic Garden, for providing much of the material for illustration.

Gardeners are notoriously generous in the sharing of their knowledge and my sincere thanks go to my numerous friends and associates in the gardening fraternity, but most of all to John H. Harvey whose enthusiasm proved to be a great source of encouragement. Thanks are also due to the Librarians of the Royal Botanic Garden, Kew, the Lindley Library, the Pharmaceutical Society of Great Britain, the Guildhall Library and the Liverpool City Library; to the Librarians and their staff of the Borough Libraries of Aylesbury, Banbury, and Chesterfield; to the Derbyshire County Council Archivist, Miss J. C. Sinar; and to Dr Harley of the Royal Botanic Garden, Kew, for his work on the genus *Mentha*.

And, always in the background, typing and retyping the manuscript, Miss Christine Brown, whose kindly diligence has proved so helpful.

I should like to thank Mrs. Katharine B. Kavanagh for her kind permission to quote lines by her late husband, Patrick Kavanagh; the lines from "Foxgloves" by Mary Webb were first published in *Poems and the Spring of Joy,* and are quoted by permission of the Executors of the Mary Webb estate and Jonathan Cape as publishers; the extract from *Green Medicine* by Margaret B. Kreig is quoted by permission of the author; and the extract from "The Sunken Garden" by Walter de la Mare is quoted by permission of the Literary Trustees of Walter de la Mare, and the Society of Authors as their representative.

Acknowledgement is also due to the following for the provision of color illustrations: Paul E. Genereux (juniper berries, p. 161); George E. Hyde (borage, p. 35; caraway, p. 89); Elsa M. Megson (bergamot, p. 17; Sissinghurst herb garden, p. 53; Wisley herb garden, p. 53); Harry Smith (jasmine, p. 143; greater periwinkle, p. 179; tobacco plant, p. 197); Western Reserve Herb Society (Western Reserve herb garden, p. 71). The photograph of angelica used on the jacket was provided by Elsa M. Megson. The remaining color photographs were taken by the author.

Tring, 1974 K.N.S.

With us ther was a Doctour of Phisyk,
In al this world ne was ther noon him lyk
To speke of phisik and of surgerye;
For he was grounded in astronomye.
He kepte his pacient a ful greet del
In houres, by his magik naturel.
Wel coude he fortunen the ascendent
Of his images for his pacient.
He knew the cause of everich maladye,
Were it of hoot or cold, or moiste, or drye,
And where engendred, and of what humour;
He was a verrey parfit practisour.
The cause y-knowe, and of his harm the rote,
Anon he yaf the seke man his bote.
Ful redy hadde he his apothecaries,
To sende him drogges and his letuaries.
For ech of hem made other for to winne;
Hir frendschipe nas nat newe to beginne.
Wel knew he the olde Esculapius,
And Deiscorides, and eek Rufus,
Old Ypocras, Haly, and Galien;
Serapion, Razis, and Avicen;
Averrois, Damascien, and Constantyn;
Bernard, and Gatesden, and Gilbertyn.

GEOFFREY CHAUCER
Canterbury Tales

Introduction

Late in the twentieth century, there are distinct signs of popular reaction against the technology which has brought civilization within sight of self-destruction. A greater awareness of the environment, of ecology, and of the balance of nature is starting to provoke a reaction against pollution, over-speculative scientific experiment, and synthetic foods. It is not surprising, therefore, that the value of natural foods and remedies have been "rediscovered."

In their unsophisticated world, our forefathers turned to the plants around them to satisfy some of the basic human requirements—sustenance and the relief of ills and discomforts included; and plants still have a great contribution to make to the solution of many medical problems, as well as providing an immense store of nutritional value. To turn back to growing herbs for both food and medicine is truly to recover an old wisdom.

PART I

A Practical Guide to Cultivation and Use

Making a Herb Garden

There is an old theory that herbs should be grown near the kitchen door, but there is little justification for the practice other than the wish to avoid a change of shoes in wet weather. All plants need a congenial environment, and greater success will reward the kitchen and medicine cupboard if the herbs selected are suited to their situations. For herbs to be cultivated successfully, they must be sheltered from prevailing winds *and* compatible with the soil rather than attempts made to change the nature of the soil. The latter condition is best met if plants are chosen to suit a certain soil; provided that a site is not badly drained or waterlogged, some types of herbs can always be grown. A heavy clay soil is least congenial for herb cultivation, but much can be achieved by the addition of compost, leaf mold, lawn clippings, seaweed, peat, and other humus-forming materials, which will lighten the soil-crumb structure. These materials should also be added to greedy, sandy soils with sharp drainage, in order to enrich them and add the body which can improve moisture retention.

Despite modern soil-conditioners (many of them organic in content) and weed-killers, there is no site preparation as thorough as digging, clearing perennial weeds and debris, then, if possible, fallowing or backsetting for a time. Land that has been disturbed throws up a crop of weeds, as if to convince itself that it can still support plant life; hoeing to keep such squatters at bay for a few weeks, while the urge to start planting the herb garden is resisted, is time very well spent. Humus-forming material may be spread over the surface and hoed in or incorporated into the top layer of soil either before or after the weeds are cleared.

Compost is derived from both kitchen scraps, such as potato peelings, citrus fruit skins, carrot tops, and so on, and garden material—weeds, hedge clippings that are not too woody, pea and potato haulms, spent perennials, lawn mowings, in fact, any organic material that will eventually rot down. Layers of such material should alternate, in a flat-topped heap that is not too large, with layers of good garden soil and a sprinkling of a proprietary compost activator, to form a compost heap. Or a wire or plastic mesh bin can be filled in layers and the contents left to rot down for six months or so. The compost is ready for use when it forms a soft crumbly brown mass.

A chalky soil is one of the few that are really difficult to change; the addition of horticultural peat, compost, and manure all help to reduce the iron-locking alkalinity; and the use of sequestrene and other such products does help to combat the iron starvation of plants (chlorosis), which is signaled by a marked yellowing of foliage. However, many herbs are not only tolerant of lime and chalk but prefer the conditions such soil offers; lavender, rosemary, dianthus (pinks), chicory, verbascum, mignonette, and cinquefoil are a few examples. Weeds are usually a fairly general indication of soil type, and moss on the surface suggests poor drainage and extreme lime conditions. Simple soil-testing equipment can be bought to identify a particular soil type, but for successful herb cultivation, as for all gardening, the land should always be in good heart before a start is made.

The long-term plan to grow a hedge as the boundary of a herb garden is a good one; it will prevent drying winds from snatching at the plants and robbing them of their aromatic qualities. And the unity of the design will enhance the herb garden itself. Informal hedges of roses, rosemary, lavender, sage, or artemisia provide a rustic effect as well as color and a minimum of labor; but a formal evergreen hedge of holly, yew, or laurel will add an air of permanence and seclusion and make the perfect backdrop. Where an old wall or house wall forms the boundary of the site on one or more sides, it is probably best to choose a lower informal hedge to complete the enclosure unless a very secluded herb garden is desired or the area is windy.

No one would describe the majority of herbs as first-class plants where a striking garden or foliage effect is required, but the best herb gardens have a delightful atmosphere of their own, and they evolve either from a collection of particularly decorative varieties or from use of plants in a repeated theme complemented by a bold design of formally shaped beds. The collection is personal, the choice of plants can be made from a universal range; but once assembled, these plants will display the curious harmony characteristic of every herb garden. The design and theme are limited only by the site: a level site provides the best canvas for a formal garden, but a sloping site can be given form with terraces or steps and still be used in a formal way. Statuary, pot plants, roses grown on posts—all go a long way towards creating a well-integrated effect.

With a circular or rectangular outline, a series of interesting designs can be achieved; perhaps the best effect is to trace the outline of each bed with plants of the same kind: santolina, violets, chives, box, red sage, or pinks are possibilities. The simplest design is to imitate the rim and spokes of a wheel, marking these out in one of the suggested plants and filling each wedge between the spokes solidly with a contrasting plant. The central hub of the wheel can be emphasized with a sundial, a statue, a fountain, a standard rose or small upright formal tree—juniper or a clipped bay tree. Another great favorite for herb collections is the checkerboard design; small square or rectangular beds are formed in staggered rows and the intervening spaces paved with brick or stone. A similar theme is possible where patches of herbs are tucked among the paving stones of a patio garden or terrace; use thyme, penny-royal, chamomile, and mints for a particularly delightful effect, because these emit their fragrance best if crushed underfoot, accidentally or otherwise!

Ideas abound for formal treatment, but if a herb border is planned, the less sophisticated it is, the better. The juxtaposition of plants, if carefully arranged, always creates a pleasing picture as one leaf form or texture acts as a foil for the next, or covers a faded neighbor. In general, the lower growing plants, such as borage, thyme, violets, marigold, nasturtium, feverfew, should naturally be set towards the front of the border and the taller ones, like sage, mullein, melilot, eupatorium, chicory, foxgloves, at the back, with plants of intermediate height in between. To add variety, though, do not adhere too rigidly to this rule.

Not many herbs will tolerate waterlogged conditions and poor drainage; the borders of a stream can be planted with yellow flags, sweet sedges, mints, balsams, marsh marigolds, and monardas. The margin of a garden pool can be embellished in the same way. The making of moisture beds is not usually associated with herb growing; but when spare time and funds allow, a fascinating collection can be assembled, consisting of the bog plants like yellow flag, watercress, acorus, balsams, marsh marigolds, and mints. Moisture beds are not suited to those plants whose roots plumb the depths seeking water but to those whose roots squirm about nearer the surface. By maintaining moist rather than boggy conditions, a wider range of herbs can be included in such a collection. Alchemilla, eupatorium, meadowsweet, bistort, and bergamot flourish in moist conditions.

The selection of plants for a herb garden is even more personal than that made for general planting and garden decoration, because usually a theme is followed and the herb garden may be a culinary array, a scented collection, a muster of medicinal plants, a natural-order garden or, at its simplest, groups of decorative herbs. And there are many plants which fall into more than one category. Following are some lists of herbs for special conditions and situations and those that may be chosen for various types of collection.

HERBS TO CHOOSE FOR SPECIAL CONDITIONS AND SITUATIONS

CLAY SOIL

angelica
chamomile
foxglove
mints
parsley

CHALK SOIL OR LIME

juniper
mignonette
periwinkle
dianthus (pinks)
rosemary
sage

SAND SOIL

broom
lavender
marjoram
rosemary
sage
savory
thyme

MOIST POSITIONS

acorus
balsam
bergamot
bistort
comfrey
meadowsweet
mints (not penny-royal)
watercress
yellow flag

SHADE

alexanders
angelica
chervil
chives
foxglove
lovage
meadowsweet
parsley
poke root
pulmonaria
sweet Cicely
valerian
violet
woodruff

WALLS

epilobium
ferns
feverfew
houseleek
pellitory
thyme
wall germander

PAVING

alchemilla
catmint
cinquefoil
cotton lavender
dwarf lavender
feverfew
penny-royal
thyme
violets

HERBS TO INCLUDE IN COLLECTIONS

COOK'S GARDEN

alecost
angelica
balm, lemon
basil
bay
bistort
borage
caraway
chervil
chicory
chives
coriander
corn salad
cumin
dill
fennel
lovage
marigold
marjoram
nettle
parsley
purslane
rosemary
sage
savory
sorrel
tarragon
thyme
watercress

MEDICINAL GARDEN

agrimony
arnica
belladonna
betony
century
coltsfoot
comfrey
eryngium
feverfew
foxglove
garlic
gentian
hemlock
henbane
horehound
hyssop
licorice
pellitory-of-the-wall
poppy
pulmonaria
self-heal
thorn apple
yarrow

POTPOURRI GARDEN

artemisia
bergamot
catmint
chamomile
cotton lavender
daphne
hyssop
iris
lavender
lily-of-the-valley
marjoram
meadowsweet
mint
rose
rosemary
sweet Cicely
thyme
verbena, lemon

NATURAL-ORDER GARDEN

COMPOSITAE	LABIATAE	LILIACEAE	SOLANACEAE	RANUNCULACEAE	UMBELLIFERAE
alecost	balm	chives	belladonna	aconite	angelica
arnica	basil	garlic	henbane	clematis	chervil
artemisia	bergamot	lily-of-the-valley	thorn apple	hellebores	cumin
chamomile	caraway			pasque flower	dill
chicory	horehound				eryngium
cotton lavender	hyssop				fennel
dandelion	marjoram				lovage
feverfew	mint				parsley
marigold	rosemary				
yarrow	self-heal				

HERBS FOR THE BEES (in order of flowering through the year)

coltsfoot
celandine
laurel
dandelion
elder
hyssop
raspberry
thyme

melilot
poppy
willow-herb
borage
mignonette
meadow-sweet
mullein
marjoram

clematis
sage
mint
balsam
chicory

ASTROLOGICAL GARDEN

SUN:	bay, chamomile, marigold, saffron, sunflower
MOON:	houseleek, purslane, watercress, yellow flag
MARS:	horseradish, lesser celandine, nettle, rhubarb
MERCURY:	calamint, caraway, elecampane, lily-of-the-valley, melilot
JUPITER:	agrimony, alecost, chicory, dandelion, sage
VENUS:	burdock, coltsfoot, elder, mint, violet, yarrow
SATURN:	belladonna, comfrey, hellebore, hemlock, valerian

GARDEN OF DYE PLANTS

RED:	alkanet, dandelion, madder
YELLOW:	cow parsley, saffron
YELLOW/ORANGE:	tansy
GREEN:	yellow flag, lily-of-the-valley
GREEN/BLACK:	elder

opposite Bergamot ('Cambridge Scarlet')

Herbs in the Eighteenth Century

Batty Langley's *New Principles of Gardening* was published in 1728, when it was becoming fashionable to bring many herbs into the kitchen garden—they were no longer confined to the apothecary's gardens and physic collections. In the work was included "The Design of a Complete Fruit, Kitchen and Physick Garden, Containing three Acres, the Walks being Excluded." The relative space apportioned to the various herbs is given here as evidence of their importance in "a Gentleman's household."

The recommended allowance within the three-acre garden was one bed of "Balm, Burgloss, Burrage and Burnet of Each 3 rods; Marjoram and Savory of Each 2 Rods, of Chamomile 4 Rods"; a second bed of "Cardus, Clary, Comfrey, Dragon and Dill of each 2 Rods and Clove Gilliflower Ten Rods." A third bed: "Dwarf Elder, Elecampane, Fennel, Feverfew of each 2 Rods, White Lilies, Lavender Cotton, Lavender Spike and Common Lavender, of Each 1 Rod and of Marigold 6 Rods." A fourth bed: "Liquorish 4 Rods, Mint 6 Rods, Violets 8 Rods and of Tansie 2 Rods." A fifth bed would contain "Angelica 6 Rods, Red and Damask Roses 6 Rods, White Poppie, Rosemary, Red Sage and Tea Sage of each 2 Rods"; a sixth bed: "Marsh Mallow, Saffron, Soloman's Seal, Wormwood, Sage, Scurvy Grass of each 2 Rods, Roman Wormwood 5 Rods, Peneyroyal 3 Rods and of Tobacco and Rue Each 1 Rod." And Langley advises an additional "Sorrel 4 Rods, Succory 4 Rods, Tarragon 3 Rods, Red Sage, Garlic, Rocambole, 2 Rods each and Jerusalem Artichokes 4 Rods."

He also expounds at some length a list of "Distilling and other Physical Herbs, as are absolutely necessary for the Services of all Gentleman's (and other) Families in general—Angelica, Chamomile, Cardus Benedictus, Comfrey, Clove Gilliflower, Dragons, Dwarf Elder, Elicampane, Feverfew, Hyssop, Lavender, Liquorish, Marjorams, Marsh Mallow, Marigolds, Garden Poppy, Rosemary, Garden Rue, Saffron, Savory, Self Heal, Southernwood, Thyme, Tobacco or Yellow Henbane and Violet."

Renovating an Old Herb Garden

There is much to be said in favor of clearing out the bulk of the indifferent plants in an exhausted garden and making a fresh start, since the opportunity is there not only to replan and replenish but also to improve the soil and renovate any existing paths and hedges.

Exhausted plants are best disposed of from an old or overgrown garden, and, once the ground has been thoroughly dug over and cleared of creeping roots and weeds, a new supply of plants can be sown or set out. Lavender bushes that have become leggy or succumbed to disease should be replaced, but where sage has become bare at the base and straggly of growth, it can be saved by building up a mound of soil around the base of the bush, burying the bare stems, and leaving only the tips of the shoots protruding. Quite quickly, roots will form at the leaf joints along the covered stems, and these shoots can be severed and replanted to replace the foundation plant. Box, santolina, roses, rosemary, and artemisias can all be pruned hard to encourage fresh and replacement growth. Stocks of herbs are available from the leading herb nurseries, markets, and some food stores; seed is always available from seedsmen and by mail order, using the catalogues of seed houses.

Cultivation

Annuals such as corn salad, purslane, basil, caraway, dill, summer savory, borage, parsley, sorrel, nasturtium, marigold, marjoram, and fennel may be sown in flats, boxes, or pots during March or better still directly into the ground in rows in a seedbed (or at their actual stations) during late April and May, once the soil has warmed. These plants will germinate, flower in most instances, and set seed in a great burst of activity before the onset of winter.

The biennials, such as verbascum, woad, and foxglove, with their more leisured approach to life, germinate and form good basal leaves the first summer, huddle through the winter, and produce flowers—and sometimes seed—the second year. Both annuals and biennials die after flowering and setting seed. For both annuals and biennials sown directly in the garden, thin out, then keep the weeds down by hoeing carefully. If there is a drought, make sure the growing plants receive extra moisture. For those started in boxes, or in a cold frame, transplant when the seedlings have a second set of true leaves or as soon as they are large enough to handle. Try to disturb the roots as little as possible. Give them enough room to grow. In those parts of the world where it is necessary to harden off the plants when the last frost is over, do so gradually by moving the containers to a protected, sunny spot outdoors during the day. After a few days, leave them outdoors overnight and finally transplant again to their final position.

Perennial herbs include sage, lavender, rosemary, artemisia, comfrey, lily-of-the-valley, mint and thyme; they make an all-the-year-round decorative contribution to the garden and come up with renewed growth each spring. Some of these can be raised from seed initially, but all can be propagated by division, taking cuttings, or by layering; the rooted young plants will be ready to move to their own stations the following spring.

There are a few perennial herbs that disappear completely below ground during the winter and are rather slow in making their reappearance the following year. It can come almost as a surprise to the herb grower to see that they are still resident in his garden. Sweet Cicely, on the other hand, sometimes hides below ground only over Christmas and the New Year and reappears with the snowdrops. Some perennials need help through damp winters; hailing as they do from native soils parched with sunshine and moistened with winter rain and sea spray, they show their disgust by behaving miserably or abandoning the struggle altogether. Protection of a mulch of peat, chopped bark, or leaf mold will frequently encourage these plants to endure, or a cover of polythene will allow them to survive in sweet oblivion until the spring.

Providing plants with shelter from prevailing winds is equally important in winter and summer; furthermore, wall protection is even more beneficial in winter, as the soil is usually drier at the base of a wall and the benefit from any sunshine is retained longer. It is not the low temperatures themselves that cause winter damage, but the dampness, fluctuations in temperature, and, frequently, early-morning sunshine on frozen plants, which thaws the leaves too quickly and causes the stems to rot.

Harvesting and Drying

The moment to harvest, what to harvest, and how to harvest are all points to be carefully considered. The time and expense of cultivation can be forfeited in an instant by incorrect harvesting and, even more certainly, by careless drying. There are five general rules for harvesting herbs: (1) gather when dry; (2) take only the part of the plant required; (3) select clean, representative plants; (4) keep types of herbs separate; and (5) handle as little as possible. Assuming that cultivation is on a domestic scale, the cardinal rule is not to gather too much material. Harvest only a quantity that can be dealt with the same day, for allowing freshly cut material to lie about encourages deterioration. The average yield is about eight pounds of fresh material to provide one pound of dried herb. In general terms, plants contain something like 70 to 85 percent water, and the objective in drying them is to remove the water content without affecting the other plant properties. Gather the clean herbs on a dry day—wherever possible, once the dew has cleared—putting the material directly into flat, shallow boxes or baskets, on to domestic trays, or, for a small quantity of plants, newspaper. It is essential to keep each type of plant separate to avoid adulterating the perfumes.

Sometimes, the whole herb is cut and used either in branches or sprigs (thyme, tarragon, rosemary and mint are usually treated in this way) or the leaves are removed after drying. Clipping off fairly large shoots is quicker and facilitates handling, but never rob a perennial plant of so much growth that it will suffer. Some plants, like santolina, catmint, and marjoram, can be cut with hand shears; otherwise, it is best to use a sharp knife, secateurs, or even good scissors.

The best time to harvest herb leaves is usually just prior to flowering, when the entire plant is of more vigorous and buoyant growth than at any other time of the season—this is the point at which the strength and effectiveness of the active principles are greatest.

Roots are harvested in autumn when the top growth has passed maturity and starts to die down; it is at this stage in the plant's development that the roots contain the maximum amount of stored food and in consequence are richest in active principles. Roots are used of plants such as valerian, eryngium, medicinal rhubarb, orris, hellebore, and yellow gentian.

Flowers are at their best just as they are first fully open. Gathering the petals the day before the flowers reach maturity rather than the day after is to be preferred, for much essential oil can be protected. Lavender flowers destined for drying, dianthus (pinks) for use in potpourri, violets for crystallizing, or borage to float in wine cups are best treated in this way. Care in handling cannot be overemphasized, as bruised petals are of little value, and the crushing of even one flower against another should be avoided. Such flowerheads as those of elder and cowslips for use in making wine are usually piled or put into crocks—the cowslips to be removed from their calyces by hand, and the elder flowers so that the corollas will loosen before they are worked free of the flower stalk.

Wherever leaves and shoots are going to be dried indoors, the room must be at the required temperature before the freshly gathered material is introduced; the ideal initial temperature is approximately 90°F. for about twenty-four hours, after which it can be reduced to 75 or 80°F. to finish off the process. The object is to reduce the water content as quickly as possible in the early stages of drying, and if this is done briskly, shriveling of the material is prevented. Shoots and leaves may be laid out in single-depth layers on sheets of newspaper, on trays, tables covered with paper, or in shallow boxes, and ought to be turned every few hours to encourage even drying. Stems of plants should be laid uniformly side by side, as this will save considerable time when handling them, once dried. Never introduce fresh material into a room where drying is in progress, or the first flush of moisture from the newly imported plants will be reabsorbed by the previous batch. Drying is complete once the stems and leaves snap easily but do not shatter. Leaves may then be pulled from stalks or rubbed off; the rubbing-down process is best done in a very slight current of air. A wise precaution is to wear a smog mask and to keep domestic animals out of the room for some hours. The dried herbs can finally be stored in bulk or in small quantities, according to requirement. Tightly lidded glass jars are best, but if the jars are made of clear glass they should be stored in a cool, dark pantry—light will fade the colour of the herb, and humidity will make them limp and encourage molds.

The first requirement is to make sure the herbs are not left in the sun after they have been gathered or during the drying process. Direct sunlight or artificial light will dissipate the natural oils, and perfume and flavor will both suffer.

Gather and prepare the shoots as quickly as possible, and avoid over-handling or bruising. The circulation of air is also important, which is why the leaves should be in a single layer and never piled up in heaps.

Obviously very few households are equipped with a special room suitable for drying herbs, and so very often a substitute has to be found. Perhaps the most convenient place is a spare room where the thermostat can be adjusted to raise the temperature (which should always be below 95°F. or the leaves will cook). Stack the trays on a table, making sure there are spaces between them for the air to circulate. Keep the room dark; alternatively use an oven, which has been set at the lowest temperature. Turn off the heat, and set an oven themometer inside the open door; when the temperature drops below 90°F., put in the trays of herbs and leave them for a little while, watching them closely.

A simple method of preserving herbs is by deep freezing. This retains the color and flavor very well, although the crisp texture will be lost when the herbs are thawed and they will be unsuitable for garnishing. Harvest and wash the herbs in cold water if necessary; shake off traces of excess moisture; remove leaves from stems, or in the case of chives, chop the leaves; place in a single layer on a plate or a tray. Put the tray in the freezer for a few minutes, until the herbs are firm. Carefully pack into small freezer bags (labeled beforehand), close tightly, and store in the freezer. Be careful not to put the bags underneath heavier cuts of meats or other packages. Bunches of herbs, for *bouquet garni* for example, may be prepared and frozen in the same way.

Another method is to blanch the herbs before freezing in the same way that vegetables are prepared for preservation. The washed herbs should be prepared by removing the stalks, or for chives, chopping, and put into an enamel colander. Blanch in boiling water for a minute, drain the excess liquid and pack loosely into freezer bags; freeze at once.

Seed must be harvested when it is mature, and while this sounds easy, a year or two of experience is usually needed to assess the precise moment. The whole plant or just the flower stalks can be cut and hung upside down to dry. Tie herbs loosely together, and hang from rafters or lines strung across a warm shed or covered yard, or a spare room or attic. Brown paper or newspaper spread below will catch any seed that is released; it is essential to deal with only one kind of plant at a time in this way. An alternative method is to enfold each bunch of plants in a large paper or cheesecloth (muslin) bag to catch the falling seed. Shake the bag before removing the stems and dried flower heads, which are discarded. A third method which can be used only in good summers and in the warmer regions of Europe and America, in areas where humidity is not too high, is to cover the maturing seed heads of the plants in the garden with similar bags, fastening the base of each bag around the stem firmly to trap the seeds. In this case, humidity is an enemy, and so, plastic bags are not suitable. Once the seeds are collected, transfer them to glass or china bottles or jars, with tight-fittings lids; the oils will not be absorbed by the glass as they would by paper or unlined wooden containers. Metal foil is suitable for keeping seeds destined for use as flavoring or in tisanes, and it should be folded a number of times to make air-tight packages.

Berries, which are really fleshy seed vessels, need to be gathered fully ripe but before the flesh darkens or softens. These may be dried off, spread out on paper, or—with small berries that grow in large clusters, like elderberries—may be hung in a dry, dust-free place for a week or so.

Potpourri

According to the Oxford English Dictionary, potpourri literally means "rotten pot" (from the French verb *pourrir* "to rot"), and was originally intended to mean a dish of various meats stewed together. Essentially a potpourri is a homogeneous mixture of flower petals and aromatic leaves together with spices and stabilizing agents; no single perfume should predominate. Once made, potpourri is stored in sachets, jars or bowls to perfume rooms, cupboards and drawers. Porcelain bowls have been made for two or three centuries specially to hold potpourri and can sometimes be found in antique shops, but there are also modern pottery containers easily available.

Recipes vary: some old ones have survived but others are too vague and unnecessarily complicated, requiring expensive and rare ingredients. Flowers with thick fleshy petals like hyacinths and lilies are not suitable ingredients because they do not dry well. Roses, carnations, lavender and honeysuckle ought to be collected immediately before they reach full maturity, and preferably after the dew has disappeared. Plants vary in the time of day when they give off their perfume most freely, usually coinciding with the timetable of the insects to be attracted for fertilization. For example the honeysuckle exhales its sweetest scent in the evening when the long-tongued moths are on the wing. However, it is difficult for the flower-gatherer to wait for the critical period for each flower, and it is more important that the petals be as dry as possible when collected.

Pluck the petals individually from the gathered flower heads and spread them out on foil-covered trays. Cover with additional foil or waxed (greaseproof) paper. Alternatively, spread them on a garden sieve, wooden tray or even cheesecloth stretched across a frame. Do not use plastic sheeting—it retains the moisture instead of letting it evaporate. Always cover with paper or foil and set out of doors during the day in a shady place to dry; take trays indoors at night. In unsuitable weather, especially if it is breezy, put the drying trays in a glasshouse where the atmosphere is buoyant and not humid, in a warm garden shed, or even in the warming drawer of an oven for a little while. Once the petals are papery but not too brittle, they remain dry and usually retain their color quite well. The time required to achieve the correct stage of dryness varies according to the moisture content of the individual flower; roses and carnations, for example, take longer than lavender or mignonette. Suitable flowers to include are roses, especially the highly scented varieties, pinks, carnations, honeysuckle, mock orange, lavender, stocks, sweet peas, mignonette, thyme, heliotrope, lily-of-the-valley, lime flowers, and a ligustrum, together with aromatic leaves such as rosemary, lemon verbena, choisya, scented-leaved geraniums, southernwood and sweet bay. Some wild herbs develop stronger aromas when they are dried, notably woodruff and bedstraws, and can also be added. Dry the leaves separately, then rub through a five-meshed sieve before adding to the petal mixture. To prepare the citrus peel (which is usually lemon although some recipes call for orange peel as well), pare the fruit very finely, discarding all the white pith, and then dry the peel in the warming drawer of the oven on a baking sheet. The dry peel can be finely minced.

In these days of short-cuts, oil of lavender and a special preparation—a potpourri maker or a potpourri reviver—can be used. For those so minded, an additional recipe has been given—the cheat's potpourri. All the recipes are fairly flexible, and other spices and flowers can be added as experiments.

Some Potpourri Recipes

An Elizabethan Recipe

Collect enough fresh rose petals to fill a half-gallon bucket or basket; sprinkle with 3 ounces of common salt. Leave for 3 days. Stir in 2 ounces finely rubbed bay salt, 2 ounces allspice, 2 ounces cloves, 2 ounces brown sugar, $\frac{1}{4}$ ounce gum benzoin, 2 ounces orris root, 2 tablespoons brandy, 4 ounces lavender heads, 4 ounces verbena leaves, and 2 ounces geranium leaves.

Put the mixture into a large stone crock. Stir every 3 days for a fortnight and if the mixture appears to be dry and lose its scent add a few more drops of brandy; a moist potpourri such as this has a stronger, and more lingering perfume than a dry mixture.

An Elizabeth II Recipe

Mix a quart measure of dried rose petals and a cup of mixed flowers of rosemary, lavender, lemon thyme, with the very finely mixed rind of one orange and one lemon. Leave for 24 hours then add a teaspoon of allspice, $\frac{1}{2}$ ounce crushed cloves and 6 dry bay leaves that have been pounded with the rolling pin. Add $\frac{1}{2}$ ounce of orris root to retain the perfume and stir the mixture daily for a week, after which it may be stored in bowls.

Connoisseur's Potpourri

A more expensive and complicated recipe begins with a quart measure of rose petals dried with 2 handfuls of common salt for a week. Mix in a large cupful of various dried flowers (lavender, rosemary, pinks, summer jasmine and honeysuckle), 3 dried, crushed sage leaves and a sprig of thyme. Blend together $\frac{1}{2}$ ounce each of cinnamon, crushed cloves, nutmeg, allspice, and 2 ounces orris root. Stir this into the rose petal mixture, pare and dry the rind of 2 lemons, and add, together with the juice. Leave for 24 hours. Oil of geranium, oil of bergamot and spirit of lavender can all or severally be added at the rate of $\frac{1}{4}$ ounce each.

Traditionally, the following recipe was said to last effectively for fifty years. Pick a peck of roses; the petals are removed, scattered with three-quarters of a pound of common salt and left for two or three days. Incorporate half a pound of finely powdered bay salt, the same quantity of allspice, cloves, brown sugar, a quarter of a pound of firm benzoin, two ounces of orris root. Add half a cupful of brandy and any kind of fragrant flowers and leaves such as lemon verbena, artemisia, carnation, jasmine, pink, lavender and heliotrope. Stir the mixture occasionally and keep it in closed jars, only raising the lid when the aroma is to be enjoyed or the room to be perfumed. If, after a time, the potpourri appears to dry, moisten it by adding brandy.

The Cheat's Potpourri

Beg, steal, buy roses, carnations, sweet peas, and lavender; gather from the fields meadowsweet, elderflowers and honeysuckle, dry the petals, and toss in a drop or two of oil of lavender, 3 crushed cloves, powdered cinnamon, borrowed from the neighbours, and 2 or 3 teaspoonsful of brandy as "medicinal". Scatter in the box of potpourri sent by Aunt Agatha four Christmases ago. Mix the ingredients together, add a drop or two of potpourri reviver and even one drop of a favourite floral perfume. Put into jars.

Petal Sachets

Gather fresh unbruised rose petals from scented roses once the dew has dispersed and spread them out to dry on paper, cheese cloth or muslin in a warm shaded place. Crush them slightly with a rolling pin, add a pinch or two of powdered orris root and a drop of oil of roses or oil of geranium. Put the mixture into muslin or taffeta bags of various shapes and decorated according to whim with embroidery, ribbon, lace or beads. The newly revived interest in handwork and Victorian crafts can be put to good domestic use. The sachets are spread among linen or suspended in wardrobes where their perfume adds a refreshing aroma.

Lavender, gathered before fully in flower, can be dried and rubbed from the stalk and used in lavender bags and sachets without the addition of any blending agent. Other sweet-scented flowers and leaves, dried first alone or in a potpourri, can be put into little bags or pillows. Rose geranium, lemon verbena, thyme, rosemary and lavender leaves combine with pinks, rose petals, marjoram, verbena, woodruff, artemisia and bergamot and a host of other sweet-smelling foliage and blossoms to provide suitable contents for

Lavender Bags

Apart from using lavender flower buds to fill scented sachets, small wicker baskets can be bought, or made, to fill with the perfumed flowers. Lavender spikes themselves, if carefully handled, can be braided or woven into pretty shapes; it is easier to work with them before they are absolutely dry to avoid breaking the stems. Braid or weave the stems alternately with mauve and white ribbon for additional decoration, and to form loops for hanging up the little decorations.

Moth Deterrents

Dry thyme, tansy, southernwood and rosemary and crush under a rolling pin on paper, or if a quantity is being dealt with put into an electric blender for a minute. Add ground cloves and put the mixture into nylon, muslin or organza bags to suspend in wardrobes. Ideally the mixture should be equal proportions of the dried ingredients, with 4 heaped tablespoons of leaves to each heaped tablespoon of dried cloves. This mixture should be firmly packed into appropriately small bags of sachets.

Beauty Treatments

Plants of the field and hedgerow have been used for many generations in the avowed belief that they have virtues of beautifying and pampering the skin. A recipe used to prevent wrinkled skin is made from poppies *(Papaver rhoeas)*. About twenty petals infused in a pint of boiling water and left to stand in a warm place for about ten minutes, strained, cooled and stored may be used to bathe the skin as a freshener, and is especially soothing to a dry skin.

For broken veins—those tiny thread-like blemishes that come from over-exposure to wind and weather—use an infusion made of a handful of leaves of wintersweet *(Hamamelis virginica)*. Let stand for ten minutes before straining and cooling. Use the tepid lotion on soaked cotton pads and bathe the face night and morning for one week in each month, especially during the winter.

Cornflowers, called *bleuet* by the French because of their value in enhancing the eyes, can be made into an eye wash. Boil half an ounce of flowers in a quart of water, starting by putting in the flowers when the water is cold and bringing them to the boil very slowly. Allow to simmer for ten minutes, strain, refrigerate and then use the liquid to bathe the eyes. When chamomile tea has been made, do not throw away any that remains in the pot, but cool it and use it in the same way as an eye bath.

For hair beauty, the least expensive preparations are those from plants. The root of *Saponaria officinalis,* soapwort, chopped into small pieces and infused for ten minutes, allowing about two ounces to a quart of water, makes an excellent soft soapy water for use instead of the second shampoo on fine or soft hair.

Perfume

The Greeks and the Romans used flowers and herbs for perfumery—but like many Roman arts, perfumery vanished from Europe during the Dark Ages. The Crusaders brought it back from its place of first origin, the Middle East. In Elizabethan times the Italians were the most famous perfumiers in Europe, and later the French, who had been organized into a guild as early as 1190. By the end of the sixteenth century, scented nosegays were commonly used to ward off diseases and unhygienic odors, a custom that persisted almost to the end of the nineteenth century. The horrors of the plague years are forever enshrined in the rhyme of "Ring a Ring o' Roses"—the line "A pocket full of posies" represents the vain efforts to escape the dreaded symptomatic ring of rose-colored spots. According to tradition, thieves and criminals who preyed on the plague-infested cities relied greatly on perfumes and tonic waters for protection against infection.

In the reign of Charles I a soap-manufacturer named Yardley paid the King a considerable sum for the monopoly of soap-manufacture in London. George Yardley, born in 1588, was to be an important figure in the development of the New World; his family were to be famous for their cosmetic products. He set out from England in 1609, and after an eventful voyage including a shipwreck arrived at Jamestown, Virginia. He was a vigorous and active man, and became a large landowner. He was a motivating force in the formation of the Elective Council, the first North American legislative body—not before a brief return to England, the reception of a knighthood there and marriage to one Temperance Flowerdew, herself related by marriage to the Earl of Leicester. Yardley was an important figure in the development of Virginian agriculture, and in particular the export of tobacco. By 1629 in England the tobacconist's became an accepted trade; the tobacco habit spread rapidly during the century, together with the taking of snuff.

Tobacco manufacture was a trade secret throughout the seventeenth and eighteenth centuries, but licorice and lavender were common components. Herbal snuffs and tobaccos were developed, including one popular "smoking mixture" made from coltsfoot leaves gathered once all the flowers had faded. The coltsfoot was hung in bunches to dry until yellowish in appearance and the mid-rib could be stripped from the lamina. Then young leaves were gathered from the comfrey and woodruff plants, and the horse-chestnut tree.

PART II
Herbs in Cooking

A Brief History

For centuries, herbs have played a vital role in making food more palatable. Although it is usually difficult to find archaeological evidence of seasonings, poppy and caraway seeds have been found at Swiss prehistoric lake sites and were most probably used as condiments. We know, too, that herbs were cultivated for culinary purposes in the early gardens of Assyria and Babylon; these include thyme, basil, bay, mint, cumin, coriander, sage, saffron, and fennel. The onion family was also known and cultivated at the time. It is probable that herbs were used as seasonings in Egypt as well, although more is known about their use in cosmetics and perfumery.

In the years when Rome was most powerful, an extraordinary number of herbs were used in foods cooked for the upper classes. Very little was eaten without a sauce or dressing of some kind, and herbs were an essential ingredient in the flavoring of these sauces. Although certain herbs and spices were imported from the East, great use was made of those plants which grew locally—especially mint, thyme, dill, lovage, rue cumin, and savory. Bread and cakes were flavored with poppy seeds, bay, fennel, and anise.

About 230 A.D., the Greek writer Athenaeus compiled *The Deipnosophists* ("Banquet of the Sophists, or Learned")—a highly informative anthology which is one of the most important sources for food descriptions of the period. It confirms the use of a number of herbs, as does the first real cookbook: *De Re Culinaria* ("About Culinary Matters") is of uncertain date and authorship; although Apicius who lived in the first century A.D. is usually credited with writing it, the only known copies date from the eighth and ninth centuries.

In England, a book of recipes was compiled about 1390 by Richard II's cooks and called *The Forme of Cury* (the old English word for "cooking"). The recipe for "King Richard's Salat" is brimful of herbs, including parsley, onions, leeks, mint, and rosemary. In France, *Le Viandier* ("The Meat Cook") was compiled about 1375 for the cooks of Charles V; its recipes feature a particularly heavy-handed use of both herbs and spices.

The first printed cookbook appeared in Renaissance Italy in 1475 and was Platina's *De Honesta Voluptate,* a title which has been translated as "Permissible Pleasures." Further proof of the importance of herbs is provided by Platina who gives advice on how to use herbs in cooking, emphasizing their medicinal properties. In England, *The Boke of Cokery,* 1500, was the first to be printed. Eighty-eight years later saw the publication of *The Good House-Wives Treasurie,* again featuring the heavy seasoning for which the period is noted, as well as an extensive use of flowers, both in salads and as sweetmeats. In 1615, the most influential of the early cookbooks—Gervase Markham's *The English House-Wife*—indicates that herbs were as popular as ever.

In the eighteenth century, numerous women wrote English cookbooks; two of the recipes from Eliza Smith's *The Compleat Housewife* are "Roast Beef with Horseradish and Pickles Around" and "A Hare with Savoury Pudding" (stuffing), with herbs again vital ingredients for flavoring. Dr. Kitchiner's book, *The Cook's Oracle,* 1817, is interesting for his specialties—condiment sauces and ketchups seasoned with herbs—which were the forerunners of today's commercial bottled sauces.

In America, the settlers were naturally influenced by their origins and their traditional ideas about food and cooking, taking with them some of the herbs of their native lands. Eventually, they also learned to use new plants found in the new land and to adapt some of the methods and ingredients popular with the Indian tribes. In 1796, the first cookbook appeared containing authentic American recipes; this was Amelia Simmons' *American Cookery,* giving plain recipes using native fruits, vegetables, and home-grown herbs. The recipe for cookies, for instance, uses coriander seed; coriander was planted in America, around 1670, by some of the very earliest colonists.

In 1828, the prolific Eliza Leslie published *Seventy-five Recipes for Pastry, Cakes and Sweetmeats* (though it included recipes for meat, sauces, etc.). Herbs feature in these recipes as they do in her *Domestic French Cookery,* 1832, indicating the growing American interest in French cooking. Herbs were also predominant in two books of southern American cookery: *The Virginia Housewife* by Mrs. Mary Randolph, published in 1824, and *The Carolina Housewife* (1847) by "A Lady of Charleston."

Today, the "cooking with herbs" cult runs the risk of being carried to absurdity in many kitchens, where racks and shelves are filled with rows of glass bottles—each labeled with a name reminiscent of a scented garden—containing enough dried leaves and seeds to cater for posterity! Most culinary flavorings can be appreciated when used only in tiny amounts and with the utmost discretion. Advice to those about to "cook with herbs" then, is first to catch your woodcock, then add a *pinch* of herbs. Palates vary and the strengths of the herbs themselves vary, and so experiment is the key for the adventurous cook, though the rules for the most frequently used herbs remain constant. Add basil, nasturtium, garlic, and tarragon judiciously, and with care; use rosemary, and thyme with caution until their flavors have been learned; mint, parsley, marigold, and chervil can be added more generously. The sweeter tastes are not so easily overdone. Violet, sweet Cicely, lemon balm, elderflower, burnet, and rose can always be used with confidence, especially in the preparation of sweetmeats.

RECIPES

Appetizers and Dips

CHEESE FINGERS

US		*UK*
½ cup	margarine	4 ounces
½ cup	all-purpose flour	4 ounces
½ cup	finely grated cheese	4 ounces
	a few drops of lemon juice	
	a pinch of salt	
1	egg yolk	1
	poppy or fennel seed, or sage leaf	

A quick savoury (appetizer) to serve with apéritifs; to make the cheese pastry, rub the margarine and flour together between the palms of the hands until it makes a crumbly dough. Add cheese, a squeeze of lemon juice, and a pinch of salt. Knead into a dough, adding a teaspoon of cold water if necessary. Brush with egg yolk, dust with poppy seed or fennel seed or rub with a bruised fresh sage leaf. Bake quickly for 8–10 minutes at 400°F. These cheese fingers may be served hot or cold.

HERB CREAM

US		UK
2/3 cups	heavy cream, whipped	¼ pint double cream
2½ tablespoons	fresh chopped herbs (any combination of parsley, lemon balm, sorrel, mint, dandelion, bistort, and fennel) or dried herbs which, reconstituted with lemon or orange juice, make the same amount	2 tablespoons
	grated rind of ½ lemon or orange	
about 2 dozen pieces altogether	cucumber "cups"; thick slices of cucumber hollowed out lightly on one side	about 2 dozen pieces altogether
	celery "boats"; 2″-long pieces of celery sticks	
	watercress to garnish	

Add chopped fresh herbs to the whipped cream; if using dried herbs, reconstitute first with either lemon or orange juice. Whichever citrus fruit is used, the grated rind should also be added to the cream. Parsley, lemon balm, sorrel, mint, dandelion, bistort, and fennel may be used in combination, or any two or three together. Spoon the cream into cucumber or celery pieces, or simply onto lettuce leaves; garnish with watercress. If the cream is whipped stiffly it can be used for spreading on canapés and served with cocktails or drinks before dinner.

HERB CHEESE

US		UK
1 cup	cream cheese or cottage cheese	8 ounces
2½ tablespoons	fresh or reconstituted dried herbs (as in preceding recipe) or use chives, watercress, caraway seed	2 tablespoons

Cream cheese or cottage cheese may be used in precisely the same way as the cream in the previous recipe, but naturally it will not need whipping! Chives, watercress, and caraway seed are alternative ingredients. The cheese provides an appetizing and nourishing accompaniment to prawns, shrimps, or smoked fish or may be served decorated with grapefruit segments or used to fill halved avocados. For sandwich fillings, cream cheese can be flavored with mint, watercress, or caraway seed.

HERB DIP

US		UK
2½ cups	plain or natural yoghurt	1 pint
3½ tablespoons	fresh tarragon, sage, parsley, or lovage	3 tablespoons
	pinch of cayenne pepper	

Combine natural or sweetened yoghurt and fresh herbs, perhaps tarragon, sage, parsley or lovage; blend well and season with a little red pepper. Serve with cheese sticks, celery sticks, or toast fingers, or the dip may be served in avocado halves or melon cups.

POTTED CHEESE

US		UK
1 cup	left-over cheese	8 ounces
$\frac{1}{4}$ cup	butter	2 ounces
1 teaspoon	brandy	1 teaspoon
	herbs or spices to season	

Using cheese and butter in the proportion of 4 to 1, there are several cheeses which may be creamed together with butter and stored. What was once an old domestic economy to keep surplus cheese also provides a tasty spread. Cream the soft cheeses—such as Stilton and Roquefort—together with the butter, a teaspoonful of brandy, and a dash of pepper. Chopped sage, oregano, basil, or rosemary may be added in small quantities. The harder cheeses, like Cheddar, must be roughly grated before being incorporated with the butter and brandy, and they can take more flavoring. Spices such as mace or nutmeg and a dash of cayenne pepper will add an extra touch of seasoning. Caraway, lovage, or fennel can also be used for variety. In all cases, after thorough blending, the mixture may be potted in wide-necked jars and covered with clarified butter. If the spread is to be consumed within the week, wrap the mixture in foil and store in the refrigerator. Remove an hour or two before serving to allow the fullness of the flavor to develop.

TOMATO CHEESE SPREAD

US		UK
$\frac{1}{2}$ cup	cottage cheese	4 ounces
$1\frac{1}{4}$ tablespoons	tomato purée	1 tablespoon
1 rounded teaspoon	peanut butter	1 teaspoon
	basil, tarragon, or rosemary to taste	

Combine cottage or curd cheese with tomato purée and peanut butter until evenly blended. Add warm-flavored herbs, such as basil, tarragon, or rosemary, to taste. This makes a delicious sandwich filling. Spread on canapés for cocktail hors d'œuvres decorated with slices of stuffed olives. It may also be put into ham rolls or stuffed into prunes and dates.

TOMATO CUPS

US		UK
4	large tomatoes	4
1 cup	cream cheese or cottage cheese	8 ounces
$2\frac{1}{2}$ tablespoons	basil, oregano, and chives, or watercress, dandelion, and sorrel	2 tablespoons

Cut the tops from the large tomatoes. Scoop out the pulp, and put in a bowl. Leave the cups to drain upside down while you make up the herb cheese. Mix the pulp with the herb-cream cheese. The best herbs to use with tomato are basil, oregano, and chives, but watercress and dandelion or sorrel are also delicious. Fill the tomato cups with the cheese, garnish with watercress or parsley, and serve on lettuce leaves.

Soups

Soup was for centuries the mainstay of the peasant diet and the quickest and most hospitable hot snack available. Andrew Boorde, a doctor and sometime monk, writing in 1542 in *A Compendyous Regyment, or a Dyetary of Health*, says: "Potage is not so moch used in al Crystendou as it is used in Englande." Then, "pease potage" and "bean potage" were common indeed, these vegetables apparently used mainly for making soup. Fennel was much used for flavoring soups and broths, and various vegetables were added for more sustenance and additional flavor. The hard bannock-like bread of the day was soaked or dipped in it, providing a filling and tasty meal.

CHEESE SOUP (URNER KÄSESUPPE) FROM SWITZERLAND

US		*UK*
½ cup	butter	4 ounces
1½ tablespoons	flour	1 tablespoon
5 cups	cold water	1 quart
1½ teaspoons	caraway seeds	1 heaped teaspoon
	crushed garlic clove (optional)	
½ cup	Swiss cheese (Emmental)	4 ounces
1 cup	milk	scant ½ pint
	nutmeg to garnish	

Melt the butter in a pan, add the flour, and brown. Remove from the heat and add cold water all at once. Cover immediately until the spluttering and steaming stops, add a heaped teaspoonful of caraway seeds and stir to render the soup smooth. Simmer gently for 15 minutes, season to taste, adding a crushed clove of garlic, if liked. Add the grated cheese and a cupful of milk. Cook for a further minute or two without boiling; serve sprinkled with nutmeg.

CHERVIL SOUP

US		*UK*
4 tablespoons	butter or oil	3 tablespoons
3 tablespoons	fresh chopped (or green-dried) chervil	2 tablespoons
2 tablespoons	flour	1½ tablespoons
1 tablespoon	cold water	1 tablespoon
4 cups	hot vegetable stock	1½ pints
	pinch of salt and white pepper	
1 tablespoon	fresh or sour cream	1 desertspoon

Sauté fresh, chopped, or green-dried chervil in the butter or oil. Add the flour, dilute with a little cold water or cold stock, then add the hot vegetable stock and a pinch of salt and white pepper. Cook for 20 minutes and add fresh or sour cream shortly before serving.

CHICKEN SOUP

US		*UK*
1	chicken carcass	1
5 cups	stock (or water and white wine in the ratio 3:1)	2 pints
2	shallots	2

1	bay leaf	1
¾ teaspoon each	thyme, parsley, marjoram, summer savory	½ teaspoon each
1 stalk	celery, diced	1 stick
	salt, white pepper	
⅓ cup	pearl barley (optional)	2⅔ ounces

The carcass of a chicken will provide a good foundation for an excellent broth; any remaining skin is best removed to avoid fattiness. Boil the carcass in stock (either fresh or made with a stock cube), or water and white wine, or water and hard (rough) cider. Add the shallots (for the delicacy of their flavor), the herbs, diced celery, and a good pinch of salt and white pepper. Simmer in a covered pot of 1½ hours. If desired, the addition of pearl barley will remove any remaining greasiness. The flavor of the soup is surpassed only by its marvelous aroma while cooking. An alternative method of preparation is to mince any left-over chicken and add it to the stock.

HERB SOUP

US		*UK*
3 tablespoons	butter or oil	2 tablespoons
3 tablespoons	flour	2 tablespoons
5 cups	well-flavored stock	2 pints
3 tablespoons	freshly mixed chopped herbs or dried mixed herbs (equaling the same amount reconstituted)	2 tablespoons
⅛ pint	cream	3–4 tablespoons

Using either dried or fresh herbs (preferably not mixing the two), a rich soup of delicate flavor can be made: Make a roux by melting the fat, adding the flour, and work gently until it amalgamates into a cream. Add a well-flavored stock and cook for 10 minutes. Meanwhile, mix together the chopped herbs (tarragon, lovage, and parsley is a good combination) with the cream in a large mixing bowl; let it stand for about 10 minutes. Add the thickened stock, blend well, and leave for half an hour. Reheat, but do not let it boil, and serve. If dried herbs are used, the flavor will be brought out better by sprinkling them onto the roux, and cooking them with the stock for 15 minutes. Add the cream immediately before serving.

POTATO AND PARSLEY SOUP

US		*UK*
2 pounds	potatoes, peeled and sliced	2 pounds
2	large onions, peeled and sliced thinly	2
5 cups	stock	2 pints
	salt	
1 teaspoon	flour (or cornstarch) to thicken	1 teaspoon
½ cup	milk	¼ pint
3 tablespoons	chopped fresh parsley	2 tablespoons
	grated cheese to garnish	

This thick, economical soup is closely linked to the "potage" of the seventeenth century.

Use large onions and potatoes, peeled, sliced, and cooked in the stock until they are very soft and may be mashed easily: add salt to taste and a little flour or cornstarch to thicken. Bring to boil, stirring constantly; add the milk; gradually scatter the chopped parsley into the creamy liquid and stir well; pour the soup over grated cheese in a warm tureen or grate cheese over the surface of the soup as it is served.

SORREL SOUP*

US		UK
2 handfuls	fresh sorrel	2 handfuls
2	shallots	2
4 tablespoons	butter	3 tablespoons
2 tablespoons	flour	1½ tablespoons
2 tablespoons	lovage	1½ tablespoons
1 teaspoon	rosemary	1 teaspoon
2 cups	chicken stock	⅘ pint
2	egg yolks	2
1 cup	cream or evaporated milk	⅓ pint
	croutons, or some cream to garnish	

"Remove midribs of sorrel leaves by folding the leaves and tearing the center rib from the top down. Chop it fine and cook in butter in which minced shallots have been browned. Stir constantly until sorrel becomes a purée. Blend in sifted flour, chopped herbs, salt and pepper; add chicken stock; bring to a boil and add egg yolk and cream. Turn off heat and stir until slightly thickened. Serve hot with croutons, or cold with a dab of thick sour cream. The finest herb soup I have ever tasted was made with ten different varieties of herbs, including wild sorrel and Good King Henry."

ANOTHER SORREL SOUP

US		UK
2–3 handfuls	fresh sorrel, washed thoroughly	2–3 handfuls
1½ tablespoons	butter	1 tablespoon
3 tablespoons	flour	2 tablespoons
	or	
2–3	floury, cooked potatoes	2–3
3 cups	stock	1¼ pints
	salt and pepper to taste	

Wash the fresh sorrel leaves very well and remove them from the stems. Put them into a large pan with butter. Put the pan over a very low heat; no liquid is required if they are cooked with extreme care. Press the leaves occasionally with the back of a wooden spoon and once they are tender, sprinkle with a little flour and then add stock very slowly and gradually to ensure that no lumps form. Instead of the flour, an alternative is to break the cooked potatoes to thicken the purée. Add salt and pepper to taste.

SORREL SOUP MAIGRE†

"Having washed and drained well two or three handfuls of sorrel, chop it very fine. Put it into a saucepan with a quart and a half of cold water, half a pound of butter, a tablespoonful of purée of sorrel, and salt and pepper sufficient to season it. As soon as the water

*Courtesy of Gertrude B. Foster, from her book *Herbs for every Garden*.

†From *Gardeners Chronicle*, 1881.

begins to boil, beat up the yolks of six eggs with sufficient milk to dilute them, and pour into the saucepan, stirring all the time. Let it boil for about five minutes, and serve with toasted or fried pieces of bread."

TOMATO SOUP

US		UK
1 cup	fresh, over-ripe tomatoes, puréed	8 ounces
	or	
½ cup	canned tomato purée	4 ounces
1 teaspoon	fresh (or green-dried) lovage or Sweet Cicely and parsley	1 teaspoon
½ teaspoon	basil	½ teaspoon
3 cups	water or light stock	1¼ pints
2½ tablespoons light cream or sour cream	cream	2 tablespoons single or soured cream
	few drops of lemon juice	
	sprinkling of chives or Parmesan cheese	

Fresh, over-ripe tomatoes may be puréed, or use canned purée; either becomes the basis of a quick, delicious thin soup. Add herbs, preferably fresh or green-dried, and the water or stock. Simmer for about 20 minutes. Blend in the cream, and add a squeeze of lemon just before removing from the heat. Serve sprinkled with Parmesan cheese, or chives if prefered.

A quick first course can be made by using a prepared tomato soup and adding ½ teaspoon of three or four of the following herbs: dried or fresh parsley, basil, chervil, lovage, summer savory, chives, or marjoram.

WATERCRESS SOUP

US		UK
1 bunch	watercress, thoroughly washed	½ pound
1 teaspoon	butter	1 teaspoon
2½ cups	well-flavored light stock (chicken or veal)	1 pint
2 teaspoons	cornstarch (corn flour) as thickener	2 teaspoons
1 cup	cold milk	8 ounces
¼ cup	cream	3 tablespoons
	a few sprigs of watercress to garnish	

Remove the thick stalks from the watercress and wash the leaves very thoroughly. Melt the butter and add the watercress; toss it lightly over a gentle heat (flame) for 2 or 3 minutes. Add stock, a pinch of salt and pepper, and simmer gently in a covered pot for half an hour. Purée in a blender or rub through a sieve, then reheat. Mix the thickener with the cold milk, and the puréed watercress, bring to the boil and simmer for 5 minutes. Blend in the cream just prior to serving, and garnish with a few sprigs of fresh watercress.

opposite Borage

CLAM CHOWDERS

The chowder controversy between New England and Manhattan is a delicate subject, and it has become more than a question of one's palate! Creamy New England chowders, ideally made from the soft-shell (or long-necked) clams are a hearty, nourishing one-course dish; the Manhattan chowder, using the hard-shell (or quahog) clams, is far more sophisticated—a thinner, less-filling soup made with tomatoes.

MANHATTAN CLAM CHOWDER

US		*UK*
36	clams, thoroughly washed	3 dozen
¼ cup	diced pork	2½ ounces
¼ cup	butter	2½ ounces
3 tablespoons	chopped onions	2 tablespoons
	crushed garlic clove	
2 tablespoons of each	finely chopped green pepper diced carrot	1⅓ tablespoons of each
1 cup	canned tomatoes	8 ounces
½ cup	chopped celery	3–4 sticks
	salt and freshly ground pepper to taste	
6 cups	cold water	2½ pints
3 cups	diced potatoes	1 pound
3 cups liquid	the liquid from the clams plus water	1¼ pints
3 or 4	cloves	3 or 4
2	crumbled bay leaves	2
2 sprigs each	parsley and thyme	2 sprigs each

Strain the liquid from the well-washed clams and reserve; then mince or chop clams. Sauté the pork in the butter until golden, add the chopped onions, a crushed clove of garlic, the finely chopped green pepper, diced carrot, and 2 tablespoons of the celery. Add the minced clams, tomatoes, the remaining celery, and salt and pepper to taste. Cook for a moment then add the cold water and diced potatoes. Bring to boil, then reduce the heat, and simmer for 10 minutes. Blend in the chopped clams and the liquid and water mixture (cider may also be used). Add, in a cheesecloth or muslin bag if preferred, the cloves, bay leaves, and a few sprigs of parsley and thyme. Simmer for 20–30 minutes.

NEW ENGLAND CLAM CHOWDER

US		*UK*
36	clams	3 dozen
¼ cup	diced pork	2½ ounces
¼ cup	butter	2½ ounces
2	sliced onions	2
6 cups	potatoes, peeled and diced	3 pounds
	salt and freshly ground white pepper to taste	
2 cups liquid	the liquid from the clams, plus water	¾ pint liquid
2	bay leaves	2

2 cups	milk or cream	¾ pint
	flour to thicken (optional)	

Wash the clams very well and cook over a low heat for a few minutes until the clams open. Mince or chop them, retaining the liquid from the shells. Sauté the diced pork in the butter; add the sliced onions, potatoes, salt and freshly ground pepper to taste. Stir in the liquid from the clams and the additional water. Crumble the bay leaves into the soup, or use a teaspoon of thyme tied in a cheesecloth or muslin bag. After a few minutes, add the chopped clams, the milk or cream and thicken with flour if desired. Simmer for 20–30 minutes.

HERB DUMPLINGS

Herb dumplings or savory fritters may be served with a wide variety of thin soups and broths. When served with soup, dumplings are best made in small balls. Add to the basic ingredients of a favorite dumpling recipe, thyme, marjoram, parsley, or mixed dried herbs. Savory fritters, including those using mixed *fines herbes*, can be cut into strips or rings and added to the soup immediately before serving.

Egg Dishes

The bland flavor and smooth consistency of cooked eggs makes them an ideal medium for the cook who wishes to experiment by adding different herbs to vary the flavor. *Fines herbes* can be strewn over omelettes and scrambled egg dishes as well as into baked eggs. If possible, use chopped fresh herbs; the flavor is really much better when combined with eggs.

EGGS IN ASPIC

US		*UK*
8	poached eggs	8
1 can	consommé, chilled	1 tin
	tarragon sprigs for decoration	

Eggs in aspic may be flavored with *fine herbes* or sage or bay. Pop a poached egg into the base of a greased ramekin dish and top it with almost-jellied cold consommé from a can. Add a tip of tarragon sprig for decoration; chill in a refrigerator until set. This simple dish, accompanied by a good mixed salad, makes an appetizing snack or light supper.

EGGS IN PASTRY

US		*UK*
½ cup	short pastry to make 4 small pastry shells	¼ pound
½ cup	thick white sauce, flavored with chopped parsley and tarragon	¼ pint, scant measure
4	poached eggs	4

Make up short pastry, according to your favorite recipe, roll out and cut into rounds; these should be baked blind (empty) in patty or muffin tins. While they are baking, poach the eggs. Make up a little thick white sauce, flavored at the last minute with chopped parsley and tarragon, put a spoonful into each pastry case and slip the poached egg on top. Serve at once.

HERBED EGGS

US		UK
4	hard-boiled eggs	4
	pinch of salt and pepper	
2 teaspoons	finely chopped parsley, chives, and tarragon	$1\frac{1}{2}$ teaspoons
1 tablespoon	yoghurt or sour cream	2 teaspoons
	sprig of parsley or watercress to garnish	

Allow an egg for each person. Hard boil the eggs, plunge into cold water, and shell immediately. Remove the yolks and combine them together with a little salt and pepper, finely chopped parsley, chives, tarragon, and the yoghurt or sour cream until the mixture is smooth. Spoon the mixture back into the egg whites, heaping it carefully; cool in the refrigerator for an hour or so before serving. Cover the dish with foil to prevent the yolk from hardening. Garnish with sprigs of parsley or watercress, or add a salad of carrot, chicory, and celery.

EGGS WITH SORREL

US		UK
1 pound	sorrel leaves	1 pound
$\frac{1}{3}$ cup	water	$\frac{1}{8}$ pint
1 tablespoon	butter	1 ounce
	salt and pepper to taste	
8	hard-boiled eggs	8
$\frac{1}{4}$ cup	light (single) cream	2 ounces

Sorrel is not to be despised as a vegetable, and a century ago, it was far more widely grown than it is today. Served with eggs, it can provide a nourishing meal. If the flavor seems a little too sharp, spinach and sorrel may be used in equal quantities, or the proportion changed according to taste. Wash the leaves, chop them, and bring to boil in salted water, or preferably stew them slowly in the oven in a fireproof dish, in which a little water, a knob of butter, and salt and pepper have been put. Cook until tender; meanwhile, mash the hard-boiled yolks with cream, then blend into sorrel, stirring to mix in smoothly. Allow two eggs per portion. Garnish the dish with the chopped whites of the eggs.

Salads

Salads always lend themselves to imaginative presentation. Ingenuity, economy, festivity, and artistry can all be achieved in the making of a salad, whether of fruit, vegetables, or cereals. In many European languages, the name is nearly the same: *salade* (French), *insalada* (Italian), *salate* (Russian), *ensalada* (Spanish), *Salat* (German); and every old book on cookery, kitchen garden herbs, and housekeeping includes "Sallet Herbs." The old proverb is a good guide: To make a perfect salad, four people are needed; a miser for the vinegar, a spendthrift for the oil, a wise man for the salt, and a madcap to combine the ingredients thoroughly. The dressing is obviously the most important ingredient of a salad. Writing in 1728, Batty Langley described the use of "sallet herbs" in *New Principles of Gardening*, stating that the tender shoots of a penny-royal could be used: "the quantity . . . is at pleasure"; but of samphire for salad use, he laid down the proportions: "when a sallet is composed of four kinds of herbs there must be of Samphire one fourth part, when five kinds, one fifth, etc." Tusser in his over-quoted *Five Hundred Points of Good Husbandrie*, 1573, listed twenty-one "Herbs and roots for sallets and souce"—including one or two items that might be surprising to twentieth-century tastes.

Stipulated proportions of the chosen ingredients seems to have been the rule: John Evelyn in his *Acetaria—a Discourse of Sallets* (1629) not only considered the most particular detail of dressing and ingredients but drew up a chart for salad plants, indicating their proportions when used together. The comparison of blanched and unblanched leaves, method of "ordering and culture," month of harvest, and proportions for inclusion are given for a long list of plants, all of which were then "sallet herbs." Evelyn's discourse includes "alexanders, artichaux, basil, baum [balm], bett, blite [mercury], brooklime, bugloss, buds [broomtops, capers, etc.], cabbage, carrots, chevile, clary, clavers, corn sallet, cress, cucumber, daisy, dandelion, dock, elder, endive, fennel, flowers (for sprinkling, but give more palateable relish being infused in vinegar; especially those of clove gilly-flower, elder, orange, cowslip, rosemary, arch-angel, sage, nasturtium, mint, bugloss), goat's beard, hops, hyssop, Jack-by-the-hedge or sauce alone, leeks, lettuce, limon, mallow, mercury, lemon, mushrooms, mustard, nettles, onion, orache, orange, parsnip, pease, pepper, parsley, pimpernel, purslane, radish, rampion, rocket, rosemary, sage, samphire, scallions, scurvy grass, sellery, skirrets, souree, sowthistle, sparagus, spinach, succory, tansy, tarragon, thistle, trick madame [stonecrop], turnep, vipers grass, wood sorrel. There are besides several remaining which tho' abdicated here with us, find entertainment still in foreign countries."

This throws light on the culinary tastes at the turn of the seventeenth century. Surprisingly, Evelyn highlights the change in status of the gourmet's favorite, cucumber: "The cucumber itself, now so universally eaten, being accounted little better than poyson, even within our memory." Evelyn continues on the preparation and serving of salads, "What care and circumspection should attend the choice and collection of Sallet herbs, has been partly show'd. I can therefore by no means approve of that extravagant fancy of some, who tell us that a fool is as fit to be the gatherer of a sallet as a wise man. Because, say they, one can hardly choose amiss, provided the plants be green, young and tender where-ever-they-meet with them. . . ." And issuing warnings against collecting poisonous plants inadvertently, Evelyn adds the flourish of the true connoisseur: "Thus by the discreet choice and mixture of the Oxoleon [oil, vinegar and salt] the composition is perfect. . . . The saladiere (Sallet dishes) be of *Porcelane* or of the *Holland Delft-Ware*. . . . the sallet gatherer likewise should be provided with a light and neatly made *Withy-Dutch-Basket* divided into several partitions." A wicker or cane basket is still the lightest and most convenient kind for collecting fresh salads and vegetables from the garden.

GREEN HERB SALAD

Mix lettuce, endive, chicory, or cabbage heart in desired proportions and sprinkle generously with fresh chopped herbs. Toss well with a classic French dressing, made with wine vinegar, olive oil, salt and pepper, all well blended. A squeeze of lemon juice is a piquant variation. Herbs to use in this way are tarragon, dill, chervil, watercress, chives, and rosemary.

PRUSSIAN SALAD

US		*UK*
4	pickled herrings or smoked trout	4
8	new potatoes, cooked and cooled	8
4	eating apples, medium size	4
4	gherkins, or small pickles	4
2 tablespoons	capers	2 dessertspoons

1	garlic clove	1
½ cup	diced cooked beet (beetroot)	4 ounces
	Dressing	
	olive oil and tarragon vinegar in ratio 3:1	
	chopped chives, parsley, and chervil to taste	
	salt and pepper to taste	

A delicious salad can be made by using pickled herrings or smoked trout. Dice the fish and chop the potatoes, apples, and gherkins. Rub the garlic clove round a bowl, put in the fish, apples, gherkins, and add the capers. Make the dressing to taste from olive oil, tarragon vinegar, chopped chives, parsley, and chervil, Toss the salad well in the dressing and allow it to marinate for an hour or so before serving. Immediately prior to serving add the diced beetroot—if this is added earlier it will "bleed" over all the ingredients to the detriment of the salad's appearance.

A very similar dish is recorded as Flemish salad, using pickled herrings and mixing in cold cooked Brussels sprouts, carrots, celeriac, new potatoes, and apples. French haricots may be added sliced and again a dressing of olive oil, tarragon vinegar, chives, chervil, and tarragon added. A few minutes before serving, bind the salad with two or three table-spoons of mayonnaise.

Herb Vinegars

Vinegar is an acid liquid prepared from a variety of plants which produce acetous fermentation; this, in the presence of oxygen, becomes acetic acid. It may be made from wine, cider, rice, corn (maize), and many other vegetable substances. Wine or cider vinegar is normally used in the preparation of herb vinegars and any one herb such as burnet, chives, lavender, mint, parsley, tarragon, basil, marjoram, lemon thyme or lemon verbena, or chervil may be used. Alternatively, rose petals may be used to make rose petal vinegar. The proportions are roughly half a cupful of fresh herb leaves, or two tablespoons of green-dried leaves to a pint of liquid; this may vary with the strength of the herb. The liquid is frequently made up of equal parts of white wine vinegar and dry white wine.

A number of herbs lend themselves to blending with vinegar, imparting flavor. The most popular in general use is tarragon vinegar, which is made with a sprig of the whole herb. The method is to pour the vinegar over the herbs in a wide-necked glass or porcelain jar and to allow it to stand for two or three weeks, stirring daily. After straining, the liquor may be bottled and stored and makes a delightful, delicately flavored salad dressing. It is usual, in the case of tarragon, to store a fresh spray in the bottle when the vinegar is finally bottled.

What some cookery recipes call "salad vinegar" seems to be made by pounding tarragon, summer savory, chives, mint, and balm and covering with wine vinegar for two weeks, then straining through a fine cheesecloth bag or very fine sieve and bottling the vinegar.

Lavender vinegar, an intriguing variety, is made by steeping several lavender spikes in white wine vinegar in the sun. Push the spikes into a bottle of wine vinegar and re-cork the bottle; stand on a sunny windowsill for two weeks. Strain, rebottle, and store until required for use as a salad dressing.

Fish Dishes

The mild flavor of most fish must be considered when cooking with herbs. Add just enough to present an intriguing piquancy, but not to mask the true taste of the fish.

COD WITH HERBS PROVENCALE

US		UK
1 pound	cod, cleaned and filleted	1 pound
1 clove	garlic	1 clove
1 teaspoon of each	chopped parsley, tarragon, and basil	1 teaspoon of each
	pinch of salt	
¼ pint	white wine	2 ounces
	sprinkling of freshly ground black pepper	
1 small can	tomato purée	1 small tin
1½ cups (uncooked)	rice	¾ pound

Crush the garlic clove and rub it over the fish, then cut cod fillet into cubes or small pieces. Sprinkle on the chopped parsley, tarragon, and basil. Sprinkle a pinch of salt and a quarter pint of white wine over the fish, adding a sprinkling of black pepper (preferably freshly ground). Allow to stand for an hour, basting occasionally to encourage the flavors to combine. Meanwhile dilute the small can of tomato purée with an equal amount of water and warm in a pan, bringing it just to boil. Lower the heat and carefully slide in the cod and all the seasonings. Simmer for 20 minutes. Serve on a bed of rice.

MUSSELS IN CIDER

US		UK
4 cups	mussels	1¾–2 pints
1 cup	cider	½ pint, scant
1	bay leaf	1
2–3 sprigs	parsley	2–3 sprigs
1	small onion, chopped	1
2–3	fennel seeds	2–3
	standard Béchamel sauce made with liquid from the mussels	
1½ tablespoons	spinach purée	1 tablespoon

Wash the mussels very well, and scrub clean, cutting off the beards. Gently simmer them in a cupful of cider—using just enough to cover them—with a bay leaf, the parsley, onion, and fennel. Once the mussels open (usually a matter of a few minutes), remove them and strain off the liquid. Make a standard Béchamel sauce, using the cider-mussel liquid and the spinach purée, or sorrel and spinach purée; stir well and cook to thicken. Mix the cooked mussels into the sauce, and turn everything into a fireproof casserole dish. Bake in a moderately hot oven for 20 minutes.

BAKED SOLE

US		UK
2	fresh sole	2
⅓ cup	butter	3 ounces

1	medium onion, finely chopped	1
1 tablespoon	chopped parsley	$\frac{2}{3}$ tablespoon
	pinch of tarragon and thyme	
$\frac{1}{2}$ cup	dry white wine	large wine glass
	liberal sprinkling of breadcrumbs	

Clean and remove the back skin of the fish. Put the knobs of butter into a fireproof dish, and sprinkle the bottom of the dish with finely chopped onion and parsley and a pinch of tarragon and/or thyme. Place the fish on top and sprinkle with a little more parsley and onion and a glassful of dry white wine. Cover the whole liberally with breadcrumbs and a dot or two of butter and bake for half an hour in a medium oven, about 375°F. Broil (grill) for a few minutes prior to serving in order to brown the crumbs. Any white fish fillets may be treated in the same way.

TROUT TARRAGON

US		*UK*
4	plump trout	4
$\frac{1}{3}$ cup	butter	3 ounces
	bunch of tarragon leaves	

Clean and dry the trout. Make several diagonal incisions in the flesh on both sides and into each, tuck a few leaves of tarragon and some butter. Set the fish on one side for an hour or so to let the flavor of the tarragon permeate the flesh. Then brush with melted butter; broil (grill) for 4 minutes on each side. Serve with melted butter and lemon juice and a green salad.

Herbs with Meat

When herbs are used with meat, quite pronounced flavors are acceptable to many palates. Sometimes the meat seems to be only just a base for the herb flavor—taken to extremes in some European sausages.

CHICKEN WITH TARRAGON

US		*UK*
1	4-pound chicken	1
3 tablespoons	olive or corn oil	2 tablespoons
3 tablespoons	whisky	2 tablespoons
2 cups	chicken stock	$\frac{3}{4}$ pint
$\frac{1}{2}$ cup	cream	4 tablespoons
1 teaspoon	fresh crushed tarragon	1 teaspoon

Cut up a chicken (or use frozen chicken pieces after thawing slowly) and sauté in the olive or corn oil until they are golden brown and the skin is sealed. Add the warm whisky and set it alight. Make up the chicken stock, from a cube or from the giblets and a small bunch of tarragon. Boil the stock furiously until it has been reduced by a third, and add this to the chicken; it should be enough to cover the meat. Cover the pan and simmer for half an hour. Lift the chicken into a serving dish, add the cream to the remaining liquid, simmer for a few minutes, and season. Strain, add a teaspoonful of fresh crushed tarragon and pour over the chicken. By covering the dish with foil or a lid and putting it into a moderately warm oven for 10–15 minutes, the aroma of the tarragon is strengthened. Small fresh leaves like tarragon and thyme need to be picked by hand from the stems and crushed under a rolling pin or pounded in a mortar to give off their flavor to advantage. If the leaves are dry, crushing with a rolling pin is all that is required.

Wrap firmly in foil and bake in a moderate oven (about 350°F) for 75 minutes. Allow the ingredients to cool in the foil, which may be removed once it is cold. Coat with melted aspic, or red-currant jelly to give the roll an attractive finish. Very thin slices of mushroom or lemon can be arranged on top, particularly if the dish is used for a summer party, or a buffet. Slice when serving. If the dish is to be served hot, turn up the heat in the oven after about an hour to 400°F for a further 15–20 minutes and remove the foil after taking the dish from the oven.

HERBED CHICKEN FOR A COLD BUFFET

US		*UK*
1	5-pound chicken, boned	1
3 tablespoons	melted butter	2 tablespoons
	salt and pepper to season	
½ cup	jellied aspic or red-currant jelly to garnish	¼ pint (scant)
	Stuffing:	
1 cup	breadcrumbs	8 ounces
1	egg, lightly beaten	1
1 teaspoon	chopped parsley	1 teaspoon
1 teaspoon	summer savory	1 teaspoon
1 teaspoon	fresh thyme	1 teaspoon
	grated rind of 1 lemon	

Bone a chicken without cutting into the flesh except along the back; this can be done by slipping a small boning knife between the bone and the flesh and working the flesh free from the carcase. The wings and the thigh and leg bones will come away quite easily by turning the flesh inside out as the bird is boned. More simply, ask your butcher to bone the chicken for you. Lay out the flesh on a board, skin down and spread the whole with this stuffing: Mix the breadcrumbs with the lightly beaten egg and add the parsley, summer savory, fresh thyme, and the grated lemon rind. Sprinkle a little melted butter with salt and pepper, and roll up. A 5-pound chicken should give a roll of about a foot in length.

CARAWAY CASSEROLE

US		*UK*
3 pounds (with bones)	lamb for stewing	3 pounds (with bones)
1½ tablespoons	butter	1 tablespoon
4	onions	4
4 tablespoons	seasoned flour (flour with salt and pepper)	3 tablespoons
8	potatoes	8
1 teaspoon	caraway seeds in cheesecloth or muslin bag	1 teaspoon
2½ cups	warmed stock	1 pint

Lamb (or mutton) lends itself well to being cooked with caraway seeds, and a "hot pot" casserole of meat, potatoes, and onions made with a good, rich meat stock can be even better if you add a small cheesecloth or muslin bag containing a teaspoon of caraway seeds. Cut up the meat in small pieces or cubes, coat with seasoned flour, and sauté for a minute or two with the onions. Put into a casserole dish, add sliced potatoes and the bag of caraway seed, cover with warmed stock. Cook. Cover the dish and stew in a medium-low oven for 1½ hours, or until the meat is tender. (Remove the bag before serving.)

LAMB CASSEROLE WITH ROSEMARY

US		*UK*
4	boned lamb steaks or fillets cut from the loin	4
	butter to coat casserole	
3–4	leeks, sliced thickly	3–4
2–3 sprigs	fresh rosemary	2–3 sprigs
	or	
2 scant teaspoons	dried rosemary	1¼ teaspoons
¼ cup	white wine	2 tablespoons
	water to cover	
	salt and pepper to season	

This light, pleasing dish has a distinctive rosemary flavor. Butter a casserole dish and cover the bottom with the sliced leeks. Lay the meat over the leeks and add the fresh or the dried rosemary, the wine, and sufficient water to cover. Season with salt and pepper; cover and cook for 1½ hours at a low heat.

HERBED CHOPS

Either lamb or pork chops can be made much more interesting by rubbing them with a herb mixture before rolling in egg and breadcrumbs and grilling in the usual way. A mixture of parsley, tarragon, marjoram, and thyme in a proportion of twice as much parsley as any other herb, together with salt, pepper and, if desired, a little grated nutmeg, is the best seasoning to use.

ITALIAN BRAISED LAMB

US		*UK*
2 slices	bacon	2 slices
3 tablespoons	olive oil	2 tablespoons
2 lb.	lean shoulder of lamb cut from the bone and cubed	2 lb.
1 small	onion, chopped	1 small
1 clove	garlic	1 clove
½ cup	canned Italian tomatoes	4 oz.
½ cup	white wine	4 ounces
5 cups	meat stock	2 pints
1 teaspoon	salt	1 teaspoon
½ teaspoon	pepper	½ teaspoon
4 tablespoons	flour	3 tablespoons
1	bay leaf	1
1 teaspoon	dried basil	1 teaspoon
1 teaspoon	dried oregano	1 teaspoon
3	egg yolks	3

3 tablespoons	lemon juice	2 tablespoons
4 tablespoons	fresh parsley, chopped	3 tablespoons

Use a deep frying pan. Fry the bacon in its own fat until it is very brown and crisp. Remove the bacon and discard. Add the olive oil to the bacon fat and when it is hot lower the heat; toss in the cubes of lamb, a few at a time. Fry until golden brown and remove to a casserole dish. Continue until all the meat is browned. In the same pan, fry the chopped onion and garlic for 5 minutes; stir in the tomatoes, add the wine and bring to the boil. Simmer for about 10 minutes to reduce the amount by half. Add the stock and stir well; bring to the boil again.

Sprinkle pepper, flour and salt over the meat, and mix. Pour the wine mixture from the frying pan over the meat, add the bay leaf, oregano and basil. Slowly bring to the boil over gentle heat, stirring occasionally. Cover the casserole and put it in a preheated oven (350°F) for 1½ or 2 hours.

Before serving lift out the lamb with a slotted spoon, and keep it hot in a serving dish and return the gravy to the pan. Allow it to stand for a few minutes then skim off the fat from the top surface. Beat the egg yolks, and add the lemon juice. Whisk a few tablespoonsful of the gravy into the yolks first, then add to the warm gravy in the pan. Cook gently for a minute until the mixture thickens, but do not boil or else it will curdle. Pour the sauce over the meat, garnish with chopped parsley and serve immediately.

PORK FILLETS À LA COLBERT

US		*UK*
4 slices	pork fillet	4 fillets
4 large	cabbage leaves	4 large
2 medium	tomatoes, finely chopped	2 medium
2 small	onions, finely chopped	2 small
½ cup	mushrooms, diced	¼ pound
	pinch of salt and pepper	
	parsley, thyme, sage, or caraway to season	
1½ tablespoons	butter	1 tablespoon
½ cup	stock	4 ounces

Tenderize fillets of pork by beating. This will make them a little thinner and wider. Blanch one large cabbage leaf for each pork fillet, then put each fillet on top of one leaf. Spread with a mixture of chopped and fried vegetables—tomatoes, onions, mushrooms, etc.—together with a little salt and pepper. Parsley, thyme, sage, or caraway may be added. Roll the leaf to enclose the meat and savory filling, tie with white cotton thread and put the four rolls into a buttered casserole, or oven dish. Cook in a moderate oven, about 375°F, for an hour; baste with stock from time to time. It is advisable to cover the dish with cooking foil or transparent cooking film to prevent the outer parts of the leaves from drying.

PORK CHOPS WITH WHITE WINE AND HERB SAUCE

US		*UK*
1 teaspoon	marjoram, chopped fresh or dried	1 teaspoon
1 teaspoon	dried basil	1 teaspoon
½ teaspoon each	salt and black pepper	½ teaspoon each
1 clove	garlic, crushed (optional)	1 clove
4	pork chops	4

$\frac{1}{4}$ cup	butter	2 ounces
$\frac{1}{2}$ cup	white wine	4 ounces
1 teaspoon	cornstarch (cornflour)	1 teaspoon
1 teaspoon	fresh, chopped parsley	1 teaspoon

Combine the marjoram, basil, salt and pepper and the garlic (if used) and coat both sides of the chops with the mixture. Sauté the chops in butter in a frying pan, turning them after about 3 minutes, and cook for the same length of time on the other side. Add half the wine, simmer gently for about 30 minutes over very low heat. Keep the pan covered. Mix the cornstarch with the remainder of the wine, and once the chops have been cooked and removed to a warm serving dish add the wine mixture to the pan. Increase the heat, stirring gently to prevent uneven thickening and to blend in the juices remaining from the meat. Once the sauce has thickened, stir in the fresh parsley. Cover the chops with the sauce before serving, or pour the sauce into a warm gravy boat and serve separately.

SAGE AND ONION STUFFING (for poultry and pork)

US		*UK*
6 small	onions	6 small
$\frac{3}{4}$ cup	milk	6 fluid ounces
$2\frac{1}{2}$ teaspoons	butter	1 tablespoon
$\frac{1}{2}$ cup	white breadcrumbs	4-5 ounces
1 tablespoon	chopped sage leaves	1 heaped teaspoon
	chopped parsley, salt and pepper to taste	

Peel and cut the onions into quarters, and boil in milk until half-cooked. Add a knob of butter and allow to melt, this will form the basis of a good moist stuffing. Add sufficient fine white breadcrumbs to absorb the liquid, the chopped sage leaves and a pinch of chopped parsley; salt and pepper to taste. Mix thoroughly and use to stuff the bird or meat. Even when cold, this is sufficiently soft to be spread on sandwiches of cold chicken or pork and helps to make the sandwich more appetizing.

APPLE HERB JELLY

This preserve can be served with cold meat or poultry. Quantity makes about 6 lb.

US		*UK*
4 lbs.	cooking apples	4 lbs.
2 quarts	water	$2\frac{3}{4}$ pints
$\frac{2}{3}$ cup	vinegar (malt or cider)	$\frac{1}{4}$ pint
	5 or 6 tablespoons chopped fresh mint, parsley, sage or thyme (not mixed, any *one* can be used)	
	small bunch of fresh herbs—whichever has been chosen above	
1 lb. to each $2\frac{1}{2}$ cups of juice	preserving sugar	1 lb. to each pint of juice
	green coloring, a few drops	

Wash and quarter the apples, put into preserving pan with water and $\frac{1}{4}$ pint malt vinegar or cider vinegar. Bring to the boil slowly, simmer for about an hour, stirring occasionally to mash the apples. Remove from the heat and spoon the juice and pulp into a cheesecloth or a muslin bag, over a large bowl to catch the juice. Add a bunch of fresh herbs to the juice and return to the pan. Boil for 5 minutes. Remove bunch of herbs and add sugar in the proportions given above keeping the pan over a low heat until the sugar has dissolved. Then boil briskly for about 10 minutes until setting point is reached. Draw from heat and add a few drops of green coloring matter and the chopped herbs. Allow the mixture to stand for 5–10 minutes without stirring and then once a skin has formed stir gently and pour into clean jars. Cover and seal.

Vegetable Dishes

Fresh herbs, usually chopped or broken into sprigs, make excellent garnishes for vegetable dishes. It is traditional to add certain herbs to vegetables, to enhance the flavor: for instance, a sprig of mint cooked with new potatoes, or added to fresh peas, and removed before serving. Sometimes, a herb can be used to dilute the strong aroma of a vegetable cooking. Caraway seeds cooked with cabbage will prevent the smell from permeating the house.

CAULIFLOWER À LA GRECQUE

US		*UK*
1 large	cauliflower	1 large
1 cup	water	½ pint
6 tablespoons	olive oil	4 tablespoons
	juice of 2 lemons	
1 teaspoon	salt	1 teaspoon
	cheesecloth or muslin bag containing:	
1 teaspoon	chervil, chopped	1 teaspoon
1 teaspoon	fennel, chopped	1 teaspoon
½ teaspoon	coriander, ground	½ teaspoon
½ teaspoon	thyme	½ teaspoon
1	bay leaf	1
	sprinkling of red pepper	

Served cold, either as an accompaniment to tongue or cold pork or as an hors d'oeuvre, this simply prepared cauliflower dish is an unusual salad. An advantage is that it can be prepared the day before, for a dinner party. Wash a cauliflower, then cut it up into small "flowerlets." Bring the water to the boil, add the cauliflower, olive oil, lemon juice, and salt. Drop the small bag containing the chopped herbs into the pan. Once boiling, reduce the heat and simmer for about 5 minutes—not more or the cauliflower will begin to fall apart. Cool the entire contents of the pan in a bowl, cover, and refrigerate overnight. Remove the cauliflower to serve and sprinkle with the red pepper.

LEEKS WITH SAGE

Leeks themselves were classed as pot herbs before the more recent kitchen garden era and were grown far more extensively in Wales, Northern England, and Scotland than elsewhere in Britain, where they were mainly used in cock-a-leekie soup. London catalogues of 1824 list "The London Flag, and the Common sorts," but in earlier catalogues, leeks were listed along with onions, parsnips, turnips, and so on as root crops; the kinds seem to have been 'French' and 'London.' Served with a cheese sauce, to which tarragon is added, leeks make a warming vegetable dish, but an old recipe for leek pie with sage is more unusual and tempting.

LEEK PIE WITH SAGE

US		UK
1	10-inch pie shell or pastry case	1
10	leeks	10
1 pinch of each	fresh parsley and sage, chopped	1 pinch of each
1	egg, lightly beaten with a little cream	1
	salt and freshly ground black pepper to taste	
2–3 slices	lean bacon	2–3 rashers
	sprinkling of breadcrumbs	

Bake blind (empty) a pastry case or pie shell, cool, and fill it with a leek mixture made in the following way. Wash the leeks very well, and trim. Slice the thick white stems into 1-inch rounds; simmer until soft in salted water (a few minutes); drain, add chopped parsley and chopped sage. Lightly beat an egg with the cream and mix with the leeks. Season to taste. Put two or three slices of lean bacon into the base of the pastry case, pour the leek and sage mixture on top, sprinkle with breadcrumbs, and bake in a medium oven (375°F) for about 20 minutes or until golden brown. Serve hot.

MUSHROOMS PROVENCALE

US		UK
¼ cup	olive oil	3 tablespoons
¼ cup	tomato purée	2 tablespoons
2–3 sprigs	thyme	2–3 sprigs
½ cup	chopped parsley	good handful
1	bay leaf	1
	salt and pepper to taste	
1 pound	fresh mushrooms (or 4 small cans of prepared button mushrooms, drained)	1 pound

Put the olive oil in a heavy frying pan, add tomato purée, thyme, parsley, and a bay leaf. Blend a few minutes, over a low heat, then season with salt and freshly ground pepper. Add washed and peeled mushrooms. If canned button mushrooms are used, strain off the brine in which they are packed. Stir and simmer for 2 minutes, then cover the pan and cook gently for 5 more minutes. Remove the bay leaf and put the mushrooms into a covered container and cool. Keep in the refrigerator until required. Serve cold as a salad, or as an hors d'oeuvre.

PURÉE OF SORREL

US		UK
1 pound	sorrel leaves	1 pound
	water to cover	
2	onions, medium	2
¼ cup	butter	2 ounces
¼ cup	flour	2 ounces
⅛ cup	sugar	1 ounce
	salt, pepper, and nutmeg to season	
⅓ cup	stock	scant ¼ pint
4	poached eggs	4

Wash and chop sorrel leaves, put them in a pan with just sufficient water to cover, and simmer them for a few minutes. Purée in a blender or rub through a fine-meshed sieve. Meanwhile, slice the onions and fry them in butter until lightly browned, add the flour and stir to thicken, then the sugar, a dash of salt and pepper and nutmeg. Add stock, or a bouillon cube dissolved in water; use enough to form a thick gravy. Cook for 2 or 3 minutes to thicken. Strain to remove the onions and combine with the sorrel purée, or add the gravy to the cooked sorrel and purée, both together in the blender. Serve with a poached egg on top of each portion.

ZUCCHINI NICOISE (COURGETTES À LA NIÇOISE)

US		*UK*
8–12, depending on size	zucchini (courgettes)	8–12, depending on size
1 teaspoon	mixed salt and tarragon	1 teaspoon
$\frac{1}{4}$ cup	butter	2 ounces
1 slice	lean bacon	1 rasher
1 of each	small carrot and onion	1 of each
5	large tomatoes (or 1 12-ounce can)	5
1 tablespoon	flour	1 dessertspoon
1 teaspoon	sugar	1 teaspoon
1 teaspoon	thyme	1 teaspoon
1 teaspoon	tarragon	1 teaspoon
2 teaspoons	lemon juice	2 teaspoons
2	garlic cloves	2

Allow two zucchini per person (or 3 if very small). Cut into half-inch slices; spread them out on a plate, sprinkle with mixed salt and tarragon, and leave them for half an hour. Melt the butter and lightly fry the lean bacon, cut up into pieces, a small onion and a carrot, both chopped. Skin the tomatoes by leaving them in boiling water for about 5 minutes and then peeling away the skins; quarter them and add to the pan and cook for a few minutes. The tomatoes will produce more liquid. Add the flour, sugar, thyme, half the tarragon and lemon juice. Crush a clove of garlic (optional) and add, stirring continuously; simmer for 15 minutes. Strain the liquid, returning it to the pan. Meanwhile, wash and dry the sliced zucchini (courgettes) and now add them to the tomato liquid. Sprinkle in a further $\frac{1}{2}$ teaspoon of tarragon. Cook for 10 minutes. Sprinkle with the remaining lemon juice. Serve well-chilled as an accompaniment to cooked meats, cold ham or cold pork, or hot with roast beef, lamb, or chicken.

Sauces

The ubiquitous branded sauces, which make every dish taste the same, are merely quick and convenient methods of providing bottled flavor. But why chill hot food with a cold sauce? A better and wider variety of flavors can be achieved by the imaginative use of herbs and a little extra preparation time.

BLENDER MAYONNAISE

US		*UK*
2	egg yolks	2
1 teaspoon	mild mustard	1 teaspoon
1 teaspoon	salt	1 teaspoon
1 teaspoon	sugar	1 teaspoon
1 teaspoon	pinch of pepper mixed with lemon juice	1 teaspoon

$1\frac{1}{4}$ cups	olive oil	$\frac{1}{2}$ pint
3 tablespoons	wine vinegar (up to)	2 tablespoons
	chopped fresh parsley as required	

A classic mayonnaise may be blended in an electric mixer, using the medium speed. Put the egg yolks, mustard, salt, sugar, pinch of pepper and lemon juice; blend on the medium speed. While the blender is going, add the olive oil drop by drop until the mixture emulsifies, then it may be added more rapidly. A little wine vinegar may be added, dropped in gradually until the mayonnaise is of the desired consistency, stiff enough to hold its shape. Turn into a container, and store in the refrigerator until needed; sprinkle with chopped parsley before serving.

GREEN MAYONNAISE

US		*UK*
	blender mayonnaise ingredients without vinegar	
3 tablespoons	dry white wine	2 tablespoons
1 teaspoon of each	freshly chopped parsley, dill, and chives	1 teaspoon of each

Make the mayonnaise as in the previous recipe, without the vinegar and use instead the dry white wine, adding the finely chopped herbs. This sauce is best chilled for 2 or 3 hours before serving, to allow the flavor to develop. It is particularly useful as an attractive dressing for buffet dishes.

BEARNAISE SAUCE

US		*UK*
5 tablespoons	wine vinegar	4 tablespoons
5 tablespoons	white wine	4 tablespoons
$\frac{1}{4}$	bay leaf	$\frac{1}{4}$
1	sprig of thyme	1
3 tablespoons each	chopped chervil, tarragon	2 tablespoons
1	shallot, finely chopped	1
	pinch of salt and pepper	
2	egg yolks, lightly beaten with a little water	2
$\frac{1}{3}$ cup	butter	3 ounces
	squeeze of lemon juice	

Put the wine vinegar and white wine in a pan, together with the bay leaf, shallot, thyme, half the chervil and tarragon, and a pinch of salt and pepper. Bring the liquid to boil and reduce to a third of the quantity. Allow it to cool considerably before adding slowly the egg yolks, lightly beaten with very little water; this is best done with the pan over a very low heat, or in a double boiler. Gradually incorporate the butter, whisking continuously. Once the sauce is thick, smooth, and hot, season with the remaining chervil and tarragon, and a squeeze of lemon juice.

FENNEL SAUCE

US		UK
½ cup	butter	4 ounces
3 tablespoons	fresh fennel leaves	2 tablespoons
	or	
	dried fennel leaves reconstituted with a little lemon juice	

A delicious addition to boiled or baked fish can be made by simply mixing the fennel leaves in melted butter, in the above proportions, and using the fresh or green-dried foliage. Fennel leaves are not at their best when dried, but if used thus, reconstitute the dried leaves in a drop of lemon juice, rather than in water.

FENNEL AND GOOSEBERRY SAUCE

From *Receipt Book* of Henry Howard, cook to the Duke of Ormond, 1710:

"Brown some butter in a saucepan with a pinch of flour, then put in a few chives shred small, add a little Irish broth to moisten it, season with salt and pepper; Make these boil, then put in two or three sprigs of fennel and some gooseberries. Let all simmer together till the gooseberries are soft."

GREEN HERB SAUCE

US		UK
1	onion, small	1
1 tablespoon	butter or oil	½ ounce
2 tablespoons	flour	1 tablespoon
½ cup of each	stock and milk combined	¼ pint of each
1½ tablespoons	sour cream or yoghurt	1 tablespoon
2 tablespoons	chopped mixed herbs	1½ tablespoons

A tasty condiment for bland meats and one which can be much varied, it is basically a stock and milk mixture to which is added sour cream, or yoghurt, and chopped mixed herbs. Use parsley, salad burnet, sage, tarragon, or oregano, remembering that some should be used more sparingly than others. Add herbs to taste. Sauté an onion in the butter or oil, add a tablespoonful of flour; cook without allowing it to brown. Add liquid stock and milk and simmer. Strain to remove the onion pieces (or purée in a blender), add the herbs and a squeeze of lemon juice, and simmer for 2 or 3 minutes. Stir in a generous spoonful of sour cream or yoghurt just before serving.

MINT SAUCE

US		UK
3 tablespoons	freshly picked mint, chopped	2 tablespoons
	or	
2 tablespoons	dried mint	1½ tablespoons
3 tablespoons	granulated sugar	2 tablespoons
2 tablespoons	boiling water	1 tablespoon
2 tablespoons	vinegar or lemon juice	1½ tablespoons

A traditional accompaniment to roast lamb or mutton, this can enhance or ruin the enjoyment of the whole course. Mint sauce previously prepared and stored in bottles is readily

The herb garden at
Sissinghurst Castle,
Kent, England.

The Royal Horticultural
Society's herb garden at
Wisley, Surrey, England.

obtainable in supermarkets and, as far as labor-saving packaged products go, is reasonably acceptable; but the sharpness of fresh mint taken from the garden adds not only piquancy to the sauce but an aroma that is naturally lacking in the prepared bottled product. A sweet-sour flavor should be the pervading quality of a well-made mint sauce, and this is achieved by the balance of finely-granulated sugar and vinegar; though the use of lemon juice *in lieu* of the vinegar makes an interesting and refreshing alternative. Whether lemon juice or vinegar is used, put the sugar in a small bowl, or directly into a gravy dish. Dissolve in the boiling water, and add the chopped, freshly picked mint. Add vinegar or lemon juice to taste, stir well, and allow it to stand for an hour before serving, to improve the flavor.

PARSLEY MAYONNAISE

US		*UK*
3 large	egg yolks	3 large
½ teaspoon	mild mustard	½ teaspoon
1¼ cups	olive oil	½ pint
1 teaspoon	fresh lemon juice	1 teaspoon
	grated rind of half a lemon	
3 tablespoons	chopped parsley	1½ tablespoons

Make a basic mayonnaise using the yolks of 3 large eggs; add the mustard, and the olive oil, drop by drop, beating continually. Sharpen the flavor with the lemon rind and fresh lemon juice. The lemon juice should be added last, only after the mixture has thickened and blended. Just before serving, sprinkle with chopped parsley.

PARSLEY SAUCE

US		*UK*
1 tablespoon	butter	½ ounce
1 tablespoon	flour	½ ounce
1¼ cups	cold milk (or stock)	½ pint
	salt to taste	
5 tablespoons	fresh parsley, chopped	4 tablespoons
1½ teaspoons	add tarragon vinegar for a more piquant sauce	½ teaspoon
1	egg, hard-boiled	1

Parsley sauce is the perfect and most popular addition to white fish, fish cakes, bacon and ham. Its savor can really only be appreciated when it is served immediately after being made.

Melt the butter, stir in flour, blend to a smooth paste, and cook for a few minutes without letting it brown. Slowly add cold milk and/or other liquid, such as stock, according to the required thickness of the finished sauce. Add a small pinch of salt. Bring to boil, cook for 3 or 4 minutes, beating or whisking to keep it smooth. Add very well-washed chopped fresh parsley; the leaves should be put in at the last minute so that they remain uncooked when served. A more piquant sauce can be made to serve with cooked ham or veal by adding a little tarragon vinegar at the last moment. These quantities produce a generous cup of sauce. The basic sauce can have a hard-boiled egg finely chopped and added with the parsley just before serving; this is particularly good for flavoring boiled capon or other poultry dishes.

SAGE SAUCE

US		UK
3–4	onions, small, finely minced	3–4
2 tablespoons	butter	1 tablespoon
2 tablespoons	flour	1 tablespoon
2 tablespoons	milk	1 tablespoon
1¼ cups	stock	½ pint
3 tablespoons	light cream	2 tablespoons
1 tablespoon	sage (fresh or dried)	1 dessertspoon
	salt and pepper to taste	

Sage sauce is always especially good with pork; the leaves will provide the same flavor whether they are used fresh or dried. To make 1¼ cups of sauce; mince the onions and sauté in butter—add flour, sauté to form a roux, and cook for a minute or two to absorb the fat, without allowing it to brown. Slowly beat in the milk, with the pan away from the heat, then return to the heat, simmer. Add half the cream, and the sage. Let the sauce simmer, again very gently, then season with salt and pepper to taste. Add the rest of the cream just before serving.

TOMATO SAUCE

US		UK
1¼ cups	strained stock, in which celery, carrots, and leek have been cooked	1 pint
1½ pounds	ripe tomatoes	1½ pounds
¼ cup	melted butter	2 ounces
2 small	onions, chopped	2
1	*bouquet garni* of fresh rosemary, basil, thyme, and bay	1
	salt and pepper to taste	
1 teaspoon	sugar	1 teaspoon
1 tablespoon	corn starch (cornflour)	1 dessertspoon
2 tablespoons	cold milk	2 dessertspoons

A somewhat thinner and much more freshly flavored version of bottled ketchup to serve with fish, pastas, or pork chops is a tomato sauce in which a *bouquet garni* has been cooked, either in a small cheesecloth (muslin) bag suspended from the handle of the pan or as a fresh bunch of sprigs; in each instance the *bouquet garni* should consist of rosemary, basil, thyme, and bay.

Wash, skin, and cut the ripe tomatoes into small pieces and put them in a pan with the melted butter and the chopped onions. Cook in a tightly covered pan for 10 minutes over a low heat, shaking frequently. Add the herbs, the strained stock in which vegetables such as celery, carrots, and leek have been cooked, salt and pepper to taste, and add a teaspoon of sugar. Simmer gently for half an hour, occasionally stirring with a wooden spoon. Purée in a blender or strain and sieve the mixture, return to the pan, and bring to boil. Meanwhile, blend the corn starch with a little cold milk, add slowly to the contents of the pan and bring everything to a boil, stirring constantly. Cook for 5 minutes, reseason, if necessary, just before serving.

QUICK TOMATO SAUCE

US		UK
1 pound	ripe tomatoes	1 pound
	salt to taste	
1 teaspoon	chopped basil	1 teaspoon
3 tablespoons	cream	2 tablespoons

A simple tomato sauce can be quickly made by cooking chopped tomatoes slowly in an open pan, such as a frying pan (they will make their own liquid). Add a pinch of salt and the chopped basil as cooking begins, and simmer gently for about 20 minutes until the fruit is pulped and smooth. Sieve, or purée in a blender, then add cream, yoghurt, or a knob of butter just before serving.

WATERCRESS SAUCE

US		UK
2 tablespoons	butter	1 ounce
2 tablespoons	flour	1 ounce
2 cups, scant	milk	¾ pint
3 tablespoons	chopped watercress	2 tablespoons
	fresh watercress sprigs to garnish	

This good, green, tasty sauce is a delicious accompaniment to hot or cold meats and sausages; it can be served hot with omelettes and cold with hard-boiled eggs. Melt the butter, stir in an equal weight of flour, and gradually add milk and a pinch of salt, stirring constantly. Throw in well-washed and chopped watercress, stir for a further minute, and garnish with fresh watercress sprigs.

Pickles and Chutneys

MOCK CAPERS

Pick the seeds of nasturtium *(Tropaeolum majus)* while they are still green. Clean them under running water, dry and spread on a baking tray. Leave in the warming oven of a stove for 3 days to dry out thoroughly. Pack into dry, clean jars, cover with cider vinegar or white wine vinegar, and cap immediately. The "capers" will be soaked and ready for use after 2 or 3 weeks.

DILL AND CUCUMBER PICKLE

Dill seeds as a flavoring for pickle are used a great deal in Germany. In earlier days the seed was also used to flavor other preserved vegetables. From the *Recipe Book* of Joseph Cooper, cook to Charles I, 1640: "Gather the tops of the ripest dill and cover the bottom of the vessel and lay a layer of cucumbers, and another of Dill till you have filled the vessel within a handful of the top. Then take as much water as you think will fill the vessel and mix it with salt and a quarter of a pound of allom to a gallon of water and poure it on them and press them down with a stone on them and keep them covered close. For that use I think the water will be best boyl'd and cold, which will keep longer sweet, or if you like not this pickle, doe it with water, salt, and white wine vinegar, or (if you please) pour the water and salt on them scalding hot which will make them ready to use the sooner."

ELDERBERRY CHUTNEY

US		UK
2 pounds	freshly picked ripened elderberries, washed and removed from the stalks	2 pounds
1	onion, chopped	1
½ teaspoon of each	cayenne pepper allspice mustard powder	½ teaspoon of each
1 teaspoon	salt	1 teaspoon
4 tablespoons	sugar	3 tablespoons
2½ cups	wine or cider vinegar	1 pint

Wash freshly picked elderberries and remove them from the stalks, and weigh out about 2 lbs. Put them in a pan and bruise the berries with a wooden spoon; add the chopped onion, cayenne pepper, all spice, mustard powder, salt, and sugar. Add the wine or cider vinegar, and bring everything to the boil. Simmer, mixing constantly, until the mixture thickens slightly, then pour into sterilized jars, cap tightly, and store carefully.

MINT CHUTNEY

US		UK
½ pound	tomatoes	½ pound
1 pound	apples	1 pound
6 small	onions	6 small
3 large	peppercorns	3 large
1 cup	fresh mint leaves	1 large cup
3¾ cups	wine vinegar	1½ pints
1¾ cups	brown sugar	1 pound
2½ cups	seedless raisins	¾ pound
1	red pepper pod or a chili	1
4 teaspoons	mustard	4 teaspoons
	or	
2 teaspoons	dry mustard powder	2 teaspoons
2 teaspoons	salt	2 teaspoons

By combining fruits, sugar, vinegar, and mint, the sweet-sour tang of mint chutney provides an excellent accompaniment to hot and cold lamb dishes. Roughly chop the tomatoes, apples, and onions, and crush the peppercorns, finely. Chop the mint leaves, which have been taken from their stalks. Put aside. Bring the vinegar almost to boil, add the brown sugar, seedless raisins, a dried red pepper pod or chili, the mustard, and salt. Stir well and when thoroughly mixed and all the sugar dissolved, turn off the heat. Add the chopped tomatoes, apples, mint, pepper, and onions, and mix in thoroughly. Have some jars in boiling water and remove and dry them one at a time, filling them to the brim, covering and sealing at once. Store in a cool dark place, or in the refrigerator. Do not heat the chutney any further; it will improve and mature with age and is not ready to use until a month after it has been made.

MINT AND APPLE CHUTNEY

US		UK
2 pounds	cooking apples	2 pounds
2½ cups	fresh mint leaves	2 cupfuls
½ pound	tomatoes	½ pound
1 pound	onions	1 pound
2 stalks	celery	2 sticks
⅔ cup	seedless raisins or sultanas	¼ pound
2 cups	cider vinegar	¾ pint
1 teaspoon	dry mustard powder	1 teaspoon
	or	
2 teaspoons	mustard	2 teaspoons
2 teaspoons	salt	2 teaspoons
½ teaspoon	freshly ground black pepper	½ teaspoon
1 cup	soft brown sugar	½ pound
⅔ cup	cider vinegar	¼ pint

Peel and core the cooking apples and roughly chop them into pieces. Add freshly picked mint leaves taken from the stalk and washed, and then coarsely chopped. Cut up the tomatoes, onions, celery, and seedless raisins, or sultanas. Cook all these ingredients together with the cider vinegar, mustard, salt, and a good pinch of freshly ground black pepper. Simmer very gently until the mixture is soft and well blended. Moisten the soft brown sugar with the cider vinegar and add to the mixture. Once the sugar is melted bring the whole to a boil, stirring continuously. Reduce the heat, simmer, and test for setting; when the consistency thickens and the pulp and liquid do not separate when dropped from the spoon, turn off the heat. Allow the mixture to remain on the stove for a short time, then pour into sterilized, warmed jars. These ingredients should make about 5 lbs. chutney.

Desserts and Sweets

ELDERFLOWER FRITTERS

US		UK
1½ cups	fresh elderflowers	½ pound
3 tablespoons	cream cheese	2 tablespoons
2	eggs	2
	rose water, a few drops	
⅛ teaspoon	cinnamon	⅛ teaspoon
¼ cup	butter	2 ounces
	finely granulated sugar for dredging	

An old recipe notes that these heavily-scented flowers should be picked when they are fresh and full, taken from their stalks, and pounded in a mortar. Mix in the cream cheese, eggs, rose water, and a pinch of cinnamon, and work the butter thoroughly until it is very well blended. Dampen your hands and roll the mixture lightly into small balls, flatten slightly between the palms and fry. Serve immediately, dredged with sugar, or roll in vanilla sugar on waxed (grease-proof) paper or aluminum foil after cooking.

ANOTHER RECIPE FOR ELDERFLOWER FRITTERS

US		UK
¼ cup	flour	3 tablespoons
⅔ cup milk	milk	⅓ pint
1	egg	1
	pinch of salt	
	freshly picked elderflower heads	
	sugar, finely granulated, or syrup	
	leaves of lemon balm or Sweet Cicely, chopped, to garnish	

These are whole elderflowers cooked in batter. The batter is made in the standard way with flour, eggs, water, or milk and a pinch of salt. Only a small amount of the batter need be made; let it rest for half an hour. Wash the flower heads, shake dry, then dip the flower heads into the batter, holding them by the stalk; and deep fry in hot oil, until golden brown. Drain on kitchen paper, dredge with sugar or syrup and chopped herbs. Sweet Cicely or lemon balm leaves can be chopped and scattered over the fritters before servings. Marigold petals can be added to the batter as an alternative variation, but the effect is spoiled if more than one herb is used at once.

ELDERFLOWER MILK

US		UK
3	elderflower heads	3
2½ cups	milk	1 pint
1 teaspoon	semolina	1 teaspoon
	sugar and salt to taste	
1	egg yolk	1
	crystallized angelica to garnish	

Gather flower heads when dry and fresh and just coming to full bloom, and strip the blossom from the stalk. Simmer gently, in the milk, adding semolina; mix in sugar and salt to taste. Remove from the heat and slowly incorporate the egg yolk. Pour the mixture into a serving dish and set aside to cool. The top may be decorated with crystallized angelica stalks before serving.

PEAR TART WITH CUMIN AND ELDERBERRY

US		UK
	pastry to line and cover a 9″-pie plate	
	or	
	pastry to line a 9″-pie plate	
6	pears, peeled and sliced	6
4–5	cumin seeds	4–5
2 teaspoons	fresh, ripe elderberries	2 teaspoons
	grated rind of ½ lemon	
2	egg whites (optional)	2
⅓ cup	confectioner's (icing) sugar	2 ounces

Make a pastry dough, and line pie plate (flan tin) with it. Combine pears and the elderberries; dried ones may be used but their color is not as attractive as the pink from fresh berries. Pile into the pastry-lined dish, and sprinkle the grated lemon rind over the filling. Top with a second layer of pastry, or with meringue made from stiffly beaten egg white whisked with a little confectioner's (icing) sugar. Bake in a moderate-to-hot oven 400°F., mark 6, for about 20 minutes. Serve hot, preferably with cream.

SCENTED GERANIUM LEAVES FOR FLAVORING

Lemon-scented, rose-scented, apple-scented, and other perfumed geranium leaves, apart from being decorative and edible, may be used in a variety of ways to add a delicate flavor to otherwise bland dishes. Rice puddings, blancmanges, junkets, and egg custards may easily be varied in flavor by a leaf or two. The scented-leaved geraniums are good pot plants and are often grown indoors as house or greenhouse decoration.

SCENTED GERANIUM WITH APPLES

US		*UK*
4	large cooking apples, washed and cored	4
¼ cup	butter	2 ounces
⅔ cup	white raisins (sultanas)	5 ounces
	or	
	candied peel	
	or	
	apple jelly	
4	scented geranium leaves	4
	pancake (golden)	
	or maple syrup to taste	

Wash and core a cooking apple for each serving. Put a dab of margarine or butter on the base of a fire-proof oven dish under each apple. Fill the core holes with white raisins (sultanas) or candied peel, or apple jelly; top each with a scented geranium leaf. Spoon pancake or maple syrup round the apples; bake in a moderate oven for about 40 minutes, or until the apples are soft but not reduced to a pulp. The geranium leaves will become crisp, and, apart from having imparted their flavor to the fruit, are also edible.

ROSE GERANIUM LEAVES WITH PEARS

US		*UK*
4 large	pears	4 large
	juice of ½ lemon	
	water	
4	rose-scented geranium leaves	4
	granulated sugar or honey to taste	
2 drops	red food coloring	2 drops
	whipped cream to garnish	

Peel, quarter, and core the pears, dropping them into water to which a few drops of lemon juice have been added, to prevent them from going brown (a few crushed sorrel leaves in the water will achieve the same effect). Remove the pears and put them into enough fresh water to cover them in an enamel or glass pan or oven dish. Stew them very slowly until they are tender. Add rose-scented geranium leaves, 1 to each whole pear, granulated sugar or honey to taste, and two drops of red vegetable coloring (cochineal) to impart a slight rose-pink color to the cooked fruit. Serve cold, decorated with whipped cream.

TANSY PUDDING OR TANSY CAKE

US		UK
1	baked 9″-pie shell	1
7	eggs	7
2½ cups	light cream	1 pint
	spinach juice to color	
	tansy juice to flavor	
	sugar, white wine, nutmeg, to taste	

Traditionally eaten at Easter, this is really a pie, or pastry case, filled with a flavored mixture. Beat the eggs well, blending in the cream. Spinach juice will add color, and tansy juice flavor. These can be made quickly in a juice extractor, or by pounding the leaves in a mortar. Fold in the juices, than add sugar, white wine, and nutmeg in small quantities until the taste is just right. Warm the cream in a saucepan, or a double boiler, until it thickens; pour into a previously baked pastry case. If it is to be served cold let it stand until set. For a hot dessert, bake for a quarter of an hour in a moderate oven (350°F.).

TART OF ARTICHOKES WITH SUGAR

A seventeenth-century recipe, using Jerusalem artichokes, recommended by Giles Rose, one of the Master Cooks to Charles II: Once they are softened by boiling, "strain them through a colander with butter and the yolks of raw eggs, salt, cinnamon, sugar, green citrar peel, put into a patty pan sheeted with fine paste; . . . when it is baked, ice it over with sugar and orange-flower water and so serve it away."

TURNOVER OR SLICE

US		UK
	sweet short-crust pastry, to line and cover a small pie pan	
5 tablespoons	bistort or sorrel leaves, chopped	4 tablespoons
3 teaspoons	sweet Cicely leaves, chopped	1 tablespoon
4 teaspoons	brown sugar	1 tablespoon
2	eggs, well beaten	2

Bistort or young sorrel leaves provide a tasty filling for a pastry slice which may be eaten hot or cold, served with cream or egg custard. Roll out short-crust pastry thinly and line a 1-inch-deep pie pan. Make a filling of chopped bistort or sorrel leaves, Sweet Cicely leaves, brown sugar, and egg. Cover the filling with a second piece of thinly rolled pastry and bake in a moderate oven for about 15 minutes, or until golden brown. Slice into narrow triangles, and serve with creamy desserts, or fruit compôtes.

UPSIDE-DOWN PUDDING

US		UK
1 can	pineapple rings, or	1 tin
4	cooking apples, sliced	4
	sponge batter for 8-inch cake pan, to which is added	
1½ teaspoons	coriander seed	1 heaped teaspoon
1½ teaspoons	honey	1 heaped teaspoon

Line a deep cake pan with either pineapple rings or thinly sliced apples. Make up a standard sponge batter, folding in the coriander seed and the honey. Pour this batter on top of the fruit, and bake in a moderate oven for 30 minutes. Cool for a minute or two, turn out of the pan and serve hot.

Candies and Confections

TO CRYSTALLIZE FLOWERS

Flowers for crystallizing need to be unblemished, dry, and fresh. Those of a good color such as violets, borage, delphiniums, and tiny rose buds give the most pleasing results. Make a syrup of one pound of sugar and a generous cup of water; boil steadily until 240°F. is reached. Drop the flower heads into the syrup, a few at a time, and maintain a minimum temperature of 240°F. for a minute. Turn off the heat and lift the flowers out on a perforated spoon and spread them carefully on a sheet of aluminium foil on a baking sheet. Dry them off in a very cool oven. Turn the flower heads once or twice during the process until they are quite dry.

TO CRYSTALLIZE, OR CANDY, ANGELICA

Young stems, cut in May or June before the plants form flower buds, are cut into pieces 2 or 3 inches in length and boiled gently in a covered pan until tender. Drain, cool, and strip off the tough outer skin, then return to the pan in the same water and simmer for a further half an hour. The stems will take on a green color. Drain again, and weigh when dry.

Allowing an equal quantity by weight of granulated sugar, spread them on a baking sheet, sprinkle the sugar over them, and leave covered in a cool, but not cold, place for two or three days. The resulting mixture is tacky and amateurishly messy and will need to be removed with a palette knife from the baking sheet. Return everything to the pan, add a few teaspoons of water to prevent burning, and slowly bring the mixture just to boiling point. Remove the pieces of angelica and drain on foil, or, better still, a cake rack. When cool, make up enough fresh syrup, measured in cups of water to cups of sugar (an equal number of each) just to cover all the stems. Add the angelica to the syrup, and simmer again for about 10 minutes. Spread the pieces, lifted from the syrup by tweezers, on a foil-covered baking sheet, and dry them off in a cool oven until they are "dry" to the touch.

CANDIED COWSLIPS *(from a manuscript of 1700)*

This is a flower candy rather than a conserve. Gather flowers when the dew has gone and use the pips only (i.e., remove the calyces and retain the petals). Candy half a pound of sugar with as little water as possible, remove from the fire, and add the flowers little by little. Shake the pan to dry them.

A FOURTEENTH-CENTURY RECIPE TO CANDY VIOLETS

"Take flourys of vyolet and boyle them, presse them, tempre them uppe wyth almounds mylke or gode cowe mylke and bye it wyth almound flor and flore of rys. Sygre yt enow and putte cream thereto colour yt wyth the same that floures be on above."

COLTSFOOT SYRUP *(from an 1850 manuscript)*

Wash coltsfoot leaves and bruise or pound them with sugar and cook gently. Put into a bag with a sprig of rosemary in it and let it drain. Boil the juice until it thickens. "It cureth old coughes."

COLTSFOOT CANDY

US		*UK*
6-quart basket	coltsfoot leaves (gathered after flowers have faded)	large basket
2½ cups	water	1 pint
2 cups	sugar	1 pound
2 cups	molasses	1 pound
¼ cup	butter	2 ounces
½ level teaspoon	bicarbonate of soda	½ level teaspoon

Roughly chop and bruise a bucketful of coltsfoot leaves, gathered once the flowers have faded. The bruising may be done with a steak beater or tenderiser. Stew the chopped leaves slowly for about an hour, then strain through a very fine nylon straining bag, such as the type used in the making of homemade wine. Press the leaves well to extract all the juice. Make a syrup by melting the sugar in the warm coltsfoot juice, molasses, and a knob of butter, simmering together until everything is melted and well blended. Boil rapidly until setting point is reached, stir in the bicarbonate of soda, and be prepared for the mixture to effervesce a little. Pour out the hot candy onto a cold marble top, and as it stiffens cut into slices and twist the slices into sticks. It can also be poured into a cherry bowl, and whipped until it begins to cool. Using well-buttered fingers, pinch off pieces and twist into little sticks.

Cakes and Buns

CARAWAY ORANGE or LEMON BUNS

US		*UK*
⅓ cup	all-purpose (plain) flour	3 ounces
¼ cup	rice flour	2 ounces
¼ teaspoon	baking powder	¼ teaspoon
¼ cup	margarine or butter	2 ounces
1	egg, lightly beaten	1
	rind of an orange or lemon, grated	
	salt	
½ teaspoon	caraway seed	½ teaspoon

Sift together the flour, baking powder, and rice flour. Rub in the butter until the mixture looks crumbly, like breadcrumbs. Add a lightly beaten egg, the grated rind, and a small pinch of salt. Blend the mixture by cutting it with a knife, adding the caraway seed. With damp hands, shape into small buns and place them on a baking sheet, and bake in a preheated hot oven (400°F.) for about 15 minutes or until evenly brown.

CORIANDER CAKE

The flavor of coriander cake recalls the Biblical reference (Exodus 16:31) ". . . and the taste of it was like wafers made with honey" and (Numbers II:7) ". . . the people went about, and gathered it, and ground it in mills, or beat it in a mortar and baked it in pans, and made cakes of it. . . ." In the East, bread is flavored with coriander seed, but in Europe it is used more widely in confectionery.

US		UK
½ cup	margarine or butter	4 ounces
½ cup	granulated (caster) sugar	4 ounces
1	egg, lightly beaten	1
1 cup	all-purpose (plain) flour	8 ounces
½ teaspoon	baking powder	½ teaspoon
1 tablespoon	coriander seed	1 dessertspoon
	milk	

Cream the fat with the sugar, adding a lightly beaten egg. Sift the flour with the baking powder, fold in, and add the coriander seed and a drop of milk. Bake in a moderate oven (375°F.) for half an hour.

HERBED BREAD

The method of preparing garlic bread can be varied and chervil or oregano substituted. Slice French bread into thick pieces, butter each, and sprinkle with herbs. Put the baguette together again, wrap it in foil, and bake in a moderate oven for 10 minutes.

MARIGOLD BUNS

US		UK
⅓ cup	butter or margarine	3 ounces
1 cup	all-purpose (plain) flour	8 ounces
½ teaspoon	baking powder	½ teaspoon
2½ tablespoons	fine granulated (caster) sugar	2 tablespoons
⅓ cup	mixed candied peel	2 tablespoons
1 flower	petals from large double marigold	1 flower
⅓ cup	milk	2½ ounces
1	egg	1

Sift the flour with the baking powder and a pinch of salt. Quickly crumble the fat into the flour mixture and blend in the sugar. Wash and dry a handful of mixed dried fruit or make up a combination of white seedless raisins (sultanas), currants, chopped citrus peel, etc. Mix it well into the batter. Soak the marigold petals in a cheesecloth (muslin) bag in hot milk for a few minutes while the cake mixture is being prepared. As the milk cools, carefully add an egg, beating well all the time to ensure a smooth custard. Add this slowly to the cake mixture, stirring and mixing continuously, but gently, and work it in thoroughly with a folding action to keep the air in the finished mixture. Drop spoonfuls of the cake mixture into well-greased muffin pans (tins) and bake for 15 minutes in a moderate oven.

SEED CAKE (PLAIN)

US		UK
1 cup	all-purpose (plain) flour	8 ounces
½ teaspoon	baking powder	½ teaspoon
½ cup	margarine or butter	4 ounces
½ cup	sugar	4 ounces
3 teaspoons	caraway seed	1 ounce
1	egg, lightly beaten	1
	milk to make a stiff consistency	

Sift together the flour, baking powder, and a pinch of salt. Rub in the fat until the mixture resembles fine bread crumbs. Add sugar, caraway seed, and mix thoroughly. Make a well in the center and add a lightly beaten egg and mix. Slowly pour in sufficient milk to bind it all together to make a stiffish dropping consistency. Put into a small greased and floured cake or loaf pan; bake in a moderate oven (375°F) for half an hour.

SEED CAKE (RICH)

US		*UK*
1 cup	butter	8 ounces
1 cup	granulated (caster) sugar	8 ounces
2	eggs	2
1 teaspoon	caraway seed	1 teaspoon
⅓ cup	candied peel	3 ounces
	a pinch of grated nutmeg	
1 cup	all-purpose (plain) flour	8 ounces
½ teaspoon	baking powder	½ teaspoon
up to ¼ cup	brandy	2 tablespoons
	or	
	the same amount of light cream	

Cream together the butter and sugar; gradually add the well-beaten eggs and a little flour at the same time to prevent curdling. Mix in the caraway seed, candied peel, and a pinch of grated nutmeg. Carefully incorporate the rest of the flour, sifted with the baking powder. A little brandy can be added as liquid, but this is optional, and creamy milk or light cream may be substituted. The cake will keep longer with the brandy in it. Bake for 1 hour at 400°F.

SCENTED GERANIUM LEAVES FOR A VICTORIA SPONGE

US		*UK*
½ cup	butter or margarine	4 ounces
½ cup	granulated (caster) sugar	4 ounces
2	eggs, lightly beaten	2
½ cup	all-purpose (plain) flour	4 ounces
¼ teaspoon	baking powder	¼ teaspoon
	enough milk to bring mixture to soft consistency	
3 or 4	rose geranium leaves	3 or 4
	confectioner's (icing) sugar to dredge	
	whipped cream and strawberry jam to fill layers (optional)	

Cream the butter or margarine with the sugar and then gradually add the lightly beaten eggs. Sprinkle in a teaspoonful or two of flour to prevent curdling, then add the remainder of the flour and baking powder mixture and a little milk, if necessary, to bring the mixture to a soft dropping consistency. Grease a small cake pan. Put three or four rose geranium leaves on the bottom and drop the cake mixture on top. Bake in a moderate oven (375°F.) for half an hour, or until firm, and turn onto a cooling rack. The leaves may be left on the cake until it is cool, and the slight impression will be obliterated by a dredging of confectioner's sugar. If desired, split the cake, then put the layers together with whipped cream and a little strawberry jam.

Tisanes

The word "tisane," itself a corruption of *Ptisin*, originally referred to a decoction of pearl barley, but its meaning has now broadened to include many drinks made with herbs.

For centuries, tisanes have been used as refreshing and soothing drinks, sometimes made from the fresh or dried leaves of a plant and sometimes from the flower heads. As soporific, warming drinks that ease the digestion, tisanes have many devotees who use them as a nightcap or as a seasonal tonic. These drinks are, in fact, simple infusions and may be served sweetened by sugar or honey or with the addition of a little cold milk if desired. Chamomile, mint, and hibiscus teas were among the provisions of the 1971 Everest Expedition team. In times of hardship and famine, tisanes have often helped to maintain strength and spirits.

"Liberty Tea" was brewed in North American homes for a long time after the revenue-producing import duties imposed by the British Parliament on the American colonies early in the 1770s. First there had been the Townshend Acts of 1767, imposing duties on American imports including tea. To stop the outcry from the colonies and the fall in British exports to America, it was agreed to drop the duties, except that on tea, which was retained at threepence per pound. Martha Bockee Flint writing in North America in 1900 said "December 1773 days were full of resolute discussion and thrilling action over a matter touching every household in the land, and in principle involving the making of a new nation. Already in February 1770 at a meeting in Faneuil Hall 300 women had bound themselves to use no tea until the import clause in the Revenue Act was repealed."

Three years later at a meeting in the same hall, in Boston, it was agreed that tea should not be landed from the vessels then lying at anchor off Griffin's Wharf. The British Government, having vested interests in the Bohea tea stocks of the near-bankrupt East India Company, had authorized the shipment of tea direct to the colonies exempt of import duty, thus granting the company the monopoly. A roaring rumpus of charade-like character, sparked off by the Radicals (or Patriots) took place in December 1773 at Boston, when "three cargoes of Bohea tea were emptied into the sea. . . ." Men, many of them respected citizens of Boston, smeared their faces with lamp black or soot from the base of kettles, stuck feathers in their hair, swathed themselves in blankets and, masquerading as Indians, boarded the ships and turned 342 tea chests into the icy waters of Boston harbor.

The women of the colonies sought then to provide substitutes for tea, and made infusions or tisanes under the umbrella title of 'Liberty Tea.' *Ceanothus americanus*, foremost of the plants used in this way, became known as New Jersey Tea, *Solidago* as mountain tea, *Monarda didyma* as Oswego tea; catmint, raspberry leaf, mint, and sage were all used and, generations after, were known as "herb tea" as opposed to "store tea."

CHAMOMILE, AGRIMONY, JASMINE, ELDER

An infusion of a few dried flower heads, covered, allowed to stand for a few minutes, strained, and served hot is refreshing and relaxing. Several recipe books recommend a stronger tisane which can be made by adding the flowerheads to a pan of boiling water, simmering for 3 or 4 minutes, then allowing it to stand before straining and serving. This method is almost halfway to being a decoction rather than a true infusion.

DILL TEA

Dill seed together with chamomile flowers is a well-known tisane, popular for relief from nervous indigestion and hiccoughs.

ROSEMARY, BALM, ANGELICA, ALCHEMILLA, NETTLE, THYME, SAGE, BERGAMOT, PEPPERMINT, LEMON BALM
A sprig, or 3 or 4 fresh leaves, can be infused with ½ pint boiling water. Cover for 5 minutes. This makes a delicately flavored, refreshing drink. Strain and serve with a slice of lemon or a spoonful of honey, or alone.

SWEET CICELY, JUNIPER, CUMIN, DILL
Infusions of the seed (berries of Juniper), especially if they are freshly crushed before using, provide a further range of flavors, generally regarded as being good aids to digestion. They may be stored cold and reheated as required.

Fruit Cups

A full range of fruit juices can now be made in the kitchen by mechanical aids; leaves of various herbs may be added before or after liquidizing the fruit. The choice of flavors is infinite. Citrus fruits make the most delicious and health-giving drinks when the rinds are pared and put into a jug, filled with hot water, together with a little sugar and the freshly made juice. When chilled, they are most refreshing. Mint or lemon balm leaves soaked in the liquid while it cools add the suggestion of their aroma to the fruit cup. Honey, as an alternative to sugar, may be used for flavoring.

ICED MINT CUP
Infuse Indian tea with chopped mint leaves, in the proportion of about one part tea to three parts mint. Allow the tea to cool, strain, and to each pint add the juice of a lemon, a small bottle of pure pineapple juice, and add ice. Float fresh mint sprigs in the serving jug and decorate with a slice of lemon.

Herbs and Alcohol

Herbs are used as flavoring agents in the preparation of a range of alcoholic beverages and juleps, in addition to being the main variant in many fruit cups. The vaguely medicinal flavor and the tonic properties of such drinks as Campari and Vermouth are imparted by the aromatic herbs which are used in their preparation. Mead, a mildly alcoholic beverage of great antiquity, was made by fermenting honeyed water with strongly flavored herbs. For sack mead, the honeyed water was generally boiled with hops, before being mixed with sack. Cowslip mead was probably the dessert version, and it was a lovely amber color.

Goldwasser, a spirit originally made at Danzig, Germany, is flavored with a number of herbs and spices, among them aniseed and cinnamon; its name is very descriptive of its appearance—golden flakes swirl in the bottle as the drink is poured.

One of the popular spiced wines of the Middle Ages and later was hippocras (also catalogued as ipocras or ypocras), which was virtually a way of utilizing sour wine! By adding honey and flavoring it with spices and herbs, the drink was rendered palatable and usable. A sleeve or stocking, known as Hippocrates' sleeves was used to strain the liquid, hence the name. Chaucer knew this wine and classed it as a "made or medicinal wine" together with clary, or claree, and piement; the former was probably flavored with clary sage.

Some branded liquors have herb flavoring from seed, root, or leaf; notable ones are Kümmel (cumin and caraway seeds, and therefore considered to be a definite aid to digestion) and two of Italian origin, edelweiss and eucaliptine. Edelweiss is descriptive of the furry sugared stick in the bottle; the liquor is flavored with herbs. Eucaliptine is flavored by eucalyptus flowers rather than the more pungent leaves. The Polish Zubrowka, literally "of the bison," is vodka to which both a faint amber color and a special flavor are added by a grass on which the bison feed. A blade of the grass is always added to the bottle. The Russian Kvass, made from potato flour, is enriched and flavored with herbs, and Greek retsina is really made aromatic with the resin of a pine tree.

Sprigs of mint or borage are often added to punches; bergamot, borage, balm, verbena, violet, rose, jasmine, bean, and sweet pea flowers can be floated on the surface to enhance the bouquet and delight the eye.

Today, Americans drink a far wider range of juleps, cobblers, and coolers than Europeans. The plethora of recipes, each with its local adherents, provide unending variations on a theme. Invariably, the subtlety of flavor is imparted by a herb or plant material, but the basis of a cobbler is either apple jack, cider, champagne, bourbon whisky, sherry, or claret. Shaved or crushed ice in quantity is used; orange and lemon slices and berries in season are added together with the bruised leaves of mint or borage.

Today, most commercially sold wines are made from grape juice, but the old wines were more unusual, home made, and served with much pride; almost any vegetable or fruit could be used. Various roots, parsnips, artichokes, beets, carrot, and eryngium, and flowers and berries like elder, cowslip, the rosy stems of rhubarb, gooseberries, blackberries, apples, pears, peaches, and apricots—practically anything that grew, in fact. Sometimes these country wines marketed in Britain were under high-sounding names; English champagne was gooseberry wine, and English port was elderberry wine.

Juleps

Behold this cordial Julep here,
That foams and dances in his crystal bounds
With spirits of balm and fragrant syrups mix'd

MILTON

A MARYLAND JULEP

Sprigs of mint
A full measure (jigger) of bourbon
A sugar lump
Crushed ice

Crush the sugar lump in the base of a tall glass; bruise 6 sprigs of mint between the fingers, drop into the glass, and add half the whisky. Allow to stand for 10 minutes. Add the remainder of the whisky, and fill the glass with crushed ice. Stir rapidly with a spoon or swizzle stick until the outside of the glass clouds. Garnish with the remaining mint sprigs.

The author is indebted to Doris Frost, former editor of *The Herbalist*, the publication of the Herb Society of America, for the two following recipes.

SOUTHERN MINT JULEP

Crush 4 sprigs of fresh mint with $\frac{1}{2}$ tablespoon of powdered or caster sugar. Add a measure of bourbon rye. Fill the tankard (mug) with cracked or crushed ice, and stir gently until the tankard is frosted. Add three mint sprigs to garnish.

BLUE GRASS MINT JULEP

For each tankard, cover 12 or 15 leaves of mint with powdered or caster sugar and add just enough water to dissolve; this needs only a sprinkling of water. Crush gently for 5 minutes. Put half the mint and liquid into a glass and half fill with crushed or shaved ice. Leave the glass in the ice box or refrigerator for at least 2 hours. An hour prior to serving, fill up with bourbon whiskey. Immediately before serving, decorate with 2 sprigs of mint and sprinkle with powdered or caster sugar and insert a drinking straw. If the contents of the glass are too frozen use an ice pick to insert the straw.

AN OLD VIRGINIAN RECIPE FOR MINT JULEP

Allow 2 teaspoons of sugar and 3 teaspoons of water to each glass. Add a generous amount of fresh mint leaves. Crush everything together with a mortar and pestle until the mixture is greenish in appearance. Put 3 teaspoons of the liquid into each glass and pack in finely crushed ice and fill up with bourbon. Garnish with a sprig of mint and serve at once. If the traditional silver goblets are unavailable, then aluminum or glass highball glasses may be used, which should be rinsed in water and then put into the freezer to frost over.

opposite Two views of the Western Reserve Herb Society's garden, Cleveland, Ohio.

PART III

A Modern Herbal

English Name	*Botanical Name*	*Natural Order*
Aconite	*Aconitum napellus*	Ranunculaceae
Acorus	*Acorus calamus*	Araceae
Agrimony	*Agrimonia eupatoria*	Rosaceae
Alecost	*Tanacetum balsamita* (Syn. *Chrysanthemum balsamita*)	Compositae
Alehoof (*See* Ground Ivy.)		
Alexanders	*Smyrnium olusatrum*	Umbelliferae
Alkanet	*Pentaglottis sempervirens* (Syn. *Anchusa sempervirens*)	Boraginaceae
Allspice	*Calycanthus floridus*	Calycanthaceae
American Spikenard	*Aralia racemosa*	Araliaceae
Angelica	*Angelica archangelica*	Umbelliferae
Arnica	*Arnica montana*	Compositae
Artemisia	*Artemisia* spp.	Compositae
Artichoke (*See* Sunflower.)		
Balm	*Melissa officinalis*	Labiatae
Balsam (*See* Jewel-weed.)		
Basil	*Ocimum basilicum*	Labiatae
Bay	*Laurus nobilis*	Lauraceae
Belladonna	*Atropa belladonna*	Solanaceae
Bergamot	*Monarda didyma*	Labiatae
Betony	*Stachys officinalis*	Labiatae
Bistort	*Polygonum bistorta*	Polygonaceae
Borage	*Borago officinalis*	Boraginaceae
Bryony, White	*Bryonia dioica*	Cucurbitaceae
Burdock, Great	*Arctium lappa*	Compositae
Burnet	*Sanguisorba* spp.	Rosaceae
Calamint	*Calamintha ascendens*	Labiatae
Caper Spurge	*Euphorbia lathyris*	Euphorbiaceae
Caraway	*Carum carvi*	Umbelliferae
Carnation	*Dianthus caryophyllus*	Caryophyllaceae
Catmint	*Nepeta cataria*	Labiatae
Celandine	*Chelidonium majus*	Papaveraceae
Celandine, Lesser	*Ranunculus ficaria*	Ranunculaceae
Centaurea	*Centaurea* spp.	Compositae
Centaury	*Centaurium minus*	Gentianaceae
Chamomile	*Anthemis nobilis*	Compositae
Cherry	*Prunus* spp.	Rosaceae
Chervil	*Anthriscus cerefolium*	Umbelliferae
Chicory	*Cichorium intybus*	Compositae
Chives	*Allium schoenoprasum*	Liliaceae
Cinquefoil	*Potentilla reptans*	Rosaceae
Clary	*Salvia horminum* *Salvia sclarea*	Labiatae
Clematis	*Clematis vitalba*	Ranunculaceae
Coltsfoot	*Tussilago farfara*	Compositae
Comfrey	*Symphytum officinale*	Boraginaceae

English Name	Botanical Name	Natural Order
Coriander	*Coriandrum sativum*	Umbelliferae
Corn salad	*Valerianella locusta*	Valerianaceae
Costmary (*See* Alecost.)		
Cotton lavender	*Santolina chamaecyparissus*	Compositae
Cow parsley	*Anthriscus sylvestris*	Umbelliferae
Cowslip	*Primula veris*	Primulaceae
Cumin	*Cumium cyminum*	Umbelliferae
Curry plant	*Helichrysum angustifolium*	Compositae
Dandelion, Common	*Taraxacum officinale*	Compositae
Daphne	*Daphne mezereum*	Thymelaeaceae
Dill	*Anethum graveolens*	Umbelliferae
Elder, Elderberry	*Sambucus nigra*	Caprifoliaceae
Elecampane	*Inula helenium*	Compositae
Eryngium	*Eryngium maritimum*	Umbelliferae
Fennel	*Foeniculum officinale*	Umbelliferae
Fenugreek	*Trigonella foenum-graecum*	Leguminaceae
Feverfew	*Chrysanthemum parthenium*	Compositae
Foxglove	*Digitalis purpurea*	Scrophulariaceae
Fritillary	*Fritillaria meleagris*	Liliaceae
Garlic	*Allium sativum*	Liliaceae
Gentian	*Gentiana lutea*	Gentianaceae
Geranium	*Geranium* spp.	Geraniaceae
Goat's rue	*Galega officinalis*	Leguminosae
Good King Henry	*Chenopodium bonus-henricus*	Chenopodiaceae
Ground ivy	*Glechoma hederacea*	Labiatae
Hellebore	*Helleborus niger*	Ranunculaceae
Hemlock	*Conium maculatum*	Umbelliferae
Hemp agrimony	*Eupatorium cannabinum*	Compositae
Henbane	*Hyocyamus niger*	Solanaceae
Horehound, Black	*Ballota nigra*	Labiatae
Horehound, White	*Marrubium vulgare*	Labiatae
Horse-radish	*Cochlearia rusticana*	Cruciferae
Hound's-tongue	*Cynoglossum officinale*	Boraginaceae
Houseleek	*Sempervivum tectorum*	Crassulaceae
Hyssop	*Hyssopus officinalis*	Labiatae
Indigo	*Indigofera tinctoria*	Leguminosae
Iris	*Iris* spp.	Iridaceae
Jasmine	*Jasminum officinale*	Oleacaea
Jewel-weed	*Impatiens* spp.	Balsaminaceae
Juniper	*Juniperus communis*	Cupressaceae
Lady's-mantle	*Alchemilla vulgaris*	Rosaceae
Lavender	*Lavandula officinalis*	Labiatae
Licorice	*Glycyrrhiza glabra*	Leguminosae
Lily-of-the-valley	*Convallaria majalis*	Liliaceae
Lime	*Tilia europaea*	Tiliaceae
Lovage	*Ligusticum officinale*	Umbelliferae
Lung-wort	*Pulmonaria officinalis*	Boraginaceae
Madder	*Rubia tinctorum*	Rubiaceae
Mallow	*Malva* spp.	Malvaceae
	Althaea officinalis	Malvaceae
Marigold	*Calendula officinalis*	Compositae
Marjoram	*Origanum* spp.	Labiatae
Meadow-sweet	*Filipendula ulmaria*	Rosaceae
Melilot, Common	*Melilotus officinalis*	Papilionaceae
Mignonette	*Reseda odorata*	Resedaceae
Milkwort	*Polygala* spp.	Polygalaceae
Mint	*Mentha* spp.	Labiatae
Mullein	*Verbascum thapsus*	Scrophulariaceae
Myrtle	*Myrtus communis*	Myrtaceae
Nasturtium	*Tropaeolum majus*	Tropaeolaceae
Nettle, Stinging	*Urtica dioica*	Urticaceae

English Name	*Botanical Name*	*Natural Order*
Nipplewort	*Lapsana communis*	Compositae
Onion	*Allium* spp.	Liliaceae
Parsley	*Petroselinum crispum*	Umbelliferae
Parsley piert (*See* Lady's-mantle.)		
Pasque flower	*Pulsatilla vulgaris*	Ranunculaceae
Pelargonium	*Pelargonium* spp.	Geraniaceae
Pellitory-of-the-wall	*Parietaria diffusa* (Syn. *P. officinalis*)	Urticaceae
Periwinkle	*Vinca major* *Vinca minor*	Apocynaceae
Poppy	*Papaver* spp.	Papaveraceae
Purslane	*Portulaca oleracea*	Portulacaceae
Pyrethrum	*Pyrethrum coccineum*	Compositae
Rhubarb	*Rheum officinale*	Polygonaceae
Rose	*Rosa gallica officinalis*	Rosaceae
Rosemary	*Rosmarinus officinalis*	Labiatae
Rue	*Ruta graveolens*	Rutaceae
Saffron	*Crocus sativus*	Iridaceae
Sage	*Salvia officinalis*	Labiatae
Samphire, Rock	*Crithmum maritimum*	Umbelliferae
Savory	*Satureja* spp.	Labiatae
Seaweeds	*Fucaceae* *Laminariaceae*	
Self-heal	*Prunella vulgaris*	Labiatae
Soapwort	*Saponaria officinalis*	Caryophyllaceae
Solomon's seal	*Polygonatum* spp.	Liliaceae
Sorrel	*Rumex acetosa*	Polygonaceae
Spikenard	*Inula conyza*	Compositae
St John's wort	*Hypericum* spp.	Hypericaceae
Sunflower	*Helianthus annuus*	Compositae
Sweet Cicely	*Myrrhis odorata*	Umbelliferae
Tansy	*Tanacetum vulgare*	Compositae
Tarragon	*Artemisia dracunculus*	Compositae
Thistle	*Silybum marianum* *Carduus benedictus*	Compositae
Thorn-apple	*Datura stramonium*	Solanaceae
Thyme	*Thymus vulgaris (et al.)*	Labiatae
Tobacco plant	*Nicotiana tabacum*	Solanaceae
Valerian	*Valeriana officinalis*	Valerianaceae
Veratrum	*Veratrum viride*	Liliaceae
Verbena, Lemon	*Lippia citriodora*	Verbenaceae
Vervain	*Verbena officinalis*	Verbenaceae
Violet	*Viola odorata*	Violaceae
Wall Germander	*Teucrium chamaedrys*	Labiatae
Watercress	*Nasturtium officinale*	Cruciferae
Willow-herb	*Chamaenerion angustifolium*	Onagraceae
Wintergreen	*Gaultheria procumbens*	Ericaceae
Witch Hazel	*Hamamelis virginiana*	Hamamelidaceae
Woodruff, Sweet	*Asperula odorata*	Rubiaceae
Yarrow	*Achillea millefolium*	Compositae

ACONITE

Aconitum napellus
RANUNCULACEAE

A poisonous plant whose lethal properties have been written about, sometimes in quite lurid terms, the monkshood is still a favorite flowering perennial in many gardens. Nurserymen who specialize in hardy perennials offer it in their catalogues, and cultivars such as 'Spark's Variety,' 'Newry Blue,' and 'Bressingham Spire' are well worth introducing into the decorative border or herb garden. The Latin name commemorates the hill Aconitus, in Pontica, where Hercules fought with Cerberus, the many-headed watchdog at the gates of the underworld; from Cerberus's foam the plant supposedly sprang venomous with poison in all its parts, from flower to root. Homeopathic chemists use the fresh flowering spike, the straight spurred flowers being preferable, but it is the roots which yield aconitine, used as a febrifuge (fever reducer) and to reduce the pulse rate. It is now little grown on drug farms; in the early years of the present century, its commercial cultivation in Britain virtually ceased because of the wide use of the cheaper German and Japanese roots. The last edition of the British Pharmacopoeia to stipulate British-grown aconite was that of 1898.

Aconitums prefer a rich cool soil, are tolerant of shade, but make better plants when grown in a sunny position. Moisture-retentive material should be added to the soil or lower plants grown around the base to shade it so that the soil does not dry out. Propagation is from seed or by division in spring or autumn, and once the plants are established, which may take a season or two, they can be left to fend for themselves. The flower spikes reach three feet or so and are strong, requiring staking only in the most exposed positions. Commercially, roots are harvested early in the autumn when they are firm and mature.

The English names of "helmet flower," "monkshood," and "old wife's hood" clearly allude to the shape of this blue flower. The name "wolf's bane" strictly belongs to *A. lycotonum,* a somewhat variable species with yellow flowers appearing later in the year; it is less poisonous than *A. napellus.* But which one of the species was used as a poison bait for wolves in the thirteenth and fourteenth centuries is certainly of little consequence now. In a representative herb collection of drug plants, monkshood should certainly be included, but it should always be handled carefully. Wear gloves, especially when dividing clumps of aconite, and be even more careful if there are cuts or scratches on the hands or arms. It is not without good reason that this herb was called by the ancients "the queen mother of poisons."

ACORUS

Acorus calamus
ARACEAE

The sweet flag, *Acorus calamus,* is not native to Britain. It ranges over the north-temperate regions of Europe, eastward to the Himalayas, and is known in central and western North America, especially in swamp conditions in Minnesota and south to Louisiana and Kansas. A plant of the water's edge, of shallow lakes and marshes, it has stout rhizomatous roots and sword-like leaves that smell of tangerine when bruised. The aroma of all its parts earns it such local names as "myrtle grass," "myrtle sedge," "cinnamon sedge," and "sweet rush." It was recommended to the allied French and British armies during the Crimean War in 1854 as their remedy against marsh pestilence—quinine being in short supply.

The sword-like leaves, three or four feet in height, are distinguishable from those of *Iris pseudacorus* by their wavy margins. The dried rhizomes are used as a febrifuge by herbalists and were also used, until World War II, by veterinary surgeons. Its main value was in perfumery, employed in the manner of orris-root, with which it has commonly been confused. French snuff *à la violette* is scented by the inclusion of acorus, and in the past it was employed in brewing and the flavoring of herbal beers. Acorus used to be cultivated commercially in the marshes of Cambridgeshire, England.

The plants may be readily propagated by division of the old clumps of rhizomes, and they will thrive in relatively dry soil;

though in the wild state, they are always indicative of boggy land. Damp ditches can be beautified by planting with the root pieces or rhizomes about a foot apart, in early autumn. The form *variegatus* has smaller leaves striped cream and gold and is a particularly handsome garden plant.

AGRIMONY

Agrimonia eupatoria
ROSACEAE

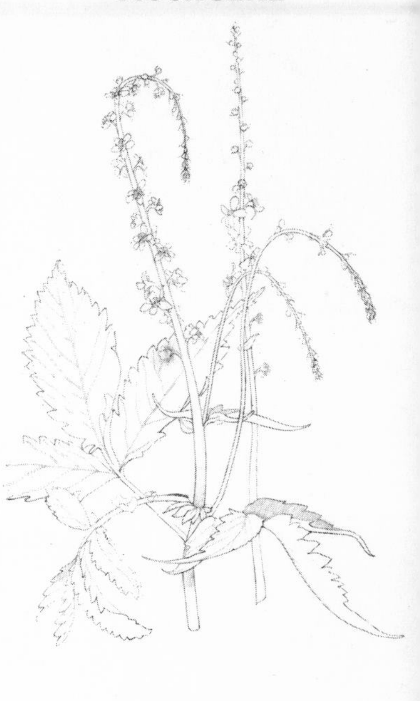

Agrimony is a native plant in Britain; its yellow flower spires, which earn it the name of "church steeples," are a familiar sight in hedgerows and field verges in all districts except Scotland. Its European range is extensive. For centuries, agrimony wine and agrimony tea have been drunk, both having a flavor reminiscent of apricots; and a few ounces of the dried whole herb enclosed in a muslin bag and suspended in home-made cider will enhance the flavor and impart its cleansing tonic qualities.

Culpeper credits agrimony with numerous virtues when taken as a drink and suggests that, bruised and applied to the joints, it alleviates gout; and mixed with "old swine's grease, it helpeth old sores, cancers, and inveterate ulcers, and draweth forth thorns and splinters of wood, nails or any other such things gotten into the flesh." And it was once believed to be an antidote to snake bite, although there is no real evidence to substantiate this claim.

Unlike most herbs, it is harvested when in flower, from June onwards, and the agrimony tea includes the flower, stem, and leaves. As a tonic drink in centuries gone by, it acquired the name "liverwort"; as Culpeper carefully explains, "The liver is the former of the blood, the blood the nourisher of the body, and agrimony the strengthener of the liver." Anne Pratt writing in 1892 says of the plant: "It has always, and not without reason, been believed to possess many tonic properties and it was mingled in all the most important drinks of the old physicians, and is still used in cottages." When the late Mrs. C. F. Leyel modernized Culpeper's herbal in 1961, she noted that agrimony is still regarded as efficacious in the treatment of rheumatism and arthritis. A teaspoon of the herb in a wineglass of hot water is the recommended strength of the tisane, infused for a quarter of an hour before drinking. The infusion is to this day considered to be of some value to the eyesight —some little confirmation of Eleanor Sinclair Rhode's derivation of the name from the Greek *argemon,* a white speck on the eye, which the plant is supposed to cure.

Conjecture, half-truth, tradition, and old wives' tales constantly surround the roles that plants have played or are purported to have played in the past. Agrimony is one of many about which very much could be written with tongue in cheek.

> Succory to match the sky
> Columbine with horn of honey
> Scented fern and agrimony
> Clover, catch-fly, —adder's tongue
> And brier-roses, dwelt among.

When Emerson wrote these lines, he must have known a Chiltern lane in England, for he describes the ecology to perfection.

Agrimony is tolerant of a wide range of soils and situations; but consider its natural habitat and do not expect it to flourish in baked solitude. It likes neighbors.

ALECOST

Tanacetum balsamita
(Syn. *Chrysanthemum balsamita)*
COMPOSITAE

Alecost, or "costmary," as it was more popularly known throughout the sixteenth and seventeenth centuries, when it was grown in every garden, imparts a spicy flavor to beer; and as its therapeutic value declined—or lost favor—it may well have been that it lingered in cultivation merely to provide an addition to home-brewed beer. Culpeper describes it as "an inhabitant in almost every garden;" and so it is justifiably classed as an old-world plant.

Closely related to tansy, it spreads quickly, with its roots scarcely below the soil surface, and should be pulled up and divided (and parts discarded) every three years or so. Give it a sunny well-drained spot in the herb garden. Its habit is strangely untidy, with yellow flowers graceless atop straggly stalks; the whole plant almost seems more appealing with flower stems removed and is certainly neater! Its lax habit evidently displeased Sir John Hill for, in his eighteenth-century *Family Herbal,* he describes costmary as "a garden plant kept more for its virtues than its beauty." Several virtues had formerly been ascribed to it, one being its beneficial action on the digestive tract. It used to be added to whey, just as chives are added to cottage cheese today. A tisane made of the leaves, either dried or fresh, was considered to be a refreshing tonic and blood-purifier; the bruised leaves, rubbed on bee stings, will relieve the pain.

In Elizabethan days, it was grown as a strewing herb, useful because of its tough texture and strong aroma. It was introduced from the Orient into Europe in the sixteenth century, where it seems to have become an economic plant quite quickly.

ALEHOOF

(*See* GROUND IVY)

ALEXANDERS

Smyrnium olusatrum
UMBELLIFERAE

An erect-growing perennial herb, named after its homeland, the coastal regions around Alexandria, in North Africa. No doubt introduced into Britain by the Romans, it has since been dubbed "Alexandrian parsley," or "horse parsley," having been used as a flavoring in the intervening centuries, though it seems little known today. The leaves have a myrrh-like aroma, adding flavor to soups, sauces, and salads.

Alexanders will clamber up cliffs and sea headlands, still managing to stand erect up to three feet in height against the fiercest gales on the Irish coast and in southern England. The yellowish-green flowers appear in April and May and are faintly scented; they are succeeded by broad, black ridged seeds which, on ripening, emit a warm spicy aroma and pungent flavor; the dark green foliage is deeply divided. The plant was used in ancient days to relieve dropsy, and the ribbed stems have been cultivated as a substitute for celery. Culpeper calls it "house parsley," "alisander," or "black pot herb," "the seed of it is that which is usually sold in apothecaries shops for Macedonian Parsley Seed!" He puts it under Jupiter's influence and says it is "therefore friendly to nature, for it warmeth a cold stomach and openeth a stoppage of the liver and spleen; it is good to expel the after birth . . ."

Propagation is simple and is effected by sowing seed in open ground in April or May; most plants will flower and seed the following year, though they may display the tendency of all umbelliferous plants to produce flowers quickly.

ALKANET

Pentaglottis sempervirens
(syn. *Anchusa sempervirens*)
BORAGINACEAE

Both these names were known to Gerard. Probably an introduced plant now naturalized in England, especially in the southwest, it is usually found in the vicinity of old demolished buildings, for it thrives on well-drained ballast. It is generally, but not prolifically, extended over Europe.

The alkanet bears the rough dark green leaves typical of the anchusas. The blue flowers are borne in twisted cymes and may be pulled from their calyces and floated in fruit cups and wine punches. Similarly, borage flowers (with which the alkanet is frequently confused) can be used to add interest to fruit drinks. The bark of the root yields a red dye which was formerly used by cabinet-makers for staining wood. The whole anchusa family yields a good indelible red dye; and the name alkanet is derived from the Spanish *alcanna,* itself taken from the Arabic *al-henna,* the henna plant.

Small and bushy, attaining only about 1½–2 feet in both height and spread, it is a first-class plant to introduce into the herb garden, and it provides summer flowers of the deepest blue from May to August and good sturdy rough leaves throughout the year.

ALLSPICE

Calycanthus floridus
CALYCANTHACEAE

An American deciduous shrub hailing from the Carolinas, sometimes seen cultivated in gardens in Great Britain, it is known in America as "Carolina allspice." A particularly lovely specimen is to be seen in the old rose garden near the dovecot at Rousham in Oxfordshire, England. *Calycanthus occidentalis,* the Californian allspice, is somewhat taller in growth, reaching perhaps ten feet, but of an untidy, straggling habit. Both have reddish flowers, but those of *C. floridus* are an unusual brown-red compared with the more orthodox purple-red of the Californian allspice. The latter compensates for its more ordinary appearance with a stronger aroma of bark and leaf. Both need a sheltered position and rich soil, but with reasonable care they are a tribute to any herb garden. The flowers have a rather strange appearance and look like clusters of strap-like petals. The Greek name gives the clue, *kalyx,* a cup or calyx, and *anthos,* a flower, emphasizing the fact that the calyces are colored like the flower and in fact appear petaloid.

Propagation is possible from seed, or from layering in July, and the presence of a protective building, or stouter shrubs, will ensure success. The calycanthus plants do not provide commercial allspice but are grown mainly for their sweet aroma in the herb garden.

AMERICAN SPIKENARD

Aralia racemosa
ARALIACEAE

Tolerantly hardy in British damp winters, the American spikenard makes an interesting addition to the herb border. Hailing from North America, its creeping rootstock supports stems rising three to five feet and bearing many clusters of greenish-white flowers in June and dark purplish berries, which birds devour, in September. It was introduced into Europe in the mid-seventeenth century and is a representative of the ginseng family; ginseng itself *(Panax quinquefolium)* grows in the rich soil of woods from Quebec and Ontario south to Alabama and westward to Minnesota and Nebraska where plant hunters have not succeeded in exterminating it. American spikenard, on the other hand, has a more southern range on the North American continent and is found in rich woodland from New Brunswick to Minnesota, South Dakota, Georgia, and Missouri. It will flourish in semi-shade and is worth adding to a herb collection for its fine foliage. The root is aromatic and exudes a viscous substance.

A. nudicaulis, the wild, false, or American sarsaparilla, attaining the same height, is also justifiably included in representative drug-plant collections. It is of some therapeutic value for the relief of pulmonary troubles, but the true sarsaparilla is a Mexican plant. The young leaves are a burnished bronze, the flowers greenish-white, and the rhizomes run about in dampish rich soil but may be kept down by raiding rabbits, who love them.

ANGELICA

Angelica archangelica
UMBELLIFERAE

Angelica, universally known by its Latin name, it seems, is a plant of the angels and archangels. The story runs that a monk was inspired by an angelic messenger in a vision or dream to use the plant therapeutically as an antidote to the plague and pestilence. The fable appears in several languages in various guises, and Culpeper advanced his own intriguing theory about the name:

> In time of heathenism when men found out any excellent herb; they dedicated it to their gods; as the bay-tree to Apollo, the oak to Jupiter, the vine to Bacchus, the poplar to Hercules. These the papists following as the patriachs, they dedicate

to their saints; as our Lady's Thistle to the Blessed Virgin, St. John's Wort to St. John, and another Wort to St. Peter, etc. Our physicians must imitate like apes (though they cannot come off so cleverly) for they blasphemously call Phansies or Hearts Ease *an herb of the Trinity,* because it is of three colours: And a certain ointment *an ointment of the Apostles* because it consists of twelve ingredients . . . [The papists called this] an herb of the *Holy Ghost;* others more moderate called it *Angelica,* because of its angelical virtues, and that name it retains still and all nations follow it so near as their dialect will permit.

Whatever one believes about its name, the uses for angelica throughout the centuries remained constant. All references agree that it cleared stomach aches and flatulence, and there seems no doubt that it has been eaten raw, stewed, candied, or taken as an infusion of leaf, stem, or root (the latter being the strongest) for a number of complaints from intestinal pains to clearing the eyes, ears, or "holes in the teeth." To bite or chew the root of angelica was a common recommendation as protection from the Great Plague of London in 1665.

The hollow stems are the characteristic by which even non-botanists recognize the plant. Even in its wild form *(Angelica sylvestris)* they are typical; but although the plant resembles closely other members of its ubiquitous natural order, the stems are of a quality inferior to that of the cultivated forms. The wild form *(A. sylvestris)* has white flowers and slightly hairy stems, whereas the garden or cultivated plant, *A. archangelica,* produces yellowish flowers in loose umbels in July and August. It is best to harvest both leaves and stems before the plant flowers and before the stems have coarsened. Strictly a biennial, an annual sowing should be made if the plants are grown for their stems; the alternative is to spare some plants to flower and seed and thus perpetuate the colony in the herb garden.

Its medicinal uses are part of the myth of plant lore, but it is popularly used in present times—the candied stem is a well-known confection for decorating cakes. Angelica's flavor resembles that of juniper berries (the seed is sometimes used to adulterate gin), and the leaves infused make a refreshing drink not unlike China tea, but much improved by the addition of a slice of lemon or a spoonful of honey according to taste. It can be used as a diuretic. The candying of angelica stem is explained on page 63.

A shady position in not too rich a soil is the ideal spot to choose, bearing in mind that the plants can grow as tall as eight feet. In the herb garden, angelica is a "back of the border" plant or can be used to good effect to give height to a central bed or form a quick screen. The leaves are a dark bright green, deeply indented, aromatic—a rare quality for plants native of the Northern Hemisphere. Seeds should be sown *in situ* in early spring, or in pots, boxes, frames, or under cloches in winter and pricked off, transplanted and set out in rows two feet apart if a crop of stems is to be harvested. The self-sown seedlings appear quickly at the end of the season and can be transplanted then or early the following spring.

ARNICA

Arnica montana
COMPOSITAE

A plant native of the mountainous regions of Europe, cultivated in both Great Britain and America, it has come to be called "mountain arnica." It is a handsome plant with a rosette of broad, ribbed leaves and golden yellowish flowers borne singly—once seen growing in the European Alps, arnica is never to be forgotten. Shunned for its crazily publicized poisonous properties, it is erroneously condemned as having the power to cause a sore throat followed by noises in the ears, stomach spasms, high blood pressure or hypertension, sleeplessness, neuralgia, debility of sight, trembling, and depression. Used in the right way arnica is one of the best-known healing herbs. Many a poisonous herb can be a blessing in disguise, and tincture of arnica, extracted mainly from the flowers, is used in homeopathic treatment. Painted on to the skin or applied as a compress, it is immediately effective in relieving intense itching, chilblains, insect bites, and the like.

In mountainous regions it is to be found at altitudes from 3,000 to 6,000 feet, and its leaves are used by the peasants to make a tobacco, in France known as *tabac des savoyards, tabac des vosges,* and *herbe aux prêcheurs.* Considered a curative since the Middle Ages, flowers are gathered in July and dried quickly, leaves being taken before flowering or in September, and the short rhizomatous root is lifted and washed in September when fully mature. All parts are used, both for the "tobacco" and for making the tincture.

ARTEMISIA

Artemisia spp.
COMPOSITAE

About 200 species of artemisia inhabit the steppes of Eastern Europe, several are to be found wild over vast areas of Europe and North Africa, and a few are natives of the British Isles. As garden escapes, or casuals, they are found in many localities especially on wasteland and on the dry thinner soils of the northern hills of England; in North America, about forty species are native and found in similar situations, though other species there have been introduced.

Most are shrubby or sub-shrubs and very decorative as garden plants. No herb garden is complete without them, be it a collection for effect or for association. Grown today primarily for their aromatic and attractively dainty foliage—the flowers are generally of no consequence—the artemisias have grown up with a wide variety of common and country names. Think of these plants mainly as old cottage-garden residents, as monastic dwellers, and as beautifiers of the vast and otherwise barren slopes of Eastern Europe. The name "artemisia" commemorates the Greek goddess of chastity, Artemis (the Roman Diana), and apart from its aroma, the plant has been grown essentially as a tonic, febrifuge, aperitif and liquor flavorer to aid digestion, quell travel sickness—and to kill flies!

Thomas Tusser recorded in 1538 that its long arching sprays of silver green foliage were used for strewing, and as the foliage was crushed underfoot, no doubt the odor was instantly released. All the artemisias give off their scent better if the foliage is crushed or rubbed between the fingers. *Artemisia absinthium,* known universally as a wormwood, is a plant native of Europe from Lapland to the Mediterranean, from Spain to Central Asia, and has been introduced into America and, in the Southern Hemisphere, to New Zealand. By tradition it is reputed to have flourished along the path of the serpent in the Garden of Eden. Undeniably one of the most universally known and valued plants of European apothecaries and botanists since medieval times, artemisia was already known to them for its use in antiquity as an antidote for the poisoning effects of fungi and hemlock and as a flavoring for drinks.

With rue, artemisia was put in the dock beside the prisoners to prevent the spread of the infectious jail fever, and in ancient times it was used by travelers as a deterrent of disease, in the form of a girdle, a garland, or a switch. In Germany it is sometimes still known as "St. John's girdle" and in Sicily as "St. John's beard." There appear to be romantic associations, too: on St. Luke's Day, with the help of artemisia, a maiden would dream of the man she was destined to marry. Its vernacular names in various districts of England are "wormwood," "warmot," "absinth," and "mongwort." It grows erect, is somewhat bushy in form and silky to touch, and has drooping dull yellow flowerheads.

The unique flavor is intensely bitter. The plant is still used medicinally today and is an important ingredient in the manufacture of Chartreuse and Pernod. All Mediterranean countries have their anise-flavored drinks, and perhaps the most popular with visitors to these southern countries is Pernod. It is reputed to have been brewed first by the improbably named Dr. Ordinaire when he escaped to Switzerland from France at the time of the Revolution, though what he actually made was absinthe. In the middle of the nineteenth century, two quite separate firms began the commercial production of absinthe and called it Pernod. "Pernod" because this, apparently, happened to be the name of both business families concerned; Hermard Pernod was the one company, and Pernod Père et Fils the other. The recipes used by both companies were similar, and wormwood was a major ingredient of the liquor they produced. In 1915 the French Government legislated against the use of the depressant, wormwood, and their livelihoods threatened, the two manufacturers of Pernod fought a joint court action. The outcome was that wormwood was dropped from the Pernod recipe and the two firms combined to manufacture Pernod 45, its own unique flavor from then on achieved by the use of *Illicium verum* and *Illicium anisatum*, colloquially known in France as *anis étoile* or *badiane*; both are native plants of China.

It is *Artemisia absinthium* that is used in the Chinese practice of moxa. Similar to acupuncture in theory, moxa is not so well known in Europe. Small cones or cylinders of artemisia, dried and powdered, are placed on points of the body defined by the moxa-charts, fired by a taper or burning joss-stick, and allowed to burn down so as to cause a small blister on the skin. The ash is then rubbed into the blister.

Artemisia abrotanum, an indigenous plant over the whole of Europe, is a cottage-garden dweller in the British Isles and is now firmly established as a garden escape in many places; it has collected a variety of common names over the years: "old man," "lad's love," "southernwood," and "maiden's ruin." Apparently, it was customary to plant it outside gardens perhaps to add it freely to nosegays given as a country favor (hence its name of "lad's love"); or perhaps its gnarled black twigs in winter were so unattractive that the cottager did not feel justified in sparing valuable ground. Its winter appearance is surely the reason for its being known as "old man." The foliage is soft to touch, green and feathery, and very aromatic. It can be incorporated with some discretion in potpourri, but a little is enough because of the intensity of its aroma. Nicholas Culpeper described it as "a gallant Mercurial plant, worthy of more esteem than it hath" and gives several odd remedies in which it was an ingredient. Mixed with roasted quince and boiled with a few bread crumbs, he asserts that it "taketh away inflammation in the eyes," and mixed with ashes and old salad oil it "restoreth the hair and cures baldness." He tells us, too, that the Germans called it "stabwort," a cure for wounds. In France it is *garde-robe* because of its power to keep moths from the wardrobe.

Artemisia vulgaris, another indigenous plant, extends over the temperate regions of the Northern Hemisphere as far north as Siberia. Despite its common name "mugwort," its uses and virtues have been extolled for centuries. The Romany mugwort tea is taken in the damp, cold days of winter as a warming nightcap, and Romany lore has it that you should therefore "wake as fresh as the spring." It is made from dried flowers, infused with boiling water. It is a known diuretic. It is also known as the friend of the traveler, and sprigs put in the shoes (ouch!) are supposed to lighten the step and shorten the road! It also acts as a deterrent to flies and moths, and is said to keep evil spirits at bay.

Artemisia verlotorum, a species bearing a very strong resemblance to *A. vulgaris,* has been dubbed "Chinese mugwort," and is indeed a native of China. Established in southeastern England since World War II, it has spread in the counties around London, despite the fact that it does not flower until October and so cannot ripen seed in England. David McLintock, however, has recorded in his *Companion to Flowers* that it has been known in Britain since 1908 and in Europe since 1873. Easily distinguishable from the commoner mugwort by its fresh greenness remaining long after the native species has faded, it is highly aromatic in all its parts and makes a useful addition to potpourri. The only way to introduce it into the garden is by acquiring a piece of rhizomatous root stock from the wild.

The sage brush of western North America is the pungent gray-leaved *Artemisia tridentata,* an evergreen introduced into British gardens about 1895. Cultivation of all the artemisias is simple. Pruning away dead, straggly, or unwanted shoots in the autumn is all that is required, or growth can be cropped right to ground level for a splendid freshly silvered supply of arching sprays the following year.

ARTICHOKE

(*See* SUNFLOWER.)

BALM

Melissa officinalis
LABIATAE

A sweet-scented perennial herb, sometimes called lemon balm on account of its aroma, balm is cultivated for use as a flavoring to stuffings for veal and poultry, sandwich spreads, and salad variation. Balm is occasionally seen as an escape, but then it is somewhat coarsened by its fight for survival. Beloved of bees, it was used by apiarists in the seventeenth and eighteenth centuries to contain bees within a hive, particularly if they were restless. The Latin name *Melissa* is from the Greek for "bee," and so apparently the plant and its attraction for bees were well known to the ancient world. In the temple of Diana, it was one of the sacred herbs.

Balm is easy to cultivate; once established in the herb garden, it remains. Its dark green sturdy leaves are not unlike those of the nettle in form, and its flowers are smallish and white. Seed sets easily in temperate zones and germinates well even after two or three years. When the bees hibernate, the plant disappears below ground for the winter.

Once dried, the leaves retain their aroma and can be included in potpourri. When destined for this use, they must be gathered dry in June or July.

BALSAM

Balsam is strictly an aromatic resinous medicinal preparation, usually insoluble in water and of varying form, used as a healing agent. It has been incorporated in the common names of a number of plants and comes originally from the Latin *balsamum* ("healing").

(*See* JEWEL WEED.)

BASIL

Ocimum basilicum
LABIATAE

Fine basil desireth it may be her lot
to grow as the gelliflower, trim in a pot
That ladies and gentles, to whom ye do
  serve
may help her, as needeth, poor life to
  preserve.

TUSSER

Basil has never been popularly used in British cooking, probably because of the hazards of raising a crop in the damp climate, but its hot clove-like flavor is being introduced increasingly into recipes, especially as Italian dishes have been popularized. It is used especially in mock turtle soup, in tomato-flavored dishes, and in cooked meats, but its intensity of flavor calls for considerable moderation in use. In the East it is regarded as a sacred herb, and the name "basil" derives from *basileus,* the Greek word for "king," possibly suggestive of its twofold power, first as a flavor of the strongest kind, and second as a preservative. It was the herb most widely employed in the past throughout Europe

for the preservation of cold meats, its strength not only masking but counteracting putrefaction.

Sweet basil, *Ocimum basilicum,* is the plant normally grown and used; and though highly esteemed in the East (it is planted outside Hindu temples in India where it is known as *Tulasi*), it is almost scorned in some western countries. In Crete, for example, it is considered of ill omen and a plant redolent of evil and the influence of the Devil. There is an English country tradition that rue and basil will not flourish in the same garden; and while the story is refuted by their cohabitation on some plots, it is based on the legend of the Basilisk, a mighty serpent endowed with a crown and which Pliny described as rearing its head and advancing bodily almost upright rather than flexing as serpents usually do. Only the weasel was cunning enough to combat the Basilisk by eating rue and, thus fortified, charging to the attack and not retreating until the enemy was dead.

The plant attains two feet in height, and the leaves are always cool to touch, grayish-green beneath, and dotted with tiny oil cells. In warm climates it is a hardy perennial, but in Britain it can at best be considered a half-hardy annual. Seeds should be sown with some protection—frame or cloche early in the year—or in open ground when frost has passed. The seedlings damp off very easily, even in sterilized no-soil composts. They dislike disturbance, and so there is much to commend a late sowing. In sandy soils in dampish, temperate climates, especially in favorable seasons, good results can be expected and two crops of leaves should be possible. The first crop should be cut before the flower buds open, but the plants must not be denuded of all their foliage, so that a second cutting can be made in September. The shoots dry quite well if laid out in warm shade or in a darkened cupboard and take on a brownish-green color, but once stripped from the stem they should be stored in airtight jars, protected from daylight.

Bush basil, *Ocimum minimum,* is smaller and hardier than the green or sweet basil and makes an excellent pot plant; both have been grown in England since the sixteenth century, and they are usually called St. Joseph's wort.

Little pots of basil were considered favor gifts by famous ladies to their visitors, and Parkinson, in his *Garden of Flowers* (1629), says: "The ordinary Basil is in a manner wholly spent to make sweet or washing waters among other sweete herbs, yet sometimes it is put into nosegays. The Physical properties are to procure a cheerfull and merry hearte whereunto the seed is chiefly used in powder." Boccaccio's story of Isabella and the Pot of Basil is immortalized by Keats, and the brushes of both Rosetti and Holman Hunt have rendered it clearly for posterity as a plant with legendary fame.

BAY

Laurus nobilis
LAURACEAE

Sweet bay, an evergreen shrub-like tree hailing from the warm slopes of the Mediterranean areas and Israel, provides the pungently aromatic leaves known as bay leaves. Laurel wreathes bestowed in ancient days on poets and dramatists were fashioned from branches of this tree, hence the honor bestowed in Britain today of Poet Laureate. A Roman gold coin of 342 B.C. has a laurel wreath modeled upon its surface. One of the evergreens formerly used for Christmas decoration, the smooth, somewhat waxy leaves dry and last well, the stalks holding them firmly even on drying. Thus, a sprig of bay leaves can be kept in the larder until the brittle "half leaf of bay" is required.

A stimulant to the appetite, bay is one of the constituents of *bouquet garni* and *court bouillon*; it is useful with poultry, game, fish, pasta, and sweet dishes such as milk puddings and blancmanges. The flavor can be overwhelming if too much is used, the strength of flavor governed by a volatile oil, which can only be retained by drying the sprays slowly and away from the sun. The leaves tend to curl on drying, which is decorative for purposes such as the symbolic bunch of herbs hanging in the kitchen; however, leaves for culinary use may be removed from the stem and pressed flat. Storage should then be in boxes or bottles.

Parkinson says of the bay:

> The Bay leaves are of a necessary use as any other in the garden or orchard, for they serve both for pleasure and profit, both for ornament and for use, both for honest civil uses and for physic, yea, both for the sick and the sound, both for the living and the dead; . . . so that from the cradle to the grave we still have use of it, we still have need of it.

A tree of the Sun, under the celestial sign of Leo, the bay has long been an accepted precaution against "all the evils of old Satan can do to the body of man, and they are not a few"—so Culpeper tells us. He continued to extol the use of berries, globose and a good dark purple when ripe. They follow yellow flowers, so inconspicuous one has to look for them in May—but the identification of the flower is the quickest way of avoiding the common confusion of this shrubby tree with the Portugal laurel, *Prunus lusitanica,* and the ordinary laurel, *P. laurocerasus.* The drastic uses to which seventeenth-century apothecaries apparently put the berries are best left to the medical profession today; but to take away or prevent bruising and disperse the congealed blood (as does witch hazel) the oil of the berry is useful. Oil of bay is extracted for use in exotic oriental perfumes and similarly in the Middle East, where the bay tree flourishes in its shrub-like form, each branch springing from the base. The Psalmists knew it as "green and vigorous in its native soil" and sing "I have seen the wicked in great power, and spreading himself like a green bay tree."

Propagation is generally regarded as quite difficult, but in Britain cuttings taken in late summer and kept in close conditions can succeed. Alternatively, a low branch may be layered in July—or, of course, seed sown in gentle heat, if seed can be obtained. It is wisest to buy a young tree, already potted; and how decorative they can be on balconies or in porchways! They adapt to clipping, and their formal form is quite often seen among the various tub-grown plants. Cold winds are their worst enemy, especially in their early years, but once established in the open ground, they survive the winters, only suffering the burning of some leaves in the bitterest winds. Despite this, the sweet bay will withstand coastal situations in the British Isles, with much buffeting of salt winds. There is a golden-leaved form offered, *L. nobilis* 'Aurea,' and the willow-leaved form, its slender leaves much paler beneath than above and as aromatic as those of the sweet bay; the latter is a very tough customer, withstanding quite severe conditions.

In North America, the bay is not hardy north of Virginia and must be taken into shelter for the winter to protect it from the freezing winds. On the other hand, it shrinks from the scorching sunshine of summer, and so it must be put into a shaded position when carried outside in the spring.

BELLADONNA

Atropa belladonna
SOLANACEAE

Highly poisonous in all its parts, belladonna is used in present-day medicine and is especially employed in ophthalmic work to dilate the pupil of the eye. Its specific name, *belladonna,* was given in recognition of the fact that Italian ladies used to take doses to enhance the sparkle of their dark eyes. The generic name, *Atropa,* is derived from the Greek *atropos,* one of the Fates who cut the thread of life, and signifies its deadly poisonous powers. Vernacular names similarly continue the reminder of its danger: "banewort," "death's herb," "devil's cherry," "dwale," "deadly dwale," "dwale-berry," "manicon," "mekilwort," "deadly nightshade," "sleeping nightshade," and "daft-berries." The last name signifies that the plant's effect is to cause giddiness or stupefaction similar to that brought on by excess alcohol.

BELLADONNA

Piers Plowman called it "dwale":

> The frere with his fisik, this folk has
> enchanted,
> and doth men drink dwale that me
> dredeth no synne.

Macbeth's men are reputed to have overcome and murdered the invading Danes, without resistance, after plying them with liquor adulterated with dwale. Etymologically the word "dwale" stems probably from a Norse word *dool,* to delay or to sleep, but has been accepted in English since Chaucer's day as synonymous with opiate. Reputedly it was belladonna which provided the fatal effects upon Mark Antony's Roman legionaries during their retreat from the Parthians. Before the Reformation it was known as a narcotic and was cultivated in monastic gardens and used to check excessive secretions and allay inflammation and boils. As a plaster, belladonna is still remembered for its efficacy in the alleviation of fibrositis, neuralgia, and other rheumatic aches and pains. Medicinally it acts rapidly as a circulation stimulant.

An inhabitant of limestone and chalky wastes and hedgerows, especially in the vicinity of old dwellings or workings, the deadly nightshade should not be confused with other nightshades, wood nightshade, *Solanum dulcamara,* and enchanter's nightshade, *Circaea lutetiana,* neither of which is poisonous.

The plant is perennial, dies back each autumn, and has a purplish stem which usually divides into three main branches which divide again; it tends to straggle or lean against other plants. The flowers are hanging and bell-like in June, dingy purple and offensive of odor, and the whole plant is foul-smelling when crushed. The two-lobed shining black berries which appear in the late summer are distinctive in appearance, and children should be warned against them.

One of the oldest drug plants, still listed as a poison in the chemists' Poison Lists, its distribution is local in England, absent in Ireland and Scotland, but scattered over the whole of central and southern Europe, throughout the Middle East to Persia and the North African coastal regions. It is an introduced plant in America. In Bohemia, superstition dubbed it "the plant of the devil," who was supposed always to keep it within sight and whose attention might be detracted from it on Walpurgis Night (the night preceding May 1, the witches' sabbath, according to German legend) by letting loose a black hen, which he would chase.

BERGAMOT

Monarda didyma
LABIATAE

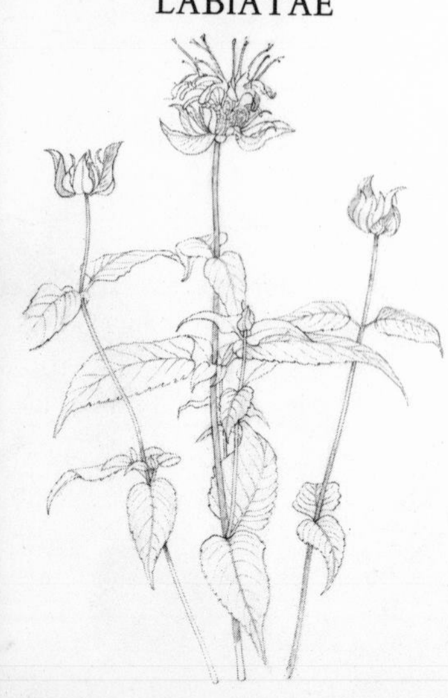

Commonly known as "Oswego tea," "monarda," or "bee balm," the plant is a native of swampy, moderately acid woodland soils of North America, from New York to Michigan, south to New Jersey, West Virginia, and Ohio. In Europe bergamot is an introduced plant and was first raised in 1745 by Peter Collinson from seed sent to him after it was collected from the shores of Lake Ontario. There, its leaves were employed to make a tea used as a gentle febrifuge, still taken today but as a refreshing tisane. The flowers are a startling red, borne in heads with red bracts between each floret so that the whole resembles a sparkling firework. Used now as a border plant, the genus is named after Dr. Nicholas Monardes, the Spanish physician and writer. His book, *Joyful news out of the new founde world,* was translated into English in 1577.

The present-day cultivars of monarda are available in pinks, mauves, and reds; and apart from a nasty habit of dying off in the centre of the clump, the plant will add astonishing gaiety to any herb garden for years. The secret is to divide the clumps in alternate years—spring or autumn—using only the outer shoots, which are the more vigorous growth, and discarding the inner, older pieces.

The flowers make a decorative addition to fruit cups, punches, and salads but should be floated in water before use so that the earwigs which love to hide deep in the corollas will escape into the water and not into the drinks! Normally, the plants attain a height of some three feet but will be stunted if deprived of moisture, thus resulting in fewer flower spikes. Both leaves and flowers are aromatic and may be included in potpourri (though this is not the plant that provides the bergamot of the perfumer).

BETONY

Stachys officinalis
LABIATAE

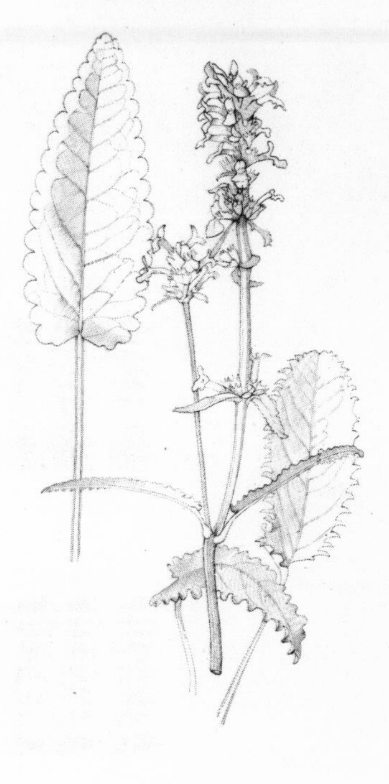

Known to many people by its former names of *Stachys betonica* or *Betonica officinalis,* which Linnaeus gave it, this herb is a native plant of open woodland and heaths from Scotland to the Mediterranean and from Spain to the Caucasus. Its several near relatives *(S. arvensis, S. germanica, S. palustris,* and *S. sylvatica)* have a fairly similar distribution, but the genus seems to be mainly represented in America by *S. hyssopifolia,* the so-called "hedge nettle" or "hyssop hedge nettle" with the typical musky odor of the family.

Betony tea, made by the infusion of dried leaves with boiling water, is a popular remedy for nervous headaches and to relieve tension and calm the nerves. The dried herb is also used as a form of herbal tobacco blended with other leaves, such as those of coltsfoot and eyebright, for the relief of pulmonary disorders. An infusion made from the fresh leaves can have a rather intoxicating effect. The bright reddish-purple flowers are pollinated by bees and carried in terminal spikes in whorls in July and August. It is a humus-loving plant, fond of woods and shaded places, and may be introduced into the herb garden by collecting seeds or "nutlets" which fall free around the plant in autumn when it grows in the wild. The generic name, *Stachys,* was given by Dioscorides and means "spike" or "ear," descriptive of the form of the plant. In the past it has been held in high repute for the treatment of numerous complaints, and it appears in lists of plants cultivated in apothecaries' gardens. There seems little doubt that it was a plant known to the infirmarers of the monasteries of Europe for treating those who were "streyt ondyd" (short of breath). In North Wales it was (and may still be) known as "herb St. Fraiid" and was gathered and dried as a cure for headaches, its special virtues supposedly endowed by the female St. Fraiid. Sir William Hooker claims its English name of betony is a corruption of Celtic words, *bew,* "head," and *ton,* "tonic" or "improve." The country names are "betayne," "wood betony," "bidney," "bishopwort," "wild hop" (referring no doubt only to the form of the actual flower head), and "vetoyu." The last mentioned name bears witness to its antiquity, for it is believed to derive from the Vettones, a tribe of Spain, and this name appears in the writings of Pliny.

BISTORT

Polygonum bistorta
POLYGONACEAE

The pink flower spikes of polygonum are known as decorative garden plants. Several species are wild, usually preferring fairly damp conditions, over the greater part of Europe and Asia but absent in Scandinavia. *Polygonum bistorta* grows profusely in northwestern England, and its early maturing leaves make it a fairly dominant feature of Lancashire and Cumberland ground cover in March and April; indeed it is from the Lake District that its vernacular and descriptive names emanate, for example "Easter-ledges." Used as a food, either in Easter-ledges pudding or as a green vegetable, the names of "Easter giant" and "Easter mangiant" are both corruptions of *mangeant,* relating to the leaves as a seasonal dish. The name "passions," which also appears to be fairly commonly known, is not suggestive of any aphrodisiac properties, as some writers infer, but is a repeated assertion of the seasonal value of the herb—Passiontide.

Polygonum is from the Greek *polys,* "many," and *gonu,* "joint," descriptive of the zigzag stem pattern of the genus, which is many-jointed. The specific name, *bistorta,* derives from *bis* "twice" and *torta* "twisted," in this instance descriptive of the doubly bent or S-shaped roots. Within

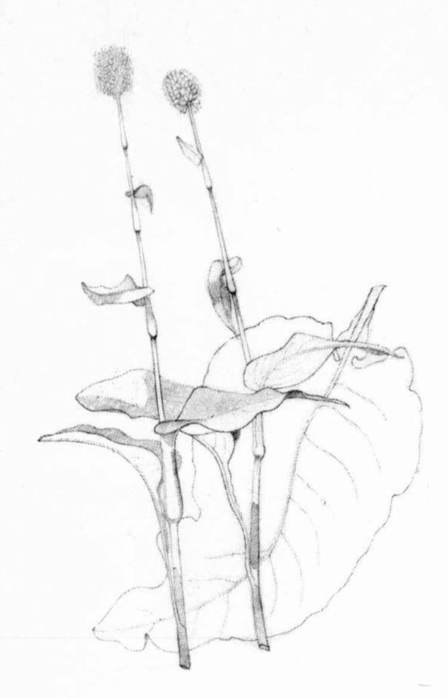

these red roots with their black skin (earning the country name of "snakeroot") lie tannic and gallic acids in remarkable amounts, providing one of the strongest known vegetable astringents. The roots of "English serpentry," as the plant has been called in times of famine, also provide comparatively large quantities of starch, and the combination of starch and astringent was reputed to shrink the intestines, reducing the quantity of food required and allaying hunger.

An astringent tonic wine used to be prepared from one part crushed bistort root and two parts alcohol (45%), which was mascerated for twenty-four hours and then added to claret to make up to eight parts. After macerating for four days, this was strained; from 1½ to 4½ fluid ounces might be taken in the course of a day. It was originally recommended in 1917 as a treatment for debility with a tendency towards tuberculosis. Its several properties as an astringent were extorted by Culpeper as a certain cure for complaints of unimaginable diversity. But its place in the herb garden is justified as both an economic and decorative plant, where it will make round patches quite quickly and will need careful tending. The roots twist about underground, spreading quite quickly; the leaves are dark bluish-green ovate, heart-shaped at the base of the plant, and best in the variety *superbum*. From June to September, upstanding rose-pink flower spikes are produced, attaining somethink like 1½ feet in height, especially in good moist soil.

BORAGE

Borago officinalis
BORAGINACEAE

If any plant can be said to bear a sense of history, an aura reminiscent of former days, it must be the borage. There is an old saying that "a garden without borage is like a heart without courage" and a Latin one, too: *Ego Borago gaudia semper ago,* "I, Borage, bring always courage." Evelyn wrote that "sprigs of borage are of known virtue to revive the hypochondriac and cheer the heart of the student." It is clear that this hairy, blue-flowered plant known to have been cultivated throughout Europe and in England in medieval times has been depended upon to refresh, invigorate, and encourage. It was added to stirrup cups as a farewell to those setting forth on crusades; and, today, it is still added to many drinks for its quality of enlivening both flavor and effect.

Corago would be a far more befitting Latin name than *Borago,* and authorities, all convinced of the truth of their theories, have attempted to explain the corruption of *Corago* into *Borago*. The Latin *burra* clearly refers to the hairiness of the plant, but the syllable *Cor* embraces a wide range of meanings—heart, soul, understanding, courage, purpose, which more closely identify the plant's usefulness. Whichever name we prefer, *or* (prefixed by *c* or *b*), stands for gold, the gold of the sun. The plant is governed by Leo, the sign of the sun.

Strictly an annual, borage can be raised from seed sown out of doors in April and May or started under some protection earlier in the year. Frequently a rosette will persist through a winter, seedlings will gather round it, and provided that old leaves are removed and the borage is given the encouragement it gives to man, fresh leaves can be available the year round. The flavor is refreshing, cucumber-like, and cooling in cordials, salads, fruit cups, and in sandwiches with cheese; the leaves are very sustaining. The flowers may be floated in fruit salads and drinks for decoration or candied like violets and used for confectionery.

Local names vary, but all emphasize the qualities of this lovely old-world plant: "bee bread," "cool tankard," "herb of gladness" to the French it is *langue de boeuf*. It is an excellent bee plant, directing the insect to the nectaries at the base of the stamen by the characteristic black eye of the deep blue flower.

opposite Caraway

BRYONY, WHITE

Bryonia dioica
CUCURBITACEAE

White bryony, native of England, Wales, and Europe (notably central Europe) but absent from Scandinavia and introduced into Scotland, is a scrambler of the hedges and heathlands. The lax stems beg support of neighbors, and it clambers by spirally coiled tendrils which arise from the leaf stalks. The five-lobed leaves always curve away from the stem, and their appearance may be why the Americans sometimes call the plant "English mandrake." The root is used in homeopathic medicine, and in Chaucer's day it was a cure for leprosy. It is white, acid and poisonous, and a powerful cathartic. The flowers are creamy yellow-green, small in comparison with the leaves, but the male larger than the female; the latter is followed by red berries. This was the counterfeit mandrake root, which Gerard exposed as a common brand, and it was used in withcraft to form the image of the person against whom a spell was to be directed.

Avoided by rabbits, but at one time added to cattle and horse fodder to enhance the glossiness of the animals' coats, the country names include "cowbind," "cow's lick," "felon-berry," "hedge grape," "snake berry," "tetter berry," "wild wood vine." Shelley used the name "cowbind":

> And in the warm hedge grew eglantine,
> Green cowbind and moonlight-
> coloured May

BURDOCK, GREAT

Arctium lappa
COMPOSITAE

A weed of wasteland and road verges before the advent of mechanical verge-cutting and chemical weed-killers, the burdock is known to children over most of the northern temperate regions of Europe for its hooked seed vessels. Children delight in throwing the little green balls, or sticky-backs, on to the backs of unsuspecting friends, for there they stay until they are pulled off. The seeds of the burdock hitch-hike everywhere and have even begged a lift across the Atlantic at some stage in the past. The plant is a naturalized immigrant in all regions of the North American continent. Its names of "cuckoo-button," "beggar's button," "cockle-burr" are all descriptive of the hooked fruit.

For skin eruptions and "old ulcers," varicose veins, and to clear the blood, a decoction of burdock leaves or root has been used by apothecaries and in herbal medicine for centuries. It has long been associated with the clearing of stones; and in the Middle Ages it was called "bardona" and was used to stimulate the kidneys and to control colic. The Missouri negroes cured colic in babies by hanging a necklace of burdock leaves around the infant's neck. In New England, the leaves were bandaged, point downwards, to the patient's ankles and wrists to absorb fever.

A handsome plant, it is erect of growth with slightly nodding stems bearing scattered pink-mauve flowers, which are followed by the burr or seed head. The leaves are heart-shaped and slightly cottony. The name, given by Dioscorides, is from the Greek *arctos*, "bear," from the coarse texture of the coat of the seed head.

Grandma's dandelion and burdock wine may spring to mind first, and many old recipes remain for this highly potent dessert wine. The root is rich in iron. The Romanies wash it, slice it, boil it in water for twenty minutes, and then sweeten the water with honey and use the decoction as a tonic. A few burdock seeds fastened in a little bag and worn round the neck in winter is a gypsy preventative for rheumatism. And that excellent naturalist and physician Dr. William Withering (famed in connection with digitalis) used to prescribe a decoction of this plant in the treatment of rheumatism.

In Ireland, land of lingering superstition and source of many plant lore stories, the roots of the great burdock *A. lappa* are used as a poultice for ringworm; however, the preparation must be carried out on the river bank opposite the patient in case the worm gets a whiff of the root and moves on!

Culpeper held an even more fantastic theory, recording:

> Venus challengeth this herb for her own, and by its leaf or seed you may draw the womb which way you please, either upwards by applying it to the crown of the head, in case it falls out; or downwards in [case of] fits of the mother by applying it to the soles of her feet; or if you would stay it in its place apply it to the navel, and that is one good way to stay the child in it. See more of it in my *Guide for Women.*

Here, Nicholas Culpeper seems to have been guarding against miscarriage, encouraging abortion, or even ensuring conception with the one plant!

BURNET

Sanguisorba spp.
ROSACEAE

The styptic quality of the burnet is revealed in its Latin name, from *Sanguis,* "blood," and *sorbere* "stopping"—a herb long used to staunch a flow of blood. Ranging over the whole of Europe, Iceland, temperate Asia and Iran, the sanguisorbas make attractive garden plants and seem to have been neglected quite unjustifiably. The American burnet *Sanguisorba canadensis* (still catalogued occasionally in Great Britain as *Poterium canadense*) is found from Newfoundland to Michigan and south to Georgia; this white-flowered species is also cultivated in British gardens and very rarely occurs as an escape. *S. officinalis* has brownish-red flowers and can reach three feet in height.

The salad burnet *S. minor* (syn. *Poterium sanquisorba*) has a similar extensive range over the whole of the temperate regions of the Northern Hemisphere. Its French name *pimpernelle* identifies it as a salad plant, and the leaves, slightly nutty in flavor, make an attractive addition to a green salad—or they may be used as a garnish, as they are prettily shaped. They may also be used with borage to flavor soups.

The roots are used as an astringent, rich in tannin and valuable in the treatment of dysentry and enteritis. In weaker doses, a tisane of the leaves or of the dried roots serves as an aperitif or stomachic.

When bruised, the leaves have a slight cucumber scent, and it was this characteristic that inspired the custom of adding them to ale to cool the tankard. It has the same refreshing association with salads and has come to be known quite reasonably, as salad burnet.

The Italians say:

L'Insalate non e buon, ne bella,
Que non e la Pimpinella!

The salad is neither good nor fair
if Pimpinella is not there!

CALAMINT, COMMON

*Calamintha ascendens**
LABIATAE

The official plant is in fact the British native *C. ascendens,* formerly *C. officinalis,* a perennial with a short but creeping rootstock found mainly on chalky soils in the whole of Europe, extending to the Black Sea. The garden or cultivated form is no different, apart from the fact that it has benefited from being cherished in country gardens over the centuries. The very close *C. arvensis* is basil-thyme by country consent, but confuses three herbs in its identity; its natural range is more extensive, from Scandinavia to Asia Minor and the Caucasus. The pale blue–mauve flowers, spotted on the lower lip, are unremarkable, but the whole plant gives off a refreshing scent if it is crushed or handled in passing, and it lends itself to paved-area planting or tucking into the cracks of an old wall. Its relative *C. nepata,* for some reason dubbed "lesser" by the prosaic English, atones for its stature by strengthening its scent, giving off a more definite mint-like aroma.

One can only describe a calamint tisane as dainty in flavor, refreshing, old-fashioned, and recalling the open air of summer on winter evenings, when it can be taken as a nightcap to ease a sluggish digestion and reduce flatulence and heartburn. A conserve can be made of the flower tops. A

* Some readers, particularly American, may know *Calamintha* as a *Satureja,* but the Royal Horticultural Society's *Dictionary of Gardening* maintains it as a genus, and the subject has recently been clarified in the *Botanical Journal of the Linnaean Society*: Vol. 65A, 344–347.

second crop is invariably obtainable during the season if the stems are cropped after the first burst of color.

CAPER SPURGE

Euphorbia lathyrus
EUPHORBIACEAE

The words "spurge" and "purge" are so close in the English language that the way in which the euphobias or milkweeds are used seems obvious. The latex, or milky fluid, which exudes from the stem upon breaking, can burn the skin. A biennial plant, which when well grown can reach three or four feet in height, caper spurge is rightly to be included in the herb garden as a British native representative of a genus of world-wide range. It is to be found more commonly in the west country and southern counties, about cottage gardens and old dwellings, and if tempted to use the "capers" in pickling, beware! They can cause serious poisoning. These fruits which develop deep in the axils among the persistent bracts are merely caper substitutes. The caper of commerce is *Capparis spinosa*. The fruits of other species found growing wild in Europe are not as conspicuous and have therefore been disregarded. Turner called the plant "Spounge gyant" and says "Thys kind of spurge hath swete seedes." Its habit and glaucous foliage demand attention.

CARAWAY

Carum carvi
UMBELLIFERAE

Grown mainly for its highly flavored seed, caraway is a biennial plant which produces a tap root in the same manner as a carrot. The root is edible and bears a similar but milder flavor to that of the seed. Seed should be sown in late summer to produce flowers the following year; a sandy or light soil suits caraway best. Seed heads for drying should be removed from the plant with care, tied and hung to dry over sheets of paper or contained in a large paper bag to catch the dried seed.

Victorian seed cake springs to mind at mention of the word "caraway," but in cookery there is a variety of ways in which the seed may be used (see page 44). As a carminative, its use in medicine has been long esteemed, and Dioscorides, in his *De Materia Medica,* recommended caraway oil: the plant was therefore known to the Ancient World, and its medicinal use appears to originate with the Arabs.

Jewish and continental European cooks use the seed far more freely than is common in traditional British or American cookery. In Germany and Austria it is added to bread—a practice increasing in Britain since World War II, and in Alsace, Munster cheese is always accompanied by a saucer of seeds to be sprinkled on to it. As the flavoring of the liqueur Kümmel, caraway finds its way into some Swiss fondues. The French seem to muddle its name completely by calling it *cumin des près,* or "wild cumin," alternatively *cumin de montagne,* and also *faux anis* and *anis des Vosges,* only emphasizing the importance of Latin nomenclature for those wishing to verify the identity of a plant.

CARNATION

Dianthus caryophyllus
CARYOPHYLLACEAE

A gray-leaved perennial of tufted growth, the pink is sometimes naturalized in the stonework of old buildings or rocky walls in Britain but is native of warm Mediterranean shores of Southern Europe and North Africa. The clove pink, so called for its clove-like aroma, is a parent of many cultivated carnations. The clove gilliflower or "carnation" is catalogued in many old books as *Caryophyllus hortensis,* "of the garden," and is recorded under this name by Philip Miller in *The Gardeners Dictionary* and earlier by John Rea. The name "gilliflower" covered many plants; the wallflower was "winter gilliflower"; "sweet rocket" or "dame's violet." *Hesperis matronalis* was "Queen's gilliflower"; both of these are early-flowering and so refute the theory that "gilliflower" is a corruption of July flower. There were

"gilli apple," a variety of apple; "stock gilliflower" *(Matthiola incana)*; "mock gilliflower" *(Saponaria officinalis)*; and "water gilliflower" (probably *Cardamine pratenisis*). So the name is more likely to be from the old French *clou de girofle* and Middle English *clowe gilofre*, or, as Chaucer used it, clovegilofre, both names being a corruption of the Arabic *quaranful*, "clove," and relating to the perfume. Stocks, wallflowers, carnations are all heavily scented, and the gilli apple may well have been a particularly aromatic variety.

In Chaucer's day, the clove gilliflower was one of the herbs imported into English gardens and grown for its flavor and scent; it became a favorite garden flower of the sixteenth and seventeenth centuries, rivaled only by the rose and the lily. The flower petals were used in Tudor and Stuart days to flavor wine and possets, and from this practice comes the popular name of "sops-in-wine." Conserves, candies, and dragees were flavored with the spicy taste, and Miller records "[it] hath been for a long time so much in use for making a Cordial Syrup of which there are two or three varieties, commonly brought to the Markets, which differ greatly in their goodness." As a physic plant it was said to "strengthen the heart," whether physically or morally we are not told, but William Coles, a contemporary of Culpeper and a physician writing in 1657, asserted that the cordial was good "in fevers, expelling the poyson and fury of the disease, and greatly comforting those that are sick of any disease where the heart hath need of relief. . . ." He goes on to describe a clove vinegar, which was used "to relieve one of a swoon"—rather in the manner that smelling salts were used 200 years later.

The petals of the scented pinks and carnations can be candied by the very time-absorbing process of painting each one with stiffened egg white and then dredging with castor sugar or powdered sugar, turning, and dredging again. The drying process needs to be carried out fairly quickly and evenly or the resultant tacky mass cannot be stored for confectionery use. The flowers may be floated in fruit cups and wine punches or used to garnish summer salads and desserts.

CATMINT

Nepeta cataria
LABIATAE

The old catnep *(N. cataria)* is the true medicinal plant, the leaves of which were used to make catnep tea, a beverage imbibed in some quantity before the import of Indian or China tea to Europe. The plant bears white flowers faintly marked with bronze-red, and although strictly speaking it is a short-lived perennial, it frequently behaves like a biennial, dying off after flowering. Frankly, it is not a rewarding plant to include in a collection except for its authenticity.

The catmint of the present day is still known and catalogued as *Nepeta mussini*. However it is in fact now called *N. faassenii*. This is a delightful plant which really needs to be planted or divided in the spring in all but the warmest districts, and which soon forms a hummock of dark gray-green, soft, aromatic foliage accompanied by mauve-blue flower spikes. Its popularity appears to have waned; fashions change sometimes without any obvious reason and catmint is not used in public parks or in newly laid private gardens nearly as frequently as it was a generation ago. The cultivar 'Six Hills' is robust of flower and is of garden origin. A perennial, it displays a tendency to die out, but division is simple if the top growth is cut back in July or August. The long gray growth is encouraged from the base, and soft cuttings can be taken in August or September and over-wintered in a cold frame in preparation for spring planting. Beloved of cats, like the old-fashioned catnep, it is sometimes impossible to get a plant established if a cat discovers its whereabouts, for any cat will so enjoy nibbling its leaves or curling up on the foliage cushion.

CELANDINE

Chelidonium majus
PAPAVERACEAE

The greater celandine is the only representative of its genus in the British flora; it is believed to have been naturalized as an escape from cultivation, or it may be a native plant that was taken into cultivation in infirmary and physic gardens and is now at large again! It is always found where there has been some human habitation. Known generally in Europe, it was cradled in Asia Minor and is now generally distributed in the eastern regions of the North American continent. The latex is not only poisonous but bitter in flavor and protects the plant from destruction by animals. The blue-green leaves are decorative, the plant is perennial and disappears during the winter, but its flowering period coincides with that of the return of the swallow to England. The name was given by Dioscorides, which leads one to question the range of distribution of the swallow as well as that of the greater celandine. The coincidence in range of plants and birds is no new theory—cowslips come with nightingales—and merely serves as a continued strand in the story of the web of life and the provision nature makes for herself. It is called "swallow-wort" by Gerard, "because it first springeth at the coming in of the swallows, or dieth when they go away . . . and because some hold the opinion that with this herbe the dams restore eyesight to their young ones." The bitter juice has been used as a treatment for ringworm as well as a cure for worts, and according to the Doctrine of Signatures, its color caused it to be considered as a remedy for jaundice.

Vernacular names in the main refer to its healing powers: "killwart," "wartflower," "wartweed," "wartwort," "wretweed," and, in Ireland, "sollendine," a corruption of celandine. Its French names translate exactly, with the exception of *felongue*.

CELANDINE, LESSER

Ranunculus ficaria
RANUNCULACEAE

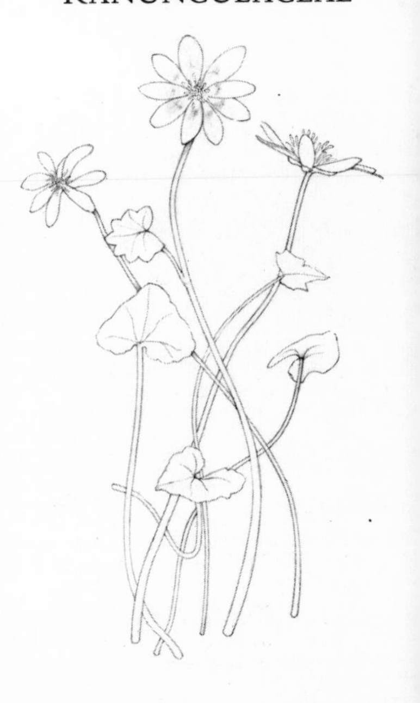

There is a Flower, the lesser Celandine
That shrinks like many more from cold
and rain,

And the first moment that the sun may
shine
Bright as the sun himself, 'tis out again!

WORDSWORTH

The lesser celandine, or pilewort, is a British and European native and has been introduced into North America. Its characteristic root nodules won it the name of pilewort through the Doctrine of Signatures; and it was used in days gone by for the treatment of piles, but Culpeper advocates it as a cure for the King's evil, "kernels by the ears and throat" or any other "wens and tumours." He goes on to say "with this I cured my own daughter of the King's evil, broke the sore, drew out a quarter of a pint of corruption, cured without any scar at all." He also says he does not know how this came to be dubbed celandine, as it bears no resemblance to the true (greater) celandine and expresses it charmingly:

I wonder what ailed the ancients to give this the name of celandine, which resembleth it neither in nature or form; it acquired its name of pilewort from its virtues, and it being no greater matter where I set it down, so as I do set it down, I humoured Dr. Tradition so much as to set him down here.

The starry, bright golden flowers appear very early in the year in hedge-banks, stream banks, and woods, the shining petals opening wide to the sun and closing tightly to gray skies and rain, as Wordsworth noted. They fade to white, looking almost as if some elf had come along and rubbed away their gloss. The little root tubers are to be found quite near the soil surface, and they are sometimes exposed by heavy rain and look like grains of corn around the base of the plant. Pigeons are said to enjoy them. The leaves may be used as a pot herb and are less acid than the other species of the buttercup family; they are eaten as a spring green in Sweden. Other vernacular English names are "foalfoot," "crain," "filding cup," "golden guineas," and "goldy knob," echoed in the French *bouton d'or*.

CENTAUREA

Centaurea spp.
COMPOSITAE

Formerly a weed of cornfields, the cornflower or blue bottle, *Centaurea cyanus,* is a native British plant and probably is also native in most of Europe and the Near East. Its attractiveness so appealed to previous generations of gardeners that when in Tudor times flower gardens were developed, and each plant no longer had to justify its existence by economic use, the cornflower was brought into cultivation. Culpeper noted that "If you please to take them from thence [cornfields] and transplant them in your Garden, especially towards the full of the moon, they will grow more double than they are and many times change colour." The seed or leaves taken in wine were recommended as effective against the plague; bruised leaves healed open wounds, and the juice dropped into the eye relieved inflammation. A decoction made from the flower heads is used as an eye bath and has long been used in alleviating eye disorders.

Other species of the large centaurea genus to include in the herb garden are *C. nigra* and *C. scabiosa,* the knapweeds, of considerable antiquity as herbs of healing. The herb has been used as a stauncher of blood and has hovered in the background in the search for the star herb in the successful treatment of cancer.

Sweet Sultan *(C. moschata)* of our gardens is a decorative form of centaurea and a good representative plant to include for its lovely brush-like flower heads. Parkinson described it as "as stranger of much beauty" for it was introduced into Europe from Turkey. It shares the virtues of its tribe; a decoction of the flower heads can be used to bathe the bruises and prevent internal bleeding and discoloration.

CENTAURY

Centaurium minus
GENTIANACEAE

Essentially a maritime plant, growing in most of the coastal areas of Britain and extending over the north temperate zones of Europe and on the eastern seaboard of the American continent, the pink-flowered centaury is selective of its camping pitch. It loves the sandy salt dunes and the old quarries, pits, or gravel workings where exposed profiles have provided a suitable habitat. Probably it would be commoner in some districts, were it not for the mechanical workings carried out on such sites.

A tisane or tonic infusion made from the fresh or dried flower tops is effective in enlivening the appetite. In France, it is used as a febrifuge, like quinine, and had been so used long before the discovery of this application for the cinchona, which was introduced into Europe in 1645 from South America. Its indications were apparently numerous in the seventeenth and eighteenth centuries, especially as a febrifuge, a revitalizer against fatigue, and a blood purifier; and as a lotion applied externally, it was commonly used to bathe ulcers and abscesses. *Herbe à Chiron,* one of its French names, echoes over the centuries the baptismal name bestowed by Dioscorides. Chiron the Centaur is said to have discovered its medicinal and healing properties when he used it to treat the arrow wound in his foot made by Hercules' weapon. In the seventeenth century, it was an ingredient of the Duke of Portland's powder, a concoction so called because it supposedly cured His Grace of gout. Vernacular names in Britain include "banwort," "bloodwort," "bitter herb," "hurdreve," and "sanctuary."

CHAMOMILE

Anthemis nobilis
COMPOSITAE

Writing in the middle of the sixteenth century, William Turner said of chamomile: "It will restore a man to hys colour shortly yf a man after the longe use of the bathe drynke of it after he is come forthe out of the bathe." In the twentieth century, it would be more credible to add chamomile to the bath water for a soothing, relaxing, and refreshing bath since the heightening of color of the skin during and after bathing is surely no longer a condition which is considered to require a remedy! Parkinson, a century later, said in his *Earthly Paradise*: "Chamomile is put to divers and sundry uses, both for pleasure and profit, both for the sick and the sound, in bathing to comfort and strengthen the sound and to ease pains in the diseased." Thus we can assume that the addition of the herb to bath water is a custom sanctioned by time; it is still used today in therapeutic herbal baths.

The name "chamomile" is vague and is used loosely to embrace a group of similar plants, the mayweeds, feverfews, and anthemis. It is most accurately allocated to *Anthemis nobilis* and *Matricaria chamomilla,* both of which have a fruity scent; the mayweeds and feverfews are by comparison stale in odor. The former is to be found both in a single- and double-flowered (cultivated) form and is a close-growing prostrate plant, compact of habit, which has traditionally been put to use in forming chamomile lawns, walks, and seats. It sends out little runners all around the plant and thus spreads, quickly covering a piece of ground.

More accurately the plants are dubbed Roman chamomile. *A. nobilis,* and German chamomile, *M. chamomilla.* (The so-called Scotch chamomile is the single-flowered form of *A. nobilis,* but for the purpose of cultivation in the herb garden it can be discounted.) The appellation "Roman" has persisted since the sixteenth century when a German botanist discovered it growing wild in the environs of Rome. Derived from the Greek *chamai,* "on the ground," and *melon,* "apple," the name originally signified "ground apple"—a plant hugging and covering the ground and reminiscent of the apple in aroma.

Has any plant such numerous virtues? Has any plant retained its favor so consistently since the days of Dioscorides? Its properties cannot be supposed or romantic. Culpeper listed ailments alleviated by chamomile as diverse as depressions, the treatment of the spleen, the relief of sprains and strains, jaundice, and flatulence; and to this day chamomile is probably the most popularly made herbal tea. It is included in wines and liquors, especially in Spain, and it is commonly used to relieve toothache and neuralgia and as an infusion to reduce fever.

Chamomile tea is best made from the cream-white double flowers of *Anthemis nobilis,* taking just the flower heads and handling them as little as possible. An infusion can be made from fresh or dried flowers—obviously more flowers being required dry than fresh. Three or four fresh flowers to a cupful of boiling water allowed to stand for a few minutes makes an aromatic, vitalizing drink. The French drink this herbal tea more frequently than most Europeans, but it is gaining popularity in England.

The finely divided leaves are of a soft green and delicate in texture, and when crushed they evoke old-world associations. Falstaff's advice that "the more it is trodden on the faster it grows" meets the present-day need for instant gardening, and so paths and banks of chamomile around present-day herb gardens are not an uncommon sight. The old herbers included a seat surrounded by this decorative daisy-like plant for their enjoyment.

Close planting is required to make a successful chamomile lawn or path; and, as in the preparation of the site for any conventional lawn, time is well spent and rewarded by the eradication of perennial weeds, the leveling of the ground, and the treading or rolling of the soil surface before planting out. The pieces or rooted divisions of chamomile should be placed four to six inches apart each way, using about one hundred plants to the square yard, and staggered for the best finished appearance. Where the land is light, or sharply drained, some moistened horticultural peat or other moisture-retentive material should be trickled into the planting hole and firmed around the long roots to encourage quick root formation. The planting is done in early May and the area hosed each evening, should the weather remain dry, during the ensuing few weeks. Do not let the plants flower. The first cut can be made with long-handled shears, but quite soon the mower with the blades set high can be taken over the lawn. The plant enjoys being crushed and will thrive for being trodden on or rolled occasionally. It

is a plant that can be used to particular decorative advantage on or near patios; and packed around the base of a sundial or bird bath or any such spot that would be frequently trodden, it is a constant source of pleasure.

A possible alternative to using young plants to start a lawn is to sow seed over the area. It is not an economical proposition; the seed must be mixed with sand to ensure an even distribution. By sowing in boxes or pans earlier in the year, pricking off, and then planting out, the results are safeguarded, even though the task is tedious.

John Evelyn, who wrote his *Kalendarium Hortense* at the end of the seventeenth century, enumerating the work to be done in the garden each month, included for October ". . . it will now be good to Beat Roll and Mow carpet walks of camomile, for now the ground is supple and it will even all inequalities." There is considerable evidence beyond conjecture that the green on which Drake was playing his famous game of bowls was of clipped chamomile. The lawn at Buckingham Palace, bedecked with receptions in summer, gives off a chamomile fragrance in the heat of the capital.

Matricaria chamomilla, an annual, has leaves similar to anthemis and single white flowers, but it grows to some two or three feet in height. The flowers may be put to the same uses as those of anthemis, but a greater quantity is required, as their properties and aroma are faint.

CHERRY

Prunus spp.
ROSACEAE

The cherry tree is reputed to have been taken to Rome in the first century B.C. by Lucullus, from Turkey, which was then known as Cerasus.

Before the knowledge of vitamins affected nutritional science, men were unwittingly using vitamin-containing plants to combat the effects of disease. The British naval surgeon who introduced the use of citrus fruit into every ship during the eighteenth century, as a measure against the scourge of scurvy, brought upon the heads of all British seamen the name of 'limey' the world over. Before the settlers arrived on the North American continent, the West Indians were using a native cherry as a source of vitamin C, without realizing it. The gypsies make a cherry tonic from the stalks of any kind of cherry by simmering an ounce in a quart of water for an hour, then straining. This decoction can be stored and sweetened if required and is administered in a tablespoon three times a day. Cherry cough syrup is a country remedy made by stewing ripe cherries from their stalks in just sufficient water to prevent them from sticking to the pan. Once the fruit is quite soft, it is strained, and to each pint, a tablespoon of vinegar and one of honey is added. The well-mixed conserve should be of the consistency of thin honey, and a teaspoonful of this luscious black liquid soothes the most troublesome cough. Proprietory cherry-bark syrups have been available for nearly two centuries.

During the cherry-picking season in Kent, England, sellers used to walk the markets and streets of London with laden baskets calling "Cherry Ripe"; they are seen only occasionally today. Together with rum, cherries made a potent liqueur known as cherry rum; and with brandy, using the kernels as well to add an almond flavor, they are still used in the making of cherry brandy—the domestic version of which was "cherry bounce."

CHERVIL

Anthriscus cerefolium
UMBELLIFERAE

One of the oldest seasoning plants known in Europe, chervil originated in south-eastern Europe and Asia Minor. In both Britain and America it is an introduced plant, and it has been cultivated in Britain since Roman times. The subtle flavor warrants its inclusion in *fines herbes* for the kitchen, and it is to be found more frequently in French gardens than in British. In Germany and Austria its main use is as a flavoring to cold meats and sausages; elsewhere it is added to cold jellied dishes, used to flavor sauces, or added as a warming ingredient to soups. One hardly ever finds it used alone, for like common salt it enhances the flavor of other ingredients, and for this reason it is included in custards and liquors.

An annual or half-hardy annual, the plant is typical in appearance of its ubiquitous tribe: the stems ribbed and hollow, the leaves daintily fern-like and dark green, resembling a fine parsley. Cultivation is straightforward provided that the seedlings are thinned and left *in situ*, for transplanting seems to encourage a flurry of activity which brings them into flower prematurely. Choose light shade for growing chervil and keep the leaves picked off regularly to encourage a fresh supply.

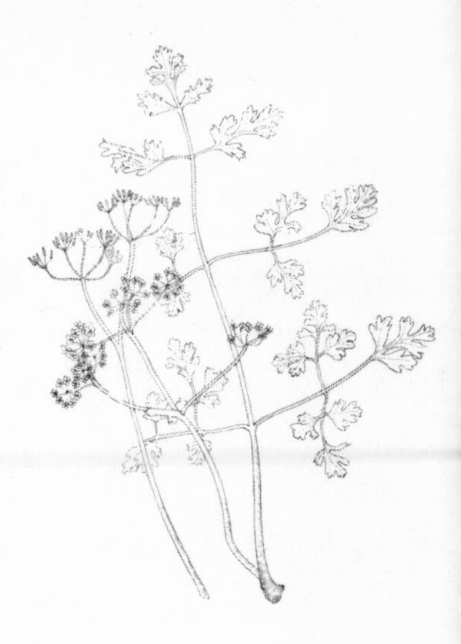

CHICORY

Cichorium intybus
COMPOSITAE

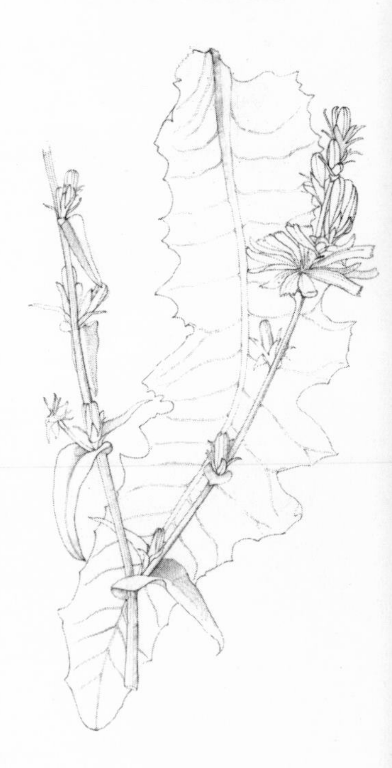

The spindle-shaped root of chicory is thick and yellow, and proves to be milky when broken. It is this root roasted and crushed that is used commercially as an additive or adulterant of coffee. The flowers, typical of their family, are of the clearest blue and are dispersed along the stem, which under cultivation attains some $3\frac{1}{2}$ feet in height. Each flower lasts but several hours and is quickly replaced by another starry bloom. Wild chicory, or succory, is native to Britain, distributed locally on light and calcareous soils, and extends over Europe northwards to Estonia and western Russia. It has been introduced into the temperate regions of Asia, North and South America, South Africa, Australia, and New Zealand. It is found by roadsides, in wasteland and arable meadow land in chalky areas, and is usually a follower of man.

The zigzag stem carries the flowers above the loose rosette of basal leaves, which are hairy and rough, and the plant varies in height from 1 to $3\frac{1}{2}$ feet, dependent upon prevailing conditions. It used to be customary to include chicory seed in ley mixtures, as cattle love the leaves and the deep root helped to break up the soil. Its country name is "bunk" or sometimes "monk's beard," probably from its French name of *barbe de capucin,* and is reminiscent of the names of other members of its family with the same form of flower, "goat's beard" and "hawk's beard." A diuretic and stomachic when used as a decoction, chicory stimulates the production of bile and has been employed in the treatment of jaundice. Its action is considered to be slow and very mild, and Tusser recommended it in 1573 as a remedy for the ague.

The flowers attract because of the clarity and perfection of their color, but the stems are difficult to break and the flower arranger will be disappointed because the blossoms appear to change place each day, as they close or fade. Linnaeus, in composing his floral clock, included the chicory flower, but the times he gave were for Upsala, where he was working. In Britain the flowers open around 6 A.M. and tire soon after noon.

A sad German legend tells how a girl waited day after day for the return of her absent betrothed and at last sank exhausted by the roadside and died of a broken heart. The blue star-like flowers sprang up on the spot, explaining the German name "watcher of the road."

CHIVES

Allium schoenoprasum
LILIACEAE

One of the onion family that has settled in all parts of the Northern Hemisphere, chives show a marked preference for rocky thin-soiled spots where it can perch high. The plant is found on the windswept cliffs in Corsica and western Portugual and on the baked mountain ranges of Greece. More usually known as a cultivated plant, it is one of the few herbs with which almost everyone has more than a nodding acquaintance. The silvery pink flower head is probably not so well known, but as a border edging in the kitchen garden or herb plot it can be used to trace the pattern of the bed. The dark blue-green grass-like leaves burst forth in tufts of bristle-like appearance and provide an unending source of supply for the kitchen. Delicately flavored in comparison with the rest of its tasty tribe, the chopped leaves are added to cottage cheese, egg dishes, and salads—and what better garnish is there for tomato salads and sandwiches?

If the leaves are to be used for culinary purposes, the flowerheads should be removed as soon as they form. Propagation can be effected by seed, but it is more usual to divide the clumps of little bulblets in late June, after flowering, and increase the stock in this way.

CINQUEFOIL

Potentilla reptans
ROSACEAE

The cinquefoil has crept its way over grassy waste places throughout the whole of Europe, the Mediterranean regions, Siberia, and Asia and has somehow gained more than a foothold in both American continents. Its dainty five (sometimes six or seven) leaflets or fingers are wholly green and fold over to form protective umbrellas for the yellow flowers when it rains. The astringent properties of its roots and leaves gave it an ancient reputation as a febrifuge, but in more modern times its main purpose is as an astringent mouthwash, which supposedly tones the gums and secures loosening teeth!

It was an ingredient of "flying ointment" which witches were wont to rub over their bodies, along with other ingredients which were strong poisons; it is generally believed that the active principles of the plants could be absorbed through the skin, inducing a state of trance. One recipe for this ointment included fat from the body of an unbaptized infant mixed with aconite, hemlock, sweet flag, poplar leaves, thorn apple, deadly nightshade, and cinquefoil.

Curiously enough, its counter-action was also employed, for such plants as St. John's wort, olive, orchis, vervain, and cinquefoil are listed as affording protection from witchcraft, and the magic that surrounds the plant may have to do with its flower's shape: a five-pointed star. Known fairly extensively in Europe as "the powerful little one"—from *Potentilla*—it has also been used as a love divination herb. When boiled in thyme and marjoram water, added to corn, and mixed with the juice of nettles and houseleeks, it had the reputation of being a powerful bait for fish. Old recipes indicate that its astringent powers were acknowledged as a remedy for haemorrhages and dysentery, when the bark of the root or the root itself, after peeling, was used to make a decoction. A similar preparation was employed for tanning.

CLARY

Salvia horminum
Salvia sclarea
LABIATAE

The clary sages are of two forms. *Salvia sclarea* is a dressy perennial often short-lived because it is given to exhibitionism, flowering itself to death, and behaving more like a biennial. The annual *Salvia horminum* (of catalogues) is a ravishing little plant, perhaps at its best in 'Pink Sundae' or a mixture marketed as 'Art Shades.' The papery bracts are conspicuous along the fifteen-inch stem; and over the past twenty years in the history of flower arrangement, it has not only become more popular, but it is being more commonly identified as clary rather than *S. sclarea*. Both thrive on lime soils.

The name "clary," or "clear eye," has evolved because the seeds soaked in water produce a mucilaginous eye bath which may be used with safety to rid the eye of grits, tiny pieces, or other foreign bodies. The leaves resemble sage leaves and as such are aromatic, their fragrance reminiscent of grapefruit. Float the papery-colored bracts in fruit salads or use them to decorate sundaes immediately prior to serving. They can, of course, be added to wine cups or punches. Clary has been used as a substitute for hops.

Over the centuries, the main use of clary has been in the treatment of the eyes. Gerard refers to it thus:

> The seeds put whole into the eyes clenseth and purgeth them exceedingly from waterish humours, rednesse, inflammation and divers other maladies or all that happen unto the eies, and taketh away the paine and smarting thereof, especially being put into the eies, one seed at a time, and no more, which is a general medicine in Cheshire and other counties there about knowne of all, and used with good successe.

The vernacular names are therefore not surprising: "Christ's eye," "clear eye," "eyeseed," "Oculus-Christi."

It is believed that clary was first brought into use in the making of beer and wine by the wine merchants of Germany. Its German name, *Muskatsalvee,* suggests that it imparts a muscat flavor, and in fact it was used together with elder flowers as an adulterant of Rhenish wine to make its flavor closer to Muscatel; hence its name, which means "muscat sage." The extracted oil, used as a perfume fixer, especially in France, is highly aromatic and known as muscat sage oil or clary sage oil.

CLEMATIS

Clematis vitalba
RANUNCULACEAE

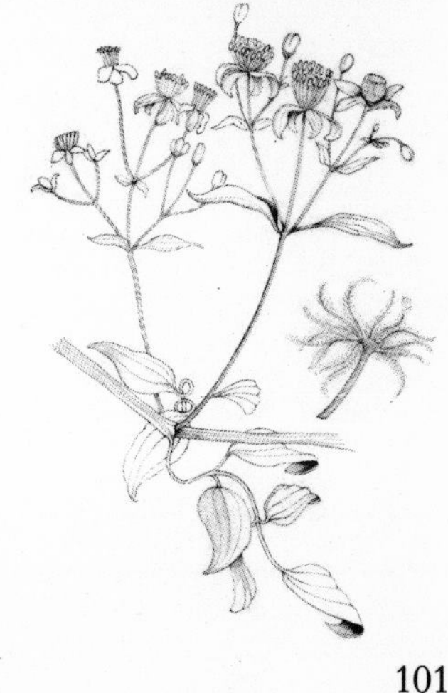

Traveller's joy, a name believed to have been bestowed upon this plant by Gerard in 1597, has become well known on both sides of the Atlantic as a plant that enfolds hedgerows. In Europe, its greenish-white flowers are fragrant, justifying Gerard's recognition of the pleasure it gave along the dusty tracks; its tangled bowers afford arbors among which birds can nest with safety. It drapes a festoon of flowers and pale green leaves over every bush within reach and seems to extend the hand of fellowship to one and all. Its essential climbing quality, characteristic of its genus, is ensured by the formation of woody foot-stalks by which it contrives to reach out and support a great mass of growth, the tensile leaf-stalks acting as clamps. The name "clematis" is derived from *clema,* a type of vine; *vita,* also meaning vine; and *alba*—white; though the original name appears to have been *Viorna*—"adorning the ways."

> But where the looped and twisted twine
> Wild clematis, bryony and woodbine
> And such reptilian growth . . .
>
> ANDREW MARVELL

A British native plant of wood margins and hedgerows, particularly inclined to select chalk and strongly alkaline soils (especially in the southern half of England), it has writhed its way over Europe from the Netherlands, where it is called *bosrank,* southwards to the Caucasus.

Little used as a healing herb today, the poisonous alkaloid clemantine has a diuretic and diaphoretic action and is obtainable from roots, leaves, and stems, though it is most potent when extracted from the leaves a little prior to flowering. Used in Pliny's time for cleansing leprous sores, its caustic nature has more recently been employed against psora, following the abuse of mercury, and in the treatment of eruptions of the scalp.

The vernacular name of "Virgin's bower," reputed to have been adopted in honor of Elizabeth I, is commonly used in both Europe and America, though in America it indicates *Clematis virginiana*. In Britain its provincial names include "gray-beard," "crocodile," "hag-rope," "love bird," "birdwith," and "willow wind." The woody stems persist throughout the winter, hence its use for basket-making while the stems are still pliable.

COLTSFOOT

Tussilago farfara
COMPOSITAE

The coltsfoot is one of the earliest plants to flower in the year, its gay yellow blooms spangling wasteland and roadsides over the whole of Europe, Asia, and North Africa. It has been introduced into America. So eager are the flowers to meet the lengthening daylight hours of February that they cannot wait for the thick leaves to form; but as the flowerheads fade into a puff of silky down, the felted heart-shaped leaves appear. Culpeper describes the leaves and roots beautifully: ". . . with a little down or frieze over the green leaf on the upper side which may be rubbed away, and whitish or mealy underneath. The root is small and white, spreading much underground, so that where it taketh, it will hardly be driven away again if any little piece be abiding therein, and from thence spring fresh leaves."

It is a plant which can be introduced into the garden only with the utmost discretion, and it should be safely confined in a large container or sunken bucket to control its wanderings. The country name of "son-before-the-father" is given because the flowers appear first. Wine made from the plant is called clayt wine and the beer is called cleats; its name of clayweed refers to its preference for clay soils. The gypsies say that wherever coltsfoot blooms, coal will be found below! Other vernacular names include "cowheave" (a cow hoof), "hoofs," "clatterclogs," and "sweep's brushes." "dummy weed" and "cough-wort" both allude to the use of the plant as a remedy for tight coughs and pulmonary congestion.

An herbal tobacco, with coltsfoot leaves its main ingredients, is still smoked by some people as a relief for asthma. Dioscorides wrote of smoking the leaves through a reed to clear mucus and catarrh, and so it has been used through 2,000 years. To make coltsfoot tobacco, the leaves are gathered in May, cut into pieces, and laid on paper to dry out of doors in the shade. When the drying process is complete, the pieces are rubbed between the hands just as a pipe smoker rubs his tobacco. The initiation is said to be difficult, but the taste is acquired quickly!

A Romany recipe to soothe coughs and colds is made with 1 oz. licorice root simmered in 3 pints water until it is reduced to 1 pint. Add this to 1 oz. coltsfoot leaves and a slice of lemon, and use honey to sweeten if required. Best taken cold, the gypsies say! A tisane made from fresh leaves relieves a hoarse throat and clears congestion; in France, where coltsfoot is called *tussilage,* it was in olden times used as the sign of a medical practitioner or physick man.

COMFREY

Symphytum officinale
BORAGINACEAE

Traditionally known as the "Saracen's root," the common comfrey is believed to have been brought back to England by the Crusaders after they had learned of its great economic value to man. As a healing herb for open wounds, as a mucilaginous product invaluable in the treatment of chest complaints, and as a bone setter, the plant was quickly put to good use as a cottage garden plant around farm workers' and country dwellers' homesteads in Britain. Its name is from the Greek *symphys,* "I grow together"; and comfrey is probably a corruption of *confirma,* "a growing together." It has a predilection for the water-side and likes shade, but it is tolerant of many conditions, always excluding baked earth.

The hispid nature of the whole plant gives it an unmistakable appearance; and the leaf stalks particularly at the base of the plant are winged. The fresh or dried leaves are still quite commonly used as a poultice or hot fomentation for sprained ankles and wrists. Its country names of "knitbone," "boneset," and "consound" stem from its use by the ancient bone-setters as a plaster or binding. The plant is rich in a watery but slightly viscous fluid which forms a paste easily and sets. The mashed white roots, which are brittle and black-skinned, can also be used as a poultice but are chiefly used to alleviate pulmonary and throat disorders, taken either as an infusion or as a milk. The gypsies know it best in this way: $\frac{1}{2}$ ounce of crushed root is combined in a saucepan with $1\frac{1}{2}$ pints of equal parts of milk and water, and simmered for 20 minutes. A wineglassful will quickly ease an irritating cough, or a spoonful taken in the night when a cough becomes troublesome will put an end to wakefulness. If milk alone is used in the preparation, the mixture is sufficiently gelatinous to set as a jelly when cooled. The root can be cooked as a vegetable; the leaves are rich in potassium and vitamin C and make a spinach-like dish when cooked; when served with a poached egg they provide a nourishing meal.

The flowers vary from creamy-white to pink and blue and are carried in June in a dangling row of bells; they are followed by black shining nuts as fruit. A tisane of flowers or leaves is useful against colds and as a refreshing tonic. It is also widely used in the treatment of stomach ulcers and is known to help the strengthening of torn tendons, allay pain in strained muscles, and, in short, earn its vernacular names of "bruisewort" and "all-heal!" An infusion of the leaves and/or roots, applied as a fomentation as hot as can be borne, is claimed to be an almost certain cure for fibrositis, even in cases where the complaint is of long standing.

Propagation is easily effected by division of the roots in early spring, for the leaves start to form bold clumps quite early. The roots are brittle and almost splinter but settle down very quickly when transplanted, provided there is moisture-retentive material around the root run.

Symphytum tuberosum, the so-called "tuberous comfrey," has stout tuberous roots and grows wild, more commonly in the northern parts of Britain, in damp localities; its flowers are creamy and the whole plant less branching than *S. officinale.* "Rough comfrey," or "prickly comfrey," is *S. asperum,* introduced in 1779 from the Caucasus as a fodder plant but now naturalized in many places. The flowers are at first pink, maturing to a clear blue.

S. officinale coccineum is the best garden form to use; its flowers are a clear crimson. *S. officinale* 'Argenteum' has silvered leaves—a plant hard to find but an attractive addition to the herb border.

CORIANDER

Coriandrum sativum
UMBELLIFERAE

Probably a native of the eastern Mediterranean, the barren shores of the Bosphorus, and the Dardanelles, coriander has been introduced into Britain and is occasionally found as an escape from cultivation, though it also appears as a weed of cultivation. The Ancient World revered the medicinal virtues of its seed for the volatile oil, which in excess can act as a narcotic, but it is generally used as a carminative. The aroma of the plant is unpleasant until the active principles reach their apogee; then, as if as a signal to the harvester, the disagreeable element changes and becomes pleasant and aromatic. The parsley-like leaves make a pot herb in Mediterranean countries and are considered to have a somewhat aphrodisiac action; they are also recommended as a complexion bleach. How widely can the uses of a herb differ! The pungency of the seeds makes coriander a useful ingredient of some curry powders, with cayenne pepper, turmeric seed, and ginger. Coriander seeds are also very familiar as a flavoring for pickles.

The flat umbels of flowers which bloom

in July are lilac in color, the seed ripening to a pale beige. Coriander is also known as Chinese parsley, and the Chinese have a legend that this plant confers immortality on those who eat it!

CORN SALAD

Valerianella locusta
VALERIANACEAE

Corn salad, or lamb's lettuce, is a slender annual, native of the whole of Europe except the extreme north, and of Madeira, North Africa, and Asia; it has been introduced into North America. Somewhat insignificant, with their washed-out lilac color, the flowers bloom in high summer, and the leaves prior to flowering are excellent as salad plants. Although it can (and does) grow almost anywhere, it is particularly quick to flourish on corn stubble; and the spoon-shaped leaves can be collected from the wild where the stubble is not fired. Usually the form cultivated is *V. olitoria,* and as white pot herb this is occasionally available in certain specialty shops, though in France quite early in spring, it is usual for greengrocers to sell small bundles of *mache*. It is a useful addition to the vegetable garden, and seed can be sown in spring or autumn; the latter sowing provides leaves through the winter in all but the most unfavored localities. Although strictly a biennial, the plant comes to maturity quickly and is usually treated as an annual. It is quite hardy, and the round leaves and rosette which form when sown in August can be cut as salad in the very early spring. A cloche or frame can be used to advantage to keep the leaves clean and encourage a better and earlier crop. Used in a mixed dish with cold boiled beetroot, corn salad is an excellent winter green salad; its flavor improves when served in this way, as parsley, watercress, and even lettuce swamp its subtle taste.

Gerard says of the plant: "In English the white potherbe, so called for that there is a black potherbe, which is called Alisander." Its other country names are "milkgrass," "cornell-sallet," and "potherb."

Batty Langley, writing in his *New Principles of Gardening* (1728) says: "Corn Sallet is a native inhabitant of the Field, but for its being a very refreshing pleasant Herb, is now received into our Gardens, and was introduced by the French and Dutch who were the first that eat it in Sallets in England."

COSTMARY

(*See* ALECOST.)

COTTON LAVENDER

Santolina chamaecyparissus
COMPOSITAE

With silver-gray foliage, conifer-like in form (hence its specific name), the cotton lavender is a plant of old-world associations. Of immense decorative use in the herb garden, the evergreen (or ever-gray) leaves are sturdy, reviving with a fresh whiteness each spring. They tolerate close clipping, which makes the plant extremely useful for the formation of low hedges or as edging to formal beds—a common practice in Tudor times. The plant is especially useful in the design of period herb gardens because its effect when used as an edging plant is unsurpassed. To maintain a groomed appearance and to keep the pattern formal, clipping should be done in March and repeated in July.

If the shrubs are allowed to grow freely, they will reach some $2\frac{1}{2}$ feet in height, and the crisp growth looks like encrusted coral. Tiny yellow button-like flowers appear in high summer, but they may be clipped off if the silver whiteness of the plant is preferred. Gently aromatic in both dampness and in warmth, cotton lavender has the alias of French lavender, although the aroma is far removed from that of the true lavender. The official properties are akin to those of wormwood. It is a stimulant; and when dried, the foliage will keep away moths in wardrobes and cupboards.

The most attractive form to introduce into the herb border is *S. neapolitana* with finer, loose foliage carried rather like a fistful of playing cards—a leaf much appreciated by floral arrangers.

COW PARSLEY

Anthriscus sylvestris
UMBELLIFERAE

The ubiquitous cow parsley, or kelk, which smothers every remaining southern English lane and is to be found ranging as far as the Caucasus, Ethiopia, and Siberia, is an introduced plant in America but native of Europe. It is strictly not a herb, but cow parsley is one of the most readily available plants for the production of a rich yellow dye. Wool when previously mordanted with alum takes on a good deep yellow which can be controlled towards a sludge-green by increasing the boiling time.

Very clearly related to chervil, cow parsley is not a plant to introduce into the herb garden; but the profusion of its creamy heads of frothy flowers might justify a hedgerow harvest for dyeing experiments. Its country names in England are "Lady's needlework," "kelk," and "Mother dere." The leaves are edible and may be chopped and added to salads and sandwiches.

COWSLIP

Primula veris
PRIMULACEAE

When Elizabeth I ruled England, the cowslip was one of the most prolific flowers to spangle the meadows in spring, and it probably remained so until the early part of this century. Cowslips thrive mainly on calcareous soils; their wrinkled leaves form a loose rosette, and the firm pale green stem carries a cluster of bright deep-yellow bells. In Elizabethan days a few freak forms seem to have been cultivated, some with two- or three-tiered flower groups along the stems and known as "hose-in-hose"; both Gerard and Parkinson speak of a double form. Shakespeare says in *A Midsummer Night's Dream*:

> The cowslips tall her pensioners be
> In their gold coats spots you see;
> Those be rubies; fairy favours,
> In their freckles live their savours

and it is the nectar enfolded in these "rubies, fairy favours" that imparts the delicate flavor to the amber-colored cowslip wine, a dessert wine.

Cowslips, or peagles (from Scottish *paigles,* "drooping with fatigue"), Culpeper calls them and reports that both wild and garden forms are well known. Their main attraction has been as a cosmetic, a cream, or toilet water, being made to remove spots and wrinkles from the skin, sunburnings and freckles, and promote beauty. They were also supposed to remedy all infirmities of the head such as vertigo, "phrensies," falling sickness, palsies, convulsions and cramps. Gerard confirms this: "A conserve made with the flowers . . . prevaileth wonderfully against the palsie."

Local English names remind us of the image of a bunch of golden keys: "Our Lady's bunch of keys," "St. Peter's keys," "culverkeys," "galligaskins," "herb paralysy," "paigle," "palsywort," "St. Peterwort." It is interesting to note that Culpeper makes an otherwise unjustified statement that the Greeks, because of the healing power of the plant for palsies, give it the name *paralysis*.

From Tudor times—and before—to Victorian days, spring festivals were gay affairs, and children and maidens gathered cowslips to toss as favors, calling them "cowslip balls" or "tossies." A bunch of flowers was tied tightly around the stalks behind the heads, and the stalks cut away so that they formed a ball. In *Our Village* by Miss Mitford, published in 1824, there is a chapter entitled "The Cowslip Ball" from which the following is taken:

> I . . . challenged Lizzie to a cowslip gathering; a trial of skill and speed to see which should soonest fill her basket . . . At last the baskets were filled and down we sat to make our cowslip ball. Everyone knows the process: to nip off the tuft of flowerets just below the top of the stalk and hang each cluster nicely balanced across a ribbon, till you have a long string like a garland; then to press them closely together and tie them tightly up.

More than the stalks need to be pulled away to make a cowslip wine. The calyces are removed as well, an intricate job, but old country people recall, with a glow on their face, the sight of a crock full of cowslip "pips" ready for winemaking. It appears to have sold well, among townspeople no doubt, at the end of the nineteenth century. An advertisement for Mott's Leicestershire Cowslip wine at about that time ran: "for Dinner, Dessert or evening. Purest, Brilliant, Slightly Sparkling, Delicious, Wholesome and Stimulating at 16s. a dozen bottles, carriage paid on orders of 2 dozen." What acres must have been covered by cowslips!

Every old cookbook seems to offer a recipe for cowslip wine, all suggesting varying quantities of flower pips, sugar, and water; some add oranges, some lemons, others suggest brandy or Rhenish wine. We read too of cowslip conserve, cowslip cream, puddings and tarts.

CUMIN

Cumium cyminum
UMBELLIFERAE

Cumin was known to the ancient civilizations and is referred to in the Bible (Isaiah 28:25 and 27) where the prophet impresses the care God takes of even the smallest seed. Jesus spoke to the scribes of "tithes of mint and cummin." The plant is grown for its seed or fruit and, like parsley and rue, is a plant of cultivation. Strongly resembling fennel in leaf and character, with the exception of the flowers which are pink or white, cumin seed has been used as a spice to flavor bread, and resembles caraway in flavor. An annual, native of Egypt, it was valued greatly in the past and has been used, like its relative, dill, as a carminative and antispasmodic. In veterinary medicine, a mixture of bay salt and cumin seed is used to treat certain disorders of pigeons.

CURRY PLANT

Helichrysum angustifolium
COMPOSITAE

A perennial, native of the Mediterranean regions, the curry plant is so called for its curry-like aroma rather than for its purpose. The small yellow flowers bloom in July and August, but it is for the attractive silver-gray foliage that this small bush is cultivated, providing as it does the perfect foil for the lingering orange flower buds. As a hummock plant, useful among stonework or a scree bed, once established it will revel in sunshine and may not always appreciate the vagaries of an inclement winter in Britain. Damage can usually be overcome by clipping back the growth in March, taking care not to cut right back into dead wood.

In the United States, it is not hardy and needs to be removed to a windowsill in a pot or protected in a cool greenhouse during the winter months.

As a moth deterrent, or to keep a musty smell away from garden sheds and outhouses, small bunches may be hung and will remain effective from one season to the next, when a fresh supply can be gathered.

Comphrey.

Foxgloves.

DANDELION, COMMON

Taraxacum officinale
COMPOSITAE

A medicinal plant known to Arabian physicians, the humble dandelion has served man as a medicine and nutrient for centuries and yet is probably one of the most scorned weeds of cultivation. Its long tap roots cling tenaciously to its foothold, the flat rosettes of leaves escape the lawnmower and the mechanical scythe, and its gay solitary flowers brighten every corner of the temperate regions of the world. The rounded heads of silver-haired seeds are beloved of children. Each hair carries away on the wind a tiny parachuted seed to move on, gypsy-like, elsewhere. "Blowball," as Ben Jonson records the name, alluded to the children's game of telling the time or forecasting the weather by counting the puffs required to disperse all the seeds from the fluffy seed head. Dandelions, as if they expected to be scorned, make a good provision for self-perpetuation. Their seed requires no dormancy and takes only three days to germinate.

In France, from February onwards, families can be seen by the roadsides, outside the towns, gathering the long leaves for salads or for cooking and serving like spinach, and dandelion tops are sold on market stalls. The nutritional value of the plant is very high; it contains calcium, sodium, sulphur, silic acid, potassium, and vitamins A, B, C, and D; the root, which is prized for dandelion coffee, is rich in insulin. As a blood cleanser even the green-dried leaves are useful in a winter diet, but the fresh spring leaves act upon the digestion by encouraging the function of the gall bladder; and the juice of a freshly harvested root is used therapeutically to stimulate the production of bile. Even an infusion of freshly chopped leaves, made from one teaspoonful to each cup of boiling water, flushes out the bile ducts and relieves associated complaints like catarrh and rheumatism. A country wine is made using both summer leaves and flowers.

The leaves can be covered (by means of a tile or plant pot with the drainage hole blocked) and blanched, much in the manner of blanching and refining endive. They then make an excellent addition to sandwiches. Three or four harvests of leaf can be made each year, and they are rich enough in iron to be considered useful in cases of anaemia.

When the roots are harvested, they should be lifted with a fork, the leaf tops removed, and the roots should be placed on sieves or racks, washed free of soil, preferably under running water. Prior to World War I, dandelion was cultivated as a commercial crop; about four pounds of seed was sown to the acre and the expected return would be four or five tons, the roots being harvested in the second autumn. There is evidence, dating from 1919, that dried English roots had previously been sold in competition with dried German roots at about 40 shillings per cwt. The roasted and ground roots sold as dandelion coffee then brought 2 shillings per pound.

It is only to be expected that a flower so well known and ubiquitous should boast a string of vernacular names. Dandelion is clearly a corruption of the French *dent de lion,* which alludes to the leaf margins. Some of its English names are "blowball," "peasant's clock," "cankerwort," "crow-parsnip," "Irish-daisy," "doon-head-clock," "fortune teller," "one-o'clocks," and "swine's snout."

Dandelion with globe of down
The schoolboy's clock in every town
Which truant puffs amain
To conjur lost hours back again.

To write of the cultivation of dandelions would probably give rise to some amusement, but obviously the roots and replenished top growth are richer for being grown in good soil or under cloche or frame protection in winter for salads. There is no need to let them flower; one flower from the crop each year will provide enough seed to maintain supplies, and the roots are usually lifted and used at the end of the second summer. During World War II, Russia obtained 80 per cent of her rubber requirements from the genus *Taraxacum.*

And over that potato field
A lazy veil of woven sun
Dandelions growing on headlands,
showing
Their unloved hearts to everyone.

PATRICK KAVENAGH
1905

DAPHNE

Daphne mezereum
THYMELAEACEAE

The mezereon, as *Daphne mezereum* is called colloquially, is a deciduous shrub found very locally in calcareous woodland in England and Europe but beloved as a garden plant for its purple heavily scented flowers which appear in February and March. They ruffle along the length of the previous year's bare wood, their exotic beauty never failing to arrest and surprise in the gray winter. The leaves follow, and later, in the late summer, the bright red berries arrive; it is mainly these berries that are employed in homeopathic medicine as a tincture in the treatment of the ears, nose and throat. The berries are poisonous and cathartic. It is of this bush that Culpeper wrote:

Though leafless, well attired and thick
beset
With blushing wreaths investing every
spray

The spurge laurel, *Daphne laureola,* is more commonly encountered in the wild state in England, extends to Wales, and inhabits light woodland and forest generally over Europe and Asia. Unlike mezereon it is evergreen; the flowers are equally exquisite but less conspicuous, they are green and bloom from February to April. The berries are black, accounting for the English and Latin specific names being confounded with the laurel. Its vernacular names confound it further: It is known as "dwarf bay," "copse laurel," "wood laurel," "sturdy lowries," and "fox poison." The juice of the berries is poisonous and causes inflammation of the skin; and the juice of the bark and berries is used in the treatment of open sores and ulcers. The roots of both species have been used to alleviate toothache, and the bark of both is regarded as poisonous.

In Greek mythology, Daphne was the daughter of the Arcadian river god and was beloved of Apollo; but her mother Garea changed her into a laurel tree to save her from Apollo's attentions. These shrubby plants are not true laurels (*Prunus lauro-cerasus* usually takes that name); the true laurel we call bay, but the general similarity in leaf form and berry has led to the association of one plant with the other. The *Daphneophoria* was a Greek festival held every ninth year in honor of Apollo and took the form of a procession, at which a chosen youth of high birth was accompanied by the *Daphneophorus,* or "laurel bearer." The laurels were entwined with ribbons representing days of the year and hung with balls to represent the sun, stars, and moon.

For the herb garden both daphnes are useful, the former standing up to exposure well, and the evergreen spurge laurel usefully tolerating the drip of trees.

DILL

Anethum graveolens
UMBELLIFERAE

The small seeds of dill are pungent and stronger in flavor than the light feathery foliage, and the whole plant can easily be confused with fennel. The name dill appears to be of Saxon origin, from *dillan,* "to lull," and the soothing properties of dill water have been turned to by generations of mothers to calm crying babies. Dill water can dispel flatulence and calm the most delicate of digestions and has a mildly soporific effect. The flavor falls generally into the anise range, and an unsweetened tisane made from the seeds is effective in alleviating hiccoughs.

The main use of dill seed is in the making of dill vinegar. This is accomplished by soaking half a cup of the seed in a quart of malt vinegar for three or four days and then straining off the liquid for storage. Alternatively, brine to which dill seeds have been added is commonly used for preserving gherkins and cucumbers. The foliage is feathery and delicate in both texture and flavor and is used in Eastern Europe and Scandinavia far more than in Britain to flavor bland vegetables and other dishes. In Poland it is cooked with new potatoes or garden peas, in much the same manner that we throw in a sprig of fresh mint, or used fresh to garnish the finished dish. Added to mushrooms, dumplings, and sauces to be served as an accompaniment to white fish, it enhances the flavor. The fresh or dried seeds can be used in all instances, but fresh foliage can only be taken from the plants either prior to flowering or from younger shoots produced after the seed has formed. Some difficulty attends the process of drying the foliage because of its filigree form; and unless some green color can be maintained there is little value in keeping it. Try drying it slowly in a darkened place in a temperature not exceeding blood heat.

An annual, the seed should be sown in fine tilth and takes about two weeks to germinate. The seed remains viable after several years of storage. Difficulty is sometimes experienced in getting dill to flourish, and a spot protected from the high sun and prevailing winds is probably most suitable; on the other hand, shade is adverse to its firm maturity because dill grows quickly once a plant is established. To grow it in the shade would only encourage etiolation. The flowers are yellow, each petal folding inwards slightly, and the seed forms about July; it may be used green or when fully ripened. In drought conditions, some watering is required to prevent stunted growth and plants producing seed in preference to foliage. It cross-fertilizes easily with fennel; and should some saved seed be used to maintain a supply of plants in the garden, bastards may well appear.

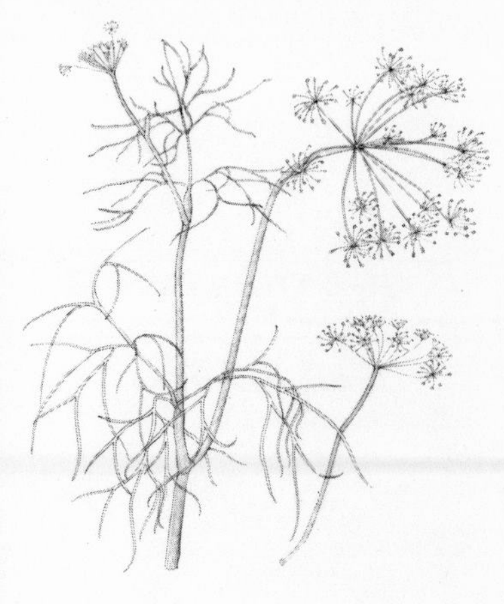

ELDER, ELDERBERRY

Sambucus nigra
CAPRIFOLIAGEAE

Culpeper writes of the elder: "I hold it needless to write any description, since every boy that plays with a pop-gun will not mistake another tree instead of the elder." The straight-growing tough branches, from which the pith may be easily extracted, have been used through the years as simple pea-shooters, whistles, and as blow-pipes for kindling fires. An ancient musical instrument, the sambuca, trombone-like in tone, was fashioned from many such reed-like sticks. The generic name, *Sambucus,* is from "Sambuca," and *nigra* alludes to the luscious, shining black berries that form in heavy clusters late in the summer.

A native of wood verges and scrub throughout Europe, Western Asia, North Africa, and the Azores, the elder has become part of the scene along British hedgerows. It prefers society to solitude and decks the lanes with creamy plate-like heads of sweetly scented lace in late June and early July, adding to the profusion where dog roses, honeysuckle, and privet abound. Mainly selective of base-rich soils, resistant to rabbits, and bursting afresh early each spring, the elder is so shrouded in superstitions and country beliefs that one would find difficulty in inventing a new one—though it would undoubtedly pass unquestioned! A century or more ago the elder was found close to habitation, for it was always planted to ward off evil spirits, thunder, witches, and all other unexplained phenomena at the time. Perhaps its close association with man has been assured by its numerous cosmetic, culinary, and medicinal properties, as though it has never been able to give of itself sufficiently in gratitude for man's company. An entire book was devoted in 1655 to its medicinal values, *The Anatomy of the Elder,* though curiously enough its properties appear to have been unknown to the Ancient World, other than as a black hair dye.

All parts of the plant are valuable. Medicinally the active principle of the bark is soft resin, and viburnic acid (identical with valeric acid), together with fat and wax, tannic acid, albumen, pectin, and a variety of salts. Both gum and starch are also present. The viburnic acid is the active principle in the alleviation of nasal catarrh, phlegm, croup, hoarseness, and the common cold, "elderberry rob" being a rustic remedy for colds and bronchitis. Causing heavy perspiring in addition to relieving bronchial congestion, it brings down the fever so frequently accompanying congestive colds. To make the rob, five pounds of ripe crushed berries are simmered together with a pound of loaf sugar until the juice has evaporated and the mixture is as thick as honey. One or two teaspoonfuls in a tumblerful of hot water is soothing to the complaint and is a mild aperient and diuretic. The benison of this hot cordial echoes today the satisfaction, which Cobbett described, of mulled elder served with nutmeg, as a nightcap—"a thing to run for." Even snuffling children do not need to be persuaded to drink the warm cordial or even take tincture of sambucus on a sugar lump.

Elderberry syrup is made in exactly the same way except that ginger and cloves are added to taste before bottling (usually about two cloves and a pinch of ginger to a pint of syrup). This is then used as a hot drink to alleviate bronchial congestion at night, two teaspoonfuls again being mixed in a tumblerful of hot water.

The bruised leaves produce an alkaloid, sambucine, and the glucoside sambunigrin; and the somewhat unpleasant odor accompanying the bruising has been found effective in the past for protecting fruit trees and vegetables by acting as an insecticide against greenfly or aphids.

And Grandma was never without her elderflower water to keep her skin soft, to keep wrinkles and freckles at bay, and to bathe her weary brow.

The timing of the flower harvest has to be determined precisely and the flowerheads gathered dry. They are then put in a pile to encourage the corollas to loosen before being sifted free of the flower stalk. If the time is not right the resultant dried flowers can be brown, or they will turn black in the heaps; and so careful observation for a few days is worthwhile. The time to choose is just as full bloom is reached. If they are gathered too soon the sifting process has to be tediously repeated, and if gathered too late the blossoms are dirty in appearance and not worth preserving. After sifting, dry off the flowers in a cool oven for a few minutes with the door open, turning or spooning the petals continuously. Once dried the flowers can be gently rolled into balls between the hands to free the stalks, and then sifted. The stalks and debris are discarded and only the petals themselves preserved. Elderflower tea at its best is made from fresh flowers; but the dried ones make a delicious tisane too, or may be added to the fresh blossoms to intensify the flavor, for like so many other plants the elder clings to its sweet perfume even in death. This tisane may be stored and reheated without sacrificing any of its fresh appeal. A pinch of dried flowers can enhance a pot of Indian tea, imparting an intriguing subtlety of flavor. The elderflower water, or *eau de sureau* as French cosmeticians call it, of the old pharmacies was not always "distilled" from the fresh flowers, as the season is so short, but blossoms were salted down for use later. The fresh flowers are nowadays gathered in profusion by home winemakers and can make a delicious high tea delicacy when fried in a thin batter—elderflower fritters. One of the problems of gathering from the hedgerows today is that the blossoms need careful washing to remove particles of dust and deposit from diesel fumes if they are to be eaten fresh in this way.

Elderberries are really one of the hedgerow harvest's greatest gifts. Green or black—that is, unripe or fully ripened—they can be used to make wine. If the heads are cut whole from the plant and hung on a string to dry, the berries will then store and provide a substitute for currants throughout the winter. A few scattered in an apple pie add flavor as well as color. Jams, jellies, chutney, vinegar, and syrup, all for the store cupboard are present-day economies in numerous households.

Culpeper draws attention to the Dane's elder, *S. ebulus,* calling it a "dwarf elder" or "wall-wort"—in all its action more drastic medicinally than the elder bush. There are more leaflets to each pinnate leaf, the creamy flowers are marked with purple, and the plant is a herbaceous perennial, not shrubby in habit. Supposedly introduced by the Danes, it is not nearly so extensive in range in Britain as *S. nigra*. Both are aperients and diuretics, and both can provide a poultice or ointment for proud flesh, ulcers, or varicose veins.

The numerous vernacular names recall its long association with man—"elder," "eldern," "ellan," "ellarne," "elnorne," "ellen-tree," all probably stemming from the Old Norse word *elda* or the Middle English verb *elden,* "to light a fire." The wood itself does not burn readily, and its pith can be removed so easily that it was put to obvious use as a bellows. "Bourtree", "boretice," "bore," and "whusselwood"—each seems to bear out the hollowed stem theme. The wood itself is comparatively heavy when seasoned but is only used for skewers or cheap rulers as a substitute for box.

Several American native elders share the virtues attributed to the European *S. nigra,* but they are less woody and of a comparatively stunted growth. *S. canadensis,* the American or sweet elder, is a somewhat short-lived green-stemmed shrub, persisting only by its runner growth. The red-berried mountain elder, *S. pubens,* with a reddish-brown pith, is found especially in rocky places and higher altitudes.

ELECAMPANE

Inula helenium
COMPOSITAE

A coarse-leaved member of the daisy family, with stout stems and bright yellow flowers, elecampane is a native of Britain, though very rarely found in the wild state nowadays. Formerly, it was cultivated in monastic gardens and has served both man and his animals from Roman times.

Famed as an ingredient of Marchalan, a Welsh thirteenth-century concoction, and referred to by Pliny, Dioscorides and Galen for its virtues, elecampane is a proud and dominant tenant of the herb border. Formerly its name was *Enula* (by which the old herbalists knew it) *campana,* because it grew in Roman fields; and the various aliases and rechristenings it has suffered all commemorate Helen, wife of Menelaus, who, tradition says, grasped a bunch of this herb when carried away by Paris.

It was as a veterinary requirement that elecampane begged its passage across the Atlantic to America, by virtue of its powers as a horse medicine and for healing sheep scab. Its vernacular names in the English language are "horseheal" and "scabwort." The leaves are bitter and aromatic, providing a mucilaginous remedy for both man and beast; and the large root is starchy, black-skinned, and aromatic. It has been used mainly as a medicament to relieve pulmonary congestion and was the basis of a sweetmeat or candy sucked to ease asthmatical breathing and, it would seem, by travelers who might encounter the poisonous fumes of marsh and river. This candy may be made by cooking small pieces of the root, coating them with hot syrup, and leaving them to set. In former days they were colored, usually pink. A decoction of the root provides a recommended tonic, and Pliny gave the advice "let no day pass without eating some of the roots of *Enula* considered to help the digestion and cause mirth." A cordial may be made by infusing the roots with white wine or white port and sugar or honey. Sometimes, as in the Haute Savoie and parts of Switzerland, raisins are added to enhance the fullness of the drink.

ERYNGIUM

Eryngium maritimum
UMBELLIFERAE

Best known as sea holly, the eryngiums or eryngios are to be found on the Atlantic coasts of Europe. A close relative, *E. campestre*—an inland form, less glabrous—ranges over Europe and Persia to Afghanistan and has been granted immigrant rights in North America. One may admire the beauty of form of these plants, wondering at the metallic blue, glaucous foliage and stem, without realizing that in the past they were much prized for their bitter roots. When candied with sugar, these were one of the valued tonics, having strong restorative properties for nervous disorders, and were sold for a considerable price.

The young shoots of *E. maritimum* are eaten in Sweden like asparagus shoots and were formerly used in this way by fisherfolk in the west country of England and in Wales.

Among the most decorative of hardy perennials, *E. amethystinum* has deeply cut basal leaves and branching heads of amethyst blue flowers, spiny and prickly and altogether startlingly beautiful. *E. × oliverianum* is a strong-growing plant with several forms all carrying good teasel-like heads, with a dark blue metallic finish. These are very good plants to include in the herb garden, because the roots can be used in the old way, and also for introducing variety of form and color second to none. The flowerheads and stems retain their gorgeous finish, even upon drying, and thus provide excellent winter material for the flower arranger.

FENNEL

Foeniculum officinale
UMBELLIFERAE

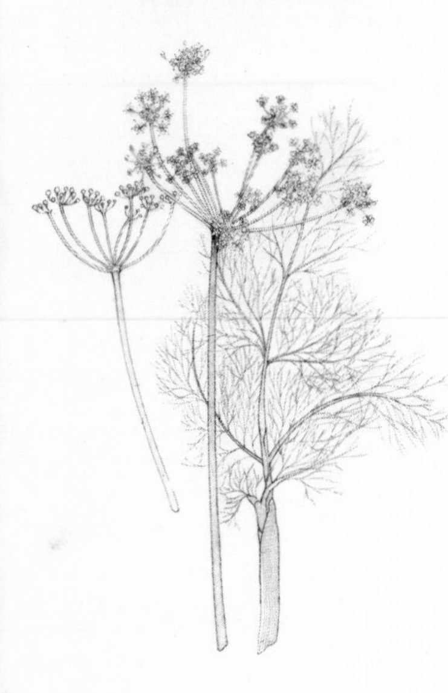

A British native herb, fennel was known to the Romans and the Anglo-Saxons, and in ancient times it was one of the nine sacred herbs. Its association with the church appears only to have been that it could be eaten on fasting days. In more recent years the seed has been amusingly called "meetin' seeds," for it was the seed of fennel that the nonconformists of the New World took to chapel meetings to sustain them through interminable sermons!

It has long been esteemed for its nourishing and slimming properties: Greek athletes included it in their diet for stamina, as a guard against overweight and an inducer of courage. The Greek name for the plant, *marathon*, is derived from *maraino*, "to grow thin."

Like the other sacred herbs, fennel was regarded as a cure for all ills. Time and authority discarded first one treatment then another, selecting the plant for use only to soothe the eyes and clear the sight. But we read that in the Middle Ages it not only comforted the stomach and counteracted dropsy but increased a woman's milk and was (at the same time) a remedy for worms in the ears. From the Household Roll of Eleanor, Countess of Leicester, wife of Simon de Montfort, we learn that in the thirteenth century, fennel was bought for threepence per pound. She was then residing at Dover Castle, where, presumably, fennel was not grown in the garden. Contemporary accounts show that 8½ pounds of fennel was a month's supply for such a family and its entourage.

An annual, the plant grows to five or six feet and forms a graceful shower of delicate leaves. It seeds itself haphazardly, and so there is always a growing generation from which to take fresh leaves for the kitchen. Alternatively, the plants can be repeatedly cut back through the summer, and the base of the plant will produce a seemingly endless supply of fresh shoots for the cook. Yellow flowers, typical of the natural order, bloom in the summer, and leaves are best taken before the plant flowers. Seed forms easily and can be harvested in September before it scatters—or the flowerheads can be shrouded with bags to catch the ripened seed as it falls. The leaves, strong in flavor, recalling both anise and celery, are used nowadays mainly in sauces which accompany fish.

As a decorative plant the so-called black fennel, *F. officinale nigra* (SYN. *F. vulgare nigra)* outshines many border perennials for effect. The delicate foliage forms sprays of bronze feathers, at first rusted and later beetle-bronze. It is worth confiscating the flowerheads before they form to enjoy the full decorative value of the foliage; and if the plants are grown four to five feet apart, their grace can be appreciated to the full.

Florence fennel (or sweet fennel, or Roman fennel), *F. vulgare dulce*, is still cultivated in the south of France as a commercial vegetable crop. The stem base, which is swollen and flattened and blanched, is sometimes seen for sale in city greengrocers. In good summers it can be expected to flourish in favored parts of Britain. The seed was particularly valued;

now, it is grown as a commercial crop in the south of France for the production of a carminative for infants and is known universally as "gripe water."

The Fennel with its yellow flowers,
In an earlier age than ours,
Was gifted with the wondrous powers
Lost vision to restore . . .
I pledge you in this cup of grief,
Where floats the fennel's bitter leaf,
The battle of our life is brief.

LONGFELLOW

FENUGREEK

Trigonella faenum-graecum
LEGUMINACEAE

One of the oldest plants of cultivation, fenugreek is often added to fodder to "sweeten" it and is one of the constituents of *kuphi*, an Egyptian embalming and incense oil. A native of southern Europe, it is a plant of cultivation only. The use of fenugreek has declined during recent years, and it is possibly only used in present-day Europe as a source of extract, the principal flavoring of imitation maple syrup, but previously it was cultivated for the mucilaginous quality of its seed. As a drug plant, it was reputed to have numerous virtues, especially in the treatment of mouth ulcers, chapped lips, and hands, and also as a digestive. Supposedly it promotes lactation and encourages an alluring roundness to the bosom; when roasted, it is used for this purpose in the harems of North Africa and the Middle East.

In the United States, it is incorporated in many spice blends like curry powder, and is included in chutneys; experiments with fenugreek, which seeds quickly after sowing, in the production of diosgenin may well lead to its use as a basis for contraceptive treatments.

FEVERFEW

Chrysanthemum parthenium
COMPOSITAE

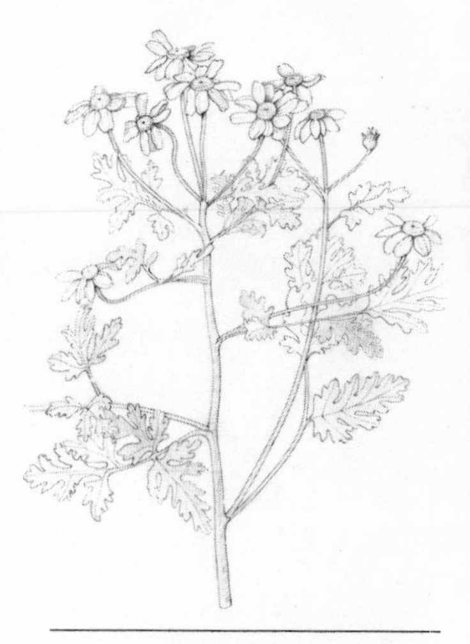

Nowadays feverfew is grown more for its decorative than its economic qualities. It is seen, not infrequently, naturalized in old walls throughout Britain. Most likely a native of southeastern Europe, Asia Minor, and the Caucasus, it is now established throughout the north temperate regions of the world. No doubt it paid for its transport as a very popular febrifuge, hence its name. The unpleasant odor of feverfew is reminiscent of rather stale chamomile, to which it is closely related, and it is as repellent as pyrethrum, another of its cousins, long grown as an insecticide. It was Dioscorides who first described the use of this attractive little herbaceous plant as an effective means of allaying fevers.

The deeply indented foliage, so similar in design to that of the garden chrysanthemum, is of a bright greenish-yellow and forms tufted growths around the crown of the plant. Decorative in the herb garden and in paving stones and walls, it will seed itself and somehow give a comfortable air to the garden.

FOXGLOVE

Digitalis purpurea
SCROPHULARIACEAE

The Latin name *Digitalis purpurea* for the foxglove was first published by Leonard Fuchs, in his *De Historia Stirpium* (1542), which is mentioned on page 195. It was he who put forward the theory of digitalin as an effective treatment of dropsy. Later, a prominent part in the story of digitalis as a drug plant was played by Dr. William Withering, a man of wide interests and a prolific writer on various learned subjects during the eighteenth century.

It was from the recipe of a country family in Shropshire that Withering first recorded the use of digitalin in the treat-

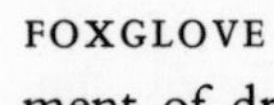

ment of dropsy, and years later he published his own theories. His studies were of necessity slow, because his patients were also his human "guinea pigs." Unfortunately, his partner Erasmus Darwin, being more eminent at the time, was credited with much of the work and, in fact, appears to have accepted the accolades. But Withering wrote his thesis on the use of digitalin and was able to report his case histories in considerable detail. He was highly regarded for this work and received recognition by being elected a Fellow of the Royal Society.

So closely identified was Withering with the plant that his memorial in Edgbaston Old Church in Birmingham, England, is embellished with the foxglove. Furthermore, his portrait, now in the Nationalmuseum, Stockholm, shows him holding the plant with which his name was associated. He died in 1799, the year when it was established that the primary action of digitalin is upon the heart, as a reducer of the pulse rate.

One of Dr. Withering's poems, published anonymously, anticipates this finding:

The Foxglove's leaves, with caution
given
Another proof of favouring Heav'n
Will happily display;
The rapid pulse it can abate;
The hectic flush can moderate
And, blest by Him whose will is fate,
May give a lengthened day.

The drug digitalin is obtained from the dark green leaves of the common foxglove, one of the few British native plants to be included in the British Pharmacopoeia. While much is imported, some of the larger manufacturing chemists cultivate *D. purpurea* in England, mainly in the west country. The drying process is not one to be undertaken by amateurs; not only must the leaves remain green when dry, they must be allowed to reabsorb some moisture to prevent shattering. The leaves are gathered either from the flowering stems in June, just before the plants bloom, or from young rosettes in September.

The foxglove is valued in the decorative herb garden for its spire-like form, which is so useful towards the back of the border. The wild or common purple foxglove revels in shade where self-sown seedlings will perpetuate the effect—sometimes taking a full eighteen or twenty months to flower. The lower leaves of the plant have a tendency to become untidy and brown and need to be removed from time to time during the season. The foxglove is happiest on light soils and where it has a cool root-run with some compost or other moisture-retentive material incorporated.

The plant is poisonous, but all foxgloves are good bee plants and claim inclusion in representative drug-plant collections, and in the bee garden and the decorative herb border. There are other species of digitalis but it is *purpurea* that is the true herb. From this species there has been some hybridizing, notably by the Reverend Henry Wilkes who introduced the Shirley Hybrids as forms of *D. purpurea* 'Gloxinoides,' the pinks and purples and whites of which were lavishly spattered with chocolate spots. By 1950, Messrs Sutton and Co., Seedsmen of Reading, England, had introduced the Excelsior Hybrids in a wide range of color but with flower bells arranged all around the stem. The spikes thus appear wider in proportion to their height than the one-sided spike of the type.

The slight tendency of the stem to arch, allowing the "bells" to fall, earns the plant its English name, from the Anglo-Saxon *foxes-gleow*—a gleow being a musical instrument of arch-form hung with graduated bells.

Mary Webb says of the foxglove belfries:

Should they startle over the land,
None would know what bells they be.
Never any wind can ring them,
Nor the great black bees that swing
them
Every crimson bell, down-slanted,
Is so utterly enchanted.

There is a host of local names: "flowaterleaves," "fox-fingers," "lady's thimble," "pop-glove" (because the unopened flowers will pop when pressure is exerted by the finger and thumb, opening to make a "finger stall"), "witches' fingers," "witches' bells," and "bluidy man's fingers."

Cultivation is simple, the plants being propagated from seed which, because it is so very fine, should be sown in a seed compost in boxes or seed pans in May, out of doors. After pricking out and planting out, once the seedlings are established the young plants will look after themselves but will need an adequate supply of water during the early stages. Losses may occur should the first winter be damp, but once the plants have flowered, self-sown seedlings will carry the banner in the herb garden for many years.

FRITILLARY

Fritillaria meleagris
LILIACEAE

The snake's head fritillary, its pendulous flower bells unique in the plant kingdom for their checkerboard markings, is sometimes to be found locally in the south of England. Believed to be a rare British native, it chooses watery meadows and is particularly common around the upper reaches of the Thames near Oxford and in the Loddon valley in Berkshire. Frequently, it is used as a garden plant to naturalize in grass and as underplanting for shrubs. Plants were brought to England by an apothecary named Noel Caperon about 1570. It was grown by Gerard in his garden, and he knew it as "checkered daffodil," or "ginnie hen flower," which suggests that it was a rare native plant, unknown to both men, and thus a collectable item from France, where Caperon found it near Orléans.

GARLIC

Allium sativum
LICIACEAE

Two species of *Allium—vineale,* crow garlic, and *sphaerocephalon,* round-headed leek—are native to Britain and northern Europe, but it is the clove garlic, although called *sativum,* which is cultivated for its very strong and distinctive flavor and which has become increasingly popular in Britain and America as a culinary additive during the past twenty years. Its country name of "Devil's posy" is from a supposed connection with the Evil One, and it has been important in Chinese mythology for centuries as a ruse against the Evil Eye. Since time immemorial, it has played the role of cleanser and antiseptic and safeguard against infectious diseases, by strengthening the senses, encouraging circulation, and hastening excretion—as do many highly seasoned foods. The pores of the skin are stimulated into action by its use. There is a belief that a clove of garlic planted near a rose bush will enhance the

perfume of the rose, because the rose, provoked by competition, will manufacture more scent.

Culpeper clearly did not like garlic and seems to have had his reservations about its all-healing and curative cleansing powers, so universally extolled. He says:

> Many authors quote many diseases this is good for, but conceal its vices. . . . Its heat is vehement and all vehement hot things send up ill favoured vapours to the brain. In choleric men 'twill add fuel to the fire; in men oppressed by melancholy it will attenuate the humour, and send up strange fancies and as many strange visions to the head; therefore let it be taken inwardly with great moderation; outwardly you may make more bold with it.

Garlic does, however, contain a volatile oil with considerable sulphurous properties and is rich in iodine, an element necessary for the healthy balance of the thyroid gland. The odor, disagreeable to some people, can be overcome to some extent if it is always used in conjunction with parsley and celery leaves.

It grows best on a light soil, enriched with some well-rotted, moisture-retentive material; and the bulbs, or sets, are usually planted about two inches deep in March, though they are perfectly hardy and will survive the winter if planted in November. Each set or clove is planted separately. By August, the foliage will have ripened and turned yellow and the cloves can be harvested and dried, their chalk-white skins decorative when strung up in the kitchen.

GENTIAN

Gentiana lutea
GENTIANACEAE

By far the most important of the gentians used medicinally is the yellow gentian, an upstanding plant of architectural attractiveness and a characteristic feature of the damp meadows of the lower Alps, Apennines, and Pyrenees in Europe. Attaining a firm three or four feet in height with opposite strongly ribbed leaves chalicing golden yellow flowers, *Gentiana lutea* was the first of its genus to be introduced into cultivation in Britain. Gerard grew it in his garden, calling it "fellwort" for its ability to cure felons, or whitlows, and it has over the years become known as "bitterwort" or "baldmoney." Its medicinal value was known to Pliny and Dioscorides; the latter reports that it was Gentius, King of Illyria from 180 to 167 B.C., who first utilized its healing qualities and named the plant. Gentian bitter, or jenzmer, is extracted from the huge spongy root, which plunges a yard or so into the pasture land which supports it. Calcareous soils are its favorite habitat and though it is prolific where it grows, colonies decrease constantly from being ravaged by the peasants and herbalists. Slow to develop, the yellow gentian can live for half a century; its stout root has no sinecure.

Autumn is the best time to lift the roots (or those parts that can be lifted, even though they are always reasonably flexible), when they are richest in gentianin, a glucoside intensely bitter of taste but almost odorless. The roots contain also a considerable amount of uncrystallizable sugar, a property long put to use by the peasants of Switzerland and Bavaria in the home production of *Enzianbranntwein* or gentian brandy. (The plant must not be confused with *Veratrum album q.v.* which bears similar leaves but acts as a cumulative poison.) The bitterness of the root of *G. lutea* renders it one of the most effective of tonics, a non-astringent. The addition of lemon or orange peel to the "brandy" makes a cordial drink to remind one of an Alpine holiday.

As a garden plant, in a bold group in good moisture-retentive soil, or as a sentinel of a damp patch, the yellow gentian presents an arresting feature. Grow it from seed germinated under glass or invest in a few plants: Where they are happy, they will outlive many of us.

GERANIUM

Geranium spp.
GERANIACEAE

The diversity of the true geranium, of which there are about 300 species scattered over the temperate regions of the world, makes identification difficult. The leaf form varies but is always elaborately and deeply indented. Some species are grown in gardens, some are naturalized in both Britain and North America, and others are native.

In the past, some have been valued for their medicinal properties as styptics, and herb Robert *(G. robertianum)* in particular in the treatment of haemorrhages. The leaves have a strong rather disagreeable smell. The small flowers are rose pink, and the whole plant somewhat straggling of habit but nevertheless dainty.

Its vernacular names are numerous: "bloodwort," "dragon's blood," "fox geranium" and "fox grass" (on account of the "foxy" smell), "knife and fork," "Robin flower," and "stinking Bob." A tea brewed from the whole herb was once used as a remedy for gout and for "red rash"; and because of the unpleasant odor of the crushed leaves, they were used as insecticides of a primitive kind, especially amongst bedding for animals.

GOAT'S RUE

Galega officinalis
LEGUMINOSAE

The light elaborate foliage of the goat's rue, topped by good spikes of flowers typical of the sweet pea family, adds good foil to the bolder plants of the herb border. Goat's rue is little used nowadays but deserves a place in a representative collection of febrifuges. It was one of the herbs traditionally used to treat the plague, because an infusion caused intense perspiration. In addition, it stimulates lactation, as its name (said to be taken from the Greek *gala,* "milk," and *ago,* "to lead") would suggest. It is a native of western Asia and southern Europe and was used as a fodder plant, especially for its stimulation of the mammary glands. Writing just over 100 years ago, Jane Loudon almost dismissed galega as "weedy plants"; but by the turn of the century when William Robinson was writing in *The English Flower Garden,* he was ready to extol their virtues as providing "an abundance of cut flowers of various hues." The plant is variable in flower color and has several varieties, including 'Alba,' and cultivars such as the mauve and white 'Duchess of Bedford,' the blue and white 'Lady Wilson,' and a very clear mauve 'Her Majesty.' Light twiggy stakes must be pushed in around the plant in the early part of the season so that its weak stems may grow through them, gaining support and providing better garden effect.

GOOD KING HENRY

Chenopodium bonus-henricus
CHENOPODIACEAE

A perennial plant, good King Henry is sometimes known as Lincolnshire asparagus and was formerly cultivated in that part of England. A British native, it is a leafy herb, rich in vitamins and iron, and used as a vegetable; cultivation is easy. The seed is very slow to germinate; and for good results, the seedlings should be thinned to 1½ feet apart, in two stages, as with many leafy vegetables. By earthing up or top dressing with leaf mold, or horticultural peat, the tips of the plant may be blanched and can then be cut and used like asparagus, making an excellent cold dish.

Its other venacular names are "Lincolnshire spinach," revealing its alternative use as a green-leaf crop, and "mercury" or

GOOD KING HENRY

"English mercury," "smiddy leaves," "smear leaves," and "flowering docken." Formerly it was much cultivated in kitchen gardens, but today grows around many English villages. The name "smiddy leaves" is thought to indicate that one of its favorite habitats was about the blacksmith's forge or smithy. As "smear leaves," it was used in the treatment of sores and ulcers and as an antiseptic for cuts and burns—no doubt very ready to hand for the blacksmith!

GROUND IVY

Glechoma hederacea
LABIATAE

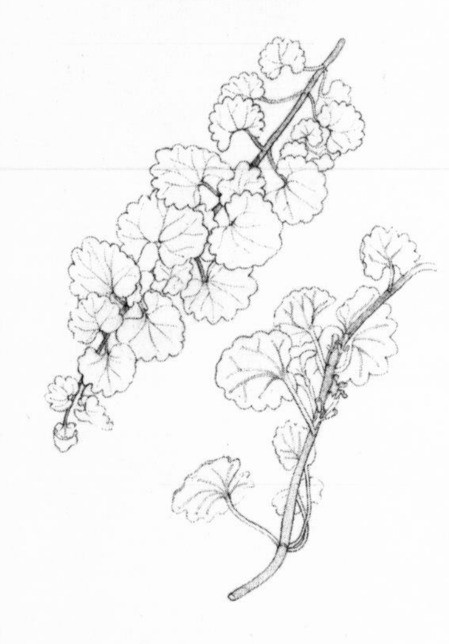

This ground-hugging plant trails its way across southern and central Europe and westward to Asia and Japan; it is also a native of Britain. On the North American continent, it is an immigrant and began its foothold in eastern Canada and the United States; but it is now trailing westward, shunned by cattle, extending its runners to bear flowers the following year.

A volatile oil is found in the glands at the back of the leaves, bestowing on the whole plant an aromatic quality. A denizen of waste ground and hedge banks, the clear flower color varies from deep blue to pinkish-mauve, probably according to the alkalinity of the soil, as is frequently the case with blue flowers. The kidney-shaped leaves are wrinkled and diminish in size towards the extremity of the square-stemmed runners.

Gerard tells us "The women of our northern parts do tun the herb Ale hoove into their ale." The leaves were formerly thrown into the vat with ale to clarify it and give it a flavor. The leaves of this little creeper have long been used all over Europe for clarifying beer, hence its names "ale hoof," "tun hoof," and "gill ale," the last a corruption of the French *quiller,* "to ferment" or "make merry." This plant was mainly superseded by hops in the sixteenth century, but in provincial areas ale hoof was often still used for 150 years. Not dreaming of relinquishing its association with refreshing and thirst-quenching drinks, people used it popularly as a brew or tisane and called it gill tea. "Gill-by-the-ground" was among the herb cries in the markets of London in Cheapside in the days of Elizabeth I and "ground ivy" more recently as a street cry of the herb women—"Here's fine rosemary, sage and thyme, come buy my ground ivy" *(Roxburgh Ballad).*

The designation of ivy alludes most probably to the evergreen character of the plant, and although various explanations have been offered, there seems little doubt that this, the simplest, is the right one. In North America, its vernacular name of field balm similarly alludes to the leaves, but in this instance to the shape. Americans avoid any further confusion by calling it "creeping Charlie," and this is interesting because its host of country names in Britain dub ground ivy always as a maiden! —Gill-over-the-ground, gill, gill hen, hedge maids, genny run-ith ground (in the north), Lizzie-by-the-hedge, Jill, hayhofe, haymaids, heihow, and heyhove. "Devil's candlestick" seems to be a fairly widespread name, but the association with the Evil One is not obvious.

The leaves are bitter, their action is diuretic, astringent, and tonic. A tisane (virtually gill tea) is made by infusing two handfuls of freshly picked leaves in a pint of boiling water. After infusion, the liquid is strained and sweetened with honey, or sometimes licorice, to alleviate the bitterness.

"Past cures it has claimed include nervous headaches, digestive troubles, and as snuff or even the juice for sniffing up the nose, the relief of deafness or ringing noises in the ears," so Gerard records; but today its value is recognized as a diuretic tonic—a spring remedy, when the leaves are at their best. The hot gill tea sweetened with honey is also effective in the treatment of coughs and colds.

HELLEBORE

Helleborus niger
RANUNCULACEAE

The Christmas rose, probably because its flowers grow with such purity and profusion during the shortest days of the year, is enshrouded in fable and legend of great antiquity. According to Greek tradition, the shepherd Melampus first realized its properties by observing its effect on his goats; later, he is said to have used it successfully to cure the daughters of Proetus, King of Argus, of mental derangement by dosing them with the milk of goats who had eaten the plant. The plant was formerly known as Melampode after Melampus, a physician of 1400 B.C. who, Pliny tells us, used it to treat nervous disorders and hysteria.

Two allied species, *Helleborus foetidus* and *H. viridis,* are found wild in England and Europe, generally in the wooded areas, though the forms seem to vary. *H. foetidus,* bear's foot or stinking hellebore, is of somewhat floppy habit in northern climes, but in the Alps it is a much more upstanding plant. The Christmas rose is a plant of cultivation in Britain, but it and other species were introduced from their native regions of the eastern Mediterranean by the Romans, who certainly knew of the plant's curative powers. Considerable ritual and ceremony attended the digging up of roots in ancient Greece by the *rhizotomi* or root-gatherers. A circle was described with the point of a sword around the plant, and then prayers were offered while the black roots were lifted. Belief in the plant's powers to cure the mania continued through the centuries, and Gerard recommends it as "good for mad and furious men, for melancholy, dull and heavie persons, and briefly, for all those that are troubled with black choler and molested with melancholy."

The Christmas rose's round flower buds of blush pink form deep in its crown in autumn and develop into pure white blossoms; its strong green foliage is itself attractive, even after the plant has flowered.

The late Margery Fish assembled a remarkable collection of hellebores at East Lambrook Manor, Somerset, England, and several old cultivars have been reintroduced comparatively recently, notable among them 'Potter's Wheel.'

HEMLOCK

Conium maculatum
UMBELLIFERAE

Famed as the ingredient of the fatal draught of Socrates, the hemlock is a plant native to Britain and is extensively distributed over Europe, Asia, and North Africa. It has been introduced into North America, certainly to Mexico, California, the West Indies, and New Zealand. Distinguished from its numerous umbelliferous relatives by its foetid smell and purple-spotted stem, it is a plant to avoid because of its poisonous qualities. The drug coniine, an alkaloid found in high concentration in all parts of the plant, is listed in the British Poisons List, and it is used in homeopathic medicine, in correct prescription, as an antidote to strychnine poisoning and as a sedative on the motor-nerve centers. Its effect is to cause giddiness to the extent of vertigo, hence its name, derived from the Greek *konos,* "spinning top." The specific name, *maculatum,* identifies the spotted stems, a feature that one should learn to recognize on the hemlock. Fatalities and illness do occur from its leaves being confused with wild parsley, its fruits with those of caraway, and even its roots with parsnips. The rotten smell should also be an identifying signal.

HEMLOCK

Hemlock is a tall graceful plant which attains six or eight feet in height. It loves moist meadows and streambanks, and its hollow bluish-white stem, with the warning spots, stands erect. The greenish-white flowers mature gradually in June and are at first entirely male and later entirely female, followed by heavy heads of flattened seeds typical of the family. The umbel has anything from twelve to twenty rays, and the herb is gathered from June to August, when both flower and fruit can be found; the plant is a biennial.

The name hemlock is from the middle English *heme-luc*, appearing as both *hemleac* and *hemlic*, or even *hymlic*, and has almost as ancient a name as *herba benedicta*, herb bennet, or St. Bennet's herb. Other names are "bad man's oatmeal," "bunk," "heckhow," "humlock," and "cambuck"—which meant "dry stalk." The present-day term "kricksies" has come to be used as imitative of the sound of the hemlock stems rattling in the wind.

HEMP AGRIMONY

Eupatorium cannabinum
COMPOSITAE

The British native hemp agrimony is a common enough plant throughout Europe, western and central Asia, and North Africa, and shows a predilection for dampish woodlands, fens, and streambanks. Its Latin name perpetuates the name of the potentate of the first century B.C., Mithridates VI Eupator. His famous concoction of as many as sixty ingredients has become so legendary and the recipe so corrupted that one tends to discard references to it, but Pliny recorded it as being a syrup, an antidote to poisons and various infections. The name of "Mithridate Confection" appears not to have been withdrawn from the London Pharmacopoeia until 1746 and may well have continued to survive in common practice, with several variants, among the quacks.

A perennial plant, bearing reddish-mauve flowers in terminal corymbs, it is visited by butterflies in July and August: This alone is reason enough to include it in the herb border. Even more decorative is *Eupatorium purpureum*, a native of North America from New Brunswick to the Gulf of Mexico and westward to Manitoba and Texas. It dwells on moist soil and low ground, throwing up numerous slightly fragrant clusters of flowers on purplish stems. Towering above surrounding plants, the "joe-pye weed" or "purple boneset" as it is called, also attracts butterflies. Joe-pye was an Indian medicine man of New England who gained fame from his treatment of typhus with this plant. "Trumpet weed" and "purple thoroughwort" are other American colloquial names. An infusion of the flowers is said to allay influenza.

HENBANE

Hyoscyamus niger
SOLANACEAE

Plants of the natural order *Solanaceae* should be carefully identified because several of them have poisonous parts. The fruits of the potato plant, for example, are poisonous as are the berries of belladonna. Henbane is a strong-smelling plant, clammy to the touch, and it appears spasmodically on waste ground, or recently disturbed land; it is poisonous. Hyoscymine, atropine, and hyosine, all alkaloids, are its main constituents, but put to good use in the correct gentle doses, they provide a preventive for travel sickness and are employed in producing hypnotic drowsiness to oblivi-ate the awareness of childbirth and yet allow the mother to fulfill her own part. In medieval times, it was called "dwale" and was used with opium to induce sleep; it was the forerunner of modern anaesthetics. (The vernacular "dwale" refers to *Atropa belladonna*.) We read also that the black seeds or nuts, heated on a tile and the vapor inhaled, would deaden toothache. Gerard says:

> The root boiled with vinegar, and the same holden hot in the mouth, easeth the pain of the teeth. The seed is used by mountebanks and tooth drawers which run about the country to cause

worms to come forth of the teeth by burning it in a chafing-dish of coles, the party holding his mouth over the fume thereof; but some crafty companions, to gain money convey small lute-strings into the water, persuading the patient that those small creepers came out of his mouth.

Somewhat curious in appearance, henbane's jagged hispid leaves have pronounced midribs. It grows to a height of 1½–2 feet and is sometimes an annual, producing flowers and fruit in the one season, but more commonly a biennial. The flowers are cream colored and daintily veined with purple, but it is an altogether sinister plant employed by and associated with sorcerers in the past. Ben Jonson includes it in his list of witches' potions.

Its vernacular names vary from "loaves of bread," "chenile," "henbell," "stinking Roger" to "belene" and "brosewort"; all herbal writers of the past, however, treat it as something to be avoided, despite the fact that it produces required drugs. It is easy enough to grow in the garden once the seed is obtained, but as with several other plants, notably aconitum, belladonna, and laburnum, children must be made aware of its dangers.

HOREHOUND, BLACK

Ballota nigra
LABIATAE

Known and recognized for its appalling smell, the black horehound bears small rose-pink flowers; though its growth is rather floppy, it looks quite attractive along the top of a dry wall. It retains the dusty appearance of white horehound but is not as hairy. The plant takes its name from the Greek *ballo,* "to reject," alluding to its offensive smell. Despite this, it seems to have been used against dog bites and as a fomentation for the treatment of gout. No longer used by herbalists, it has been replaced by alternatives which are pleasanter to use.

HOREHOUND, WHITE

Marrubium vulgare
LABIATAE

Probably known best for its use as horehound candy, white horehound is a downy perennial plant. The tiny white flowers are borne in dense whorls during July, August, and September. A British native plant, it appears throughout Scotland, Ireland, Wales, and the southern and eastern coasts of England; it also ranges generally over Europe, central and western Asia, and the Canary Isles. The somewhat untidy growth, with whitish wrinkled leaves, is characteristic, but did not prevent its being taken into every East Anglian cottage garden in Georgian times; it was cultivated for beer-making, the whole herb being used. Ground and mixed with common salt, both black horehound, *Ballota nigra (q.v.),* and the hairy white horehound have long been an accepted antidote and remedy for bites from raging dogs. Michael Drayton wrote:

> Here hore-hound 'gainst the mad
> dog's ill
> By biting, never failing

The ground herb was mixed into snuff or used alone in Regency days. Its nasal and pulmonary-clearing properties had been employed and respected for centuries. In her book *Country Things,* Alison Uttley writes nostalgically of sipping a variety of cold cures in childhood, like blackcurrant tea and linseed tea, camphorated sugar and horehound goodies. The candy is made from the extracted juice, boiled with sugar. In the modern kitchen, a liquidizer can be put to good use to provide the juice briskly and efficiently, but in the good old days, the pestle and mortar were used to produce some juice, or the leaves were boiled in a very little water to extract it. Then an equal amount of sugar was added, and the mixture boiled until setting point; when cooled, the candy was cut into squares.

Taken as a tisane sweetened with a spoonful of honey, it relieves chest congestion, breaks phlegm, and is universally one of the most popular herbal chest remedies. Culpeper knew it for this prop-

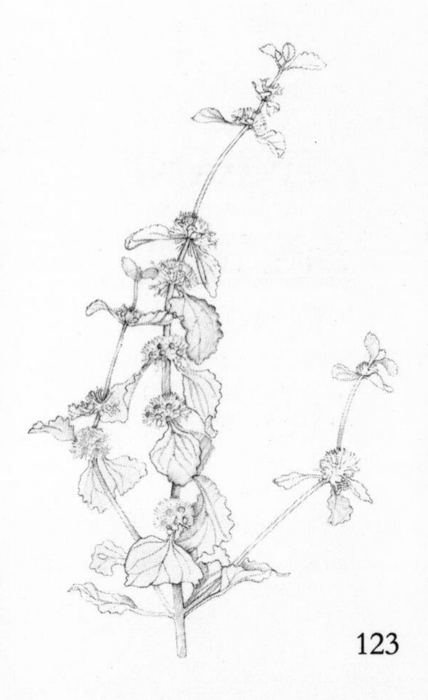

erty, and Gerard recommended a syrup using the fresh leaves as "a most singular remedie against the cough and the wheezing of the lungs . . . and doth wonderfully ease such as have been long sick of any consumption of the lungs, as hath been often proven by the learned physicians of our London College."

By common consent, it is one of the five bitter herbs of the *Mishna,* which the Jewish people took during the Passover. The name *mara,* "bitter," and the Hebrew name *marrab* for "bitter juice" are both descriptive of its flavor. The gypsies use *Marrubium vulgare* to ward off flies, but it is a useful bee plant. Easy of cultivation, it is readily propagated from seed sown out of doors in spring or late summer, or established plants can be divided. Indeed, it is advisable to divide them regularly because of the plant's lax habit; if the effects of old age are not allowed to ravage its appearance further, it will remain a useful addition to any herb garden.

HORSE-RADISH

Cochlearia rusticana
CRUCIFERAE

The coarse roots of this plant require deeply worked soil when they are cultivated in the kitchen or herb garden; and the crop should be cleared once it has been harvested to prevent it from becoming an irradicable garden weed. Propagation in the first instance is by root cuttings, and two years must be allowed for the roots to mature. An introduced plant in both Britain and North America, it has become naturalized in places and can become an invasive weed where it is allowed to colonize.

The sharp biting flavor of the root substantiates its popularity as a condiment, either as an accompaniment to roast beef, traditional in the English cuisine, or as an ingredient of tasty dips for prawns and cocktail savories. The root is always grated before being used, both to release the flavor and to break down the fiber, making it a sufficiently smooth ingredient. An electric blender is useful in the preparation of horse-radish sauce. It is an appetite stimulant, strongly diuretic, and an aid to digestion. The leaves are coarse and not unlike dock leaves with serrated edges; when they are young, they may be roughly chopped and used as a salad ingredient.

HOUND'S-TONGUE

Cynoglossum officinale
BORAGINACEAE

Growing some two feet high and flowering in June and July, houndstongue is a plant well worthy of a place in the garden. It is upstanding in habit, with a stem decoratively clothed in leaves: Their shape gives the plant its name; reddish-purple veined flowers are borne in long curved cymes above the foliage. It may well be a plant with which to confound one's friends for it seems little known. Saline, sandy, gravel, or limey soils suit it best, and it suffers exposure and drought with impunity. In these days of increasing urbanization, it should perhaps be more commonly cultivated, for it is reputed to prevent dogs from barking—a belief with the same origins as that of Chaucer's day, when it was used for the alleviation of stuttering.

Not commonly found in the wild state, although a British native, it is most frequently seen in coastal tracts and is probably an introduced plant generally in northern Europe and North America. It was included at one time in the pharmaco-

opposite Fennel (with the yellow flowers) behind a row of lavender

poeias of both London and Edinburgh, and it was used more recently by herbalists on the continent of Europe than in England, the roots pounded to provide *materia medica* for pills used in the treatment of head colds. Combined with hog's lard, it was formerly a household salve for burns and scalds, which accounts for one of its country names, "scaldhead." Other vernacular names are "gipsy flower," "rose noble," and "dog's tongue." The bun-like seeds, strictly tiny nuts, covered in hooked spines, ensure dispersal by animals and can be sown in August to provide perennial, sometimes even biennial, plants. Every passer-by, every animal, is a potential agent for carrying away the seed. In parts of America, houndstongue has reached weed-like proportions, colonizing readily upon the wastes

HOUSELEEK

Sempervivum tectorum
CRASSULACEAE

In the strange but characteristic growth of the houseleek, the finer distinctions between species are sometimes barely discernible; sufficient to say that the fleshy leaves huddle together in a close rosette, and each rosette nudges room from its neighbor. The whole colony forms a conglomerate growth which encrusts roofs and walls and will survive in the pitiless glare of the sun on mountain slopes over most of southern Europe, the Atlas range of North Africa, and in Asia. Cool to the touch, each wedge-shaped leaf is a living reservoir enabling the plant both to survive and to flourish under seemingly adverse conditions. Slow to establish, the tough growth will eventually adorn walls, old roofs, steps, and paths, giving an air of permanency.

The old Dutch name was *Donderbloom,* "thunderflower," counterpart of one of the English country names, "thunder-plant," and reminiscent of a widespread European belief in the Dark Ages that to have sempervivum growing on the roof was a charm against being struck by lightning. Charlemagne (768–814 A.D.), King of the Franks and the first Emperor of the Holy Roman Empire, in his "Ordinances" demanded by mandate that all farmers and tenants on the Imperial Estates should plant houseleeks upon their roofs as protection against evil, pestilence, fire, and war.

The Saxons brought it to Britain along with the name "homewort," and throughout the Middle Ages it was esteemed as a symbol of vivacity, with its ability to flourish and flower despite adversity. More practical and prosaic readers may readily suggest that *Sempervivum tectorum,* or "ever-living plant of the roof," was merely put there to keep slates or other roofing material in position! Elizabeth Haldane in *Scots Gardens in Old Times* reminds us of the close connections between Britain and France, in saying that the thatched roof of a cottage was considered a convenient habitat for the houseleek "which is carefully cultivated in France under the title of *fouet,* being thought efficacious for medicinal purposes." Fouet was at that time, apparently, also the Scottish name for the plant, and it is further known as "fow" which means to cleanse. In Italy, there are local antipathies about uprooting it from roofs. Its country names are numerous in Britain: "hockerie-topner," "house-green," "huslock" (a corruption of houseleek), "imbreke," "jobarbe," "jubarb," "Jupiter's beard," "sungreen," "suphelt," and as recently as 1952, an authoritative flora handbook proclaimed the name "welcome home husband however drunk you be!"

A native of the Greek islands, it is under the dominion of Jupiter and symbolizes vivacity, and probably tenacity, too, for a dislodged rosette will survive for months without any visible form of nourishment. The Greeks regarded it as an aphrodisiac and named it *hypogeson* because it grew on the high parts or eaves of buildings. The Old English name *leac,* from the Anglo-Saxon, became "houseleek."

Herbalists today regard it as one of the safest remedies for inflammation and swelling of almost any part of the body, and a poultice of the bruised leaves is recommended. Culpeper stated that the "leaves bruised and laid upon the crown or seam of the head, stayeth bleeding at the nose very quickly." He also referred to it by the name of sengreen. Externally, the juice may be safely used as an antiseptic on grazes, cuts, or burns. The fresh juice extracted directly from a fleshy leaf into the eye will relieve inflammation and dispel styes. An ointment used in the treatment of burns and scalds was a country remedy; the chisel-shaped leaves can be pressed to exude much liquid.

The barrenness of its habitat and its undemanding nature make it an easy plant to cultivate. Sometimes it can appear slow to establish, undecided whether to remain or not; but planting the tiny rosette offsets at any time between March and June in paving cracks or around the edges of clay pots will encourage roots to form, for they love a porous environment. Seed, as fine as dust, can be sown, but with considerable uncertainty as to the progeny, for the species hybridizes very freely.

HYSSOP

Hyssopus officinalis
LABIATAE

Beloved of bees and butterflies, the shrubby hyssop adds old-world charm and association to the herb garden. Formerly much cultivated for medicinal use, it is now most famous as the plant that adorns the walls of Beaulieu Abbey in Hampshire, England—previously a Cistercian monastery. Native of southern Europe and ranging eastwards into central Asia, it is not the hyssop of the Bible. The terminal spikes of small violet-blue (sometimes pink or white) flowers are in bloom from early July to September and provide an excellent edging plant or low internal hedge. A plant that lends itself to clipping, hyssop—like santolina and box—can be persuaded to form the boundary to a herb plot or to outline a knot pattern or *par terre*.

Pungent in aroma, it was once used as a strewing herb. However, it is generally too strong for culinary use, although it has been recommended as a seasoning (with discretion) for broths. Its main virtue is as an infusion: Hyssop tea is made from a few flowers; it relieves catarrh and is claimed to have expectorant, stimulant, and carminative properties. Pliny wrote of Hyssopites, a wine made from the plant using the leaves.

Hedge-hyssop, *Gratiola officinalis,* belongs to the natural order *Scrophulariaceae* and is a native of marshy land in southern Europe. It seems to have fallen out of cultivation, the last mention of it appearing in William Robinson's *The English Flower Garden* as "Dwarf perennial plants of the Figwort family. Of little use outside botanic gardens . . ."; but this is the hyssop that formed the basis of the apothecaries' *eau médicinale* and was in earlier times referred to as *gratia dei* and as an esteemed remedy for dropsy, acting as a diuretic, but apparently of nauseous taste.

INDIGO

Indigofera tinctoria
LEGUMINOSAE

Until the end of the last century the blue dye, indigo, was obtained almost exclusively from vegetable sources, *Indigofera tinctoria* being the principal plant. The name is from *indigo,* the blue dye, and *fero,* "to produce." The chief world source has for many years been India where the species *I. sumatrana* was cultivated for the purpose. Evidence of the dye has been traced in Egyptian tombs, as well as Inca graves; and the plant was cultivated in Carolina, Georgia, and other American states from the mid-eighteenth century onwards when slave labor made competition with the Orient possible. Much of the indigo produced found its way to the United Kingdom.

From an early date, indigo was known but not specifically grown in Europe. Woad was the only plant grown to produce the blue dye used by Europeans until the opening up of sea routes to India. The British East India Company and the Dutch East India Company both carried on an indigo trade with India, which subsequently declined when plantations cultivating indigofera on a commercial scale were set up in Carolina and Georgia. However, trade later swung back to India when the southern states of America turned their attentions to the more profitable cultivation of tobacco and cotton.

The wild indigo of the North American continent is *Baptisia tinctoria,* or indigo broom as it is confusingly called; it bears the same acacia-like foliage as indigofera but has yellow rather than pink flowers. Baptisia makes a bushy plant 2 or $2\frac{1}{2}$ feet tall and is quite a hardy import in British gardens, whereas *Indigofera tinctoria* must be grown in a large pot and have the winter protection of a conservatory or greenhouse.

IRIS

Iris spp.
IRIDACEAE

The yellow flag iris *(Iris pseudacorus)* is one of the most distinctive plants in marginal vegetation throughout Europe, covering many watery meadows and enfolding the banks of rivers and canals. For hundreds of years it has been employed as a dye plant: The rhizomes produce a black ink dye and the flowers provide yellow, the commonest color obtainable from vegetable material. The specific name clarifies its confusion with the sweet flag, *Acorus (q.v.),* another denizen of marshy localities. Recognized as *fleur de lis,* and called flower-de-luce by Shakespeare, the golden-yellow flowers bloom in June.

In days gone by, a colony of "flags" along the river bank indicated a ford, for the creeping roots or rhizomes, broken and torn by hooves and wheels, drifted downstream and established themselves in the shallows to root again. It was in the sixth century that Clovis, King of the Franks, discovered a ford on the Rhine indicated by yellow flag irises and brought his army to safety from the overpowering Goths, near Cologne. Quite naturally he adopted the flower as his emblem. In the twelfth century, Louis V of France adopted the *fleur-de-lis* emblem during the crusades. Thereafter, it was emblazoned upon the escutcheons of the kings of France. When Edward of England claimed the crown of France, the *fleur-de-lis* was added to the English coat of arms and remained there until 1801 (nearly 250 years after Calais had been reclaimed by the French). The Plantagenet standard bearing the *fleur-de-lis* of France is the emblem on the arms of Eton College, founded by Henry VI. Shakespear noted the point in *Henry VI, Part I*:

> Cropp'd are the flower-de-luces in
> your armes;
> of England's coat one half is cut away.

The name "lily" when applied to the iris is merely a confusion of common usage, dating back across the centuries to Biblical times when we read of the lilies of the field. It would appear to be a comprehensive dubbing for any conspicuous or particularly showy flower. The name "rose" was also used erroneously to describe any plant that was not utilitarian.

The English names are "legion-flag," "flagons," "Jacob's sword," "laister," "levers," "lug," "maiken," "meklin," "yellow saggan," "seggs," "water seg," "seggin," "shaldon," "skeg," "sword lily," and "fliggers." The last name was supposedly given because the slightest breeze moves the sword-like leaves; another country name, "cucumber," is descriptive of the seed capsule.

Iris florentina (now strictly *Iris germanica florentina*), the Florentine iris, provides the orris root of commerce, the name apparently a corruption of iris root. *I. germanica* and *I. pallida* are also known to have been grown as substitutes for, or even adulterants of, orris root, chiefly in the region of Florence in northern Italy. From Dante we learn that the ancient arms of the city of Florence depicted a white iris on a red ground, indicating the importance of the commercial cultivation of the iris in the district at that time. It appears that the Florentine iris was naturalized in Tuscany, having been introduced from Macedonia, its home. In Greek and Roman medicine, orris was used in ointments and oils.

The rhizomes are lifted in August, once they are mature, cleared of rootlets, stripped free of the brown outer skin, and dried. Although the fresh roots have no particular scent, on drying they are delicately perfumed of violets, and the sweet odor strengthens if they are kept for a year or two. Chalky in appearance, they are ground and incorporated in dentifrices and toilet preparations. As an ingredient of potpourri, orris-root improves the mixture because it helps to retain or bind the perfumes, and it also strengthens any mixture.

Both the yellow flag and the Florentine iris are easy of cultivation and make attractive perennial additions to a herb garden. The soil must be well prepared with moisture-retentive material—or the margin of a pond or boggy patch can be enhanced with a few rhizomes of yellow flag. They will spread quite quickly. Divide the rhizomes after flowering. The earlier the work is carried out, the easier it will be, since the stringy roots become badly entangled on fresh rhizomes late in the season.

JASMINE

Jasminum officinale
OLEACAEA

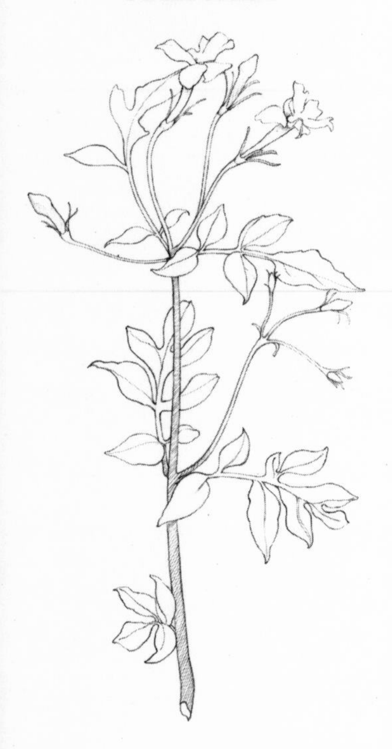

Young blossomed Jessamines;
Such fragrant flowers do give most
odorous smell.

When Spenser wrote these lines, he captured the evasive sense of mystery that surrounds the summer jasmine. This plant is of Eastern association and is far more heavily perfumed in those climates than in the temperate regions. The supple and pliant branches of *Jasminum officinale* suggest a binding and all-enfolding quality. In fact, Hindus use them to make neck garlands for their friends as a show of binding affection. In Italy, the flowers used to be entwined in bridal headdresses; a coronet of jasmine and orange blossom assured the bride of certain constancy and love. There was in that country a saying that she who is worthy of being decorated with jasmine is rich enough for any husband. According to legend, jasmine was introduced by the Duke of Tuscany who jealously guarded it as a treasure, wishing to preserve it solely for his own plant collection, but the wonderful fragrance tempted his gardener to take a sprig for his sweetheart on her birthday, a natural enough gesture. The girl planted the spray, it rooted and flourished, bringing her much wealth from the sale of its precious blossoms—wealth she took with her in marriage to the dismissed gardener.

In a few fragrant plants, one of which is the jasmine, the scent does not exist as such in the flower but is emitted slowly as long as the petals are fresh; thus, in the art of perfumery the process of *enfleurage* is used to capture the natural essence. A perfume particularly difficult to capture, jasmine has been a constituent of *eau de chypre*; and although synthetic perfumes are available, the true *eau de jasmine* is much prized.

The name is derived from the Persian *yasmin*. *J. officinale*, the summer jasmine of our gardens, is a species native of Persia and northern India. It was introduced into Europe in the mid-sixteenth century, and grafted stock of this plant worked with the Spanish or Catalonian jasmine *(J. grandiflorum)* is today grown extensively in the environs of Grasse and Cannes in France, centre of the perfume industry. The plants are set out in rows about three feet apart and remain as erect bushes, with large flowers blooming over a long period from June to September.

Medicinally, an oily extract obtained by boiling the leaves has been used to anoint the head in the belief that it relieves a variety of eye complaints; similarly, an oil obtained from the roots is administered to reduce lactation during the weaning of infants.

Immensely valuable for the herb garden, the summer jasmine can be easily grown, and there is every possible justification to do so. Lax in habit, ligneous, it flowers on the young wood, and so it must be pruned in the autumn after flowering; otherwise, the whole growth will become a tangled mass. Cast over a low fence or wall or to enclose a seat or arbor, it can provide a soothingly scented corner for a warm afternoon.

JEWEL-WEED

Impatiens spp.
BALSAMINACEAE

Perhaps balsam would be a better general heading for the interesting impatiens group, but arbitrary decisions have to be made when vernacular names are used. Rightly named jewelweed, *Impatiens capensis* (syn. *I. fulva, I. biflora*) spatters the banks of rivers in southern England with its brilliant orange flowers, sometimes making the backwaters of the Thames and its tributaries a blazing wonderland, especially at sunset. There is no other wild flower of this arresting hue in Britain, and as it paints its way along the southern waterways, the colonies are still increasing. An immigrant from America, it extends from Nova Scotia to Oregon and south to Missouri and Florida, where "spotted touch-me-not," "snap weed," "wild balsam," and "silver cap" are the country names. Its relative *I. glandulifera* (syn. *I. roylei*) preceded it from India and must have arrived by sea at Liverpool. It was in the dock areas and along the Manchester Ship Canal that it first took foothold in the British Isles and came to be called wild balsam. There, along the slimy banks of already polluted rivers of the industrial regions of southwest Lancashire, it reveled in some profusion in the 1920s.

It is a suitable plant to introduce into wild gardens with some discretion, because the seeds germinate boldly the following spring, producing two of the largest seed leaves in the garden. It is not a true herb, but all the impatiens including the British yellow-flowered native, *I. noli-me-tangere,* have an acrid juice against which old herbals issue warnings.

The golden- and yellow-flowered species has been used externally as a decoction for the treatment of warts, corns, and other foot troubles. The "keep away" has conjured up the local name of "touch-me-nots," but to touch the ripened fruit and note the reflex action, explosive and surprising as it is in *I. glandulifera,* is a great temptation.

JUNIPER

Juniperus communis
CUPRESSACEAE

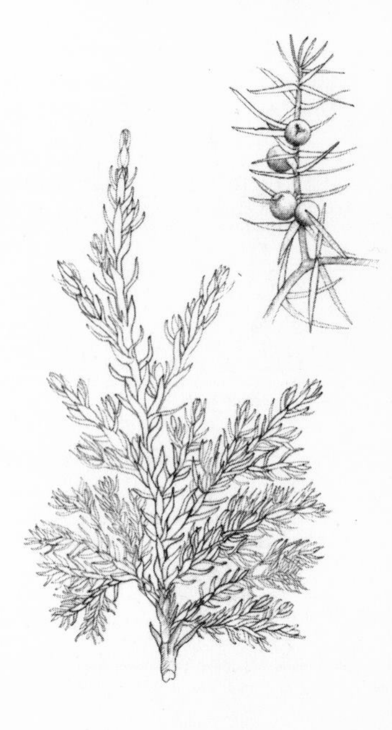

The evergreen juniper, unlike most conifers, produces luscious blue berries which are harvested about October. It is a native of chalk and lime-stone regions of Britain, notably of Box Hill in Surrey, the chalky downs of Hampshire, and the limestone escarpments of the Pennine range in north Lancashire. Juniper is also quite widely distributed across the European continent from the Arctic to the mountain ranges of North Africa. It occurs in North America from Massachusetts to Alaska, south to North Carolina and westward to the Rocky Mountains. Its southern limit is New Mexico.

The berries may be dried in a warm, shaded place but should be used within a year because they lose their aroma and properties if kept longer. They yield a volatile oil used in medicine and to flavor gin (the word itself being derived from the French *genévrier,* "juniper"). Supposedly able to rejuvenate, the berries are sometimes used as a condiment and may be ground when dried in a pepper mill like peppercorns. The berries take a long time to ripen, and green ones seem to be always on the tree, but it is useless to harvest them before they are really ripe. In warm climates, a resinous gum can be collected from incisions made in the bark.

Medicinally, the distilled oil of juniper is a diuretic, stomachic, carminative, and sudorific; and an infusion of berries in wine is a stimulant to the appetite, but too strong a dose can prove an irritant to renal conditions. In Sweden, a beer is brewed from juniper berries.

An evergreen shrub, that will tolerate exposure and thin soil, the juniper may be planted in the herb garden as a representative plant, in one of its many forms. *J. communis 'Compressa,'* for instance, is a gem for the rock garden with glaucous gray foliage; and the Irish juniper, suited to formal gardens, provides a good columnar form so useful among the low-growing herbs.

LADY'S-MANTLE

Alchemilla vulgaris
ROSACEAE

Native of Europe, north and western Asia, and the North American continent, wandering on into Greenland, the little green lady's mantle was known to Culpeper as a wound stauncher and cleanser. Its vernacular name was probably bestowed because of the immaculate daintiness of its pale green leaves, always jeweled after rain dew and, some say, shaped like a draped cloak.

Alchemilla mollis is a garden form to grow among the paving stones, at the border's edge or atop a low wall, for it has a glowing green delicacy that should not be hidden by neighbors. Of the thirteen species listed by Clapham, Tutin, and Warburg (in *Flora of the British Isles*) most wander over the coolest regions of the temperate zones, and *A. alpina* is a stormer of the heights, ascending over 4,000 feet in the Cairngorms, Pyrenees, Alps, and Greenland. "Dew mantle" is its mountain name, because its leaves always glisten with the excess moisture it expels at these heights; or more prosaically, "five-leaved lady's mantle," because the radical leaves are segmented almost to the base.

"Alchemilla"—the plant of the alchemists—is the name the genus earned in the Middle Ages when its dew was hopefully used for the production of the Philosopher's Stone, the solid substance supposed by alchemists to possess the property of changing other metals into silver or gold. In fact the only known purpose to which the liquid was usefully put was in Culpeper's day, when a decoction was made with it to prevent miscarriage. He also recommends it as a beautifier for the bosom. In modern herbal practice, a tisane is considered to lessen excessive menstruation, and so Culpeper was well informed in associating the plant with "female complaints."

The gypsies know parsley piert as an alchemilla, and it has been classified as so for many a long year, but its up-to-date name is *Aphanes arvensis* (though one will still find it described as alchemilla). Common throughout the British Isles in gravelly places, this alchemilla blooms lowly but prettily in July and has been employed for centuries as a certain cure for gallstones. The country names of "piercestone" or "breakstone" are descriptive of this action. Modern herbalism combines it subtly with comfrey, or slippery elm bark as demulcents. The tisane of the dried herb is soothing and relaxes the muscles of the lower abdomen. Herb pillows, used to encourage sleep, at one time contained this dried herb and its roots.

LAVENDER

Lavandula officinalis
LABIATAE

The name lavender comes from the Latin *Lavandus,* "to be washed," indicating how it was used in the ancient world when sprigs were flung into baths to perfume the water. Undoubtedly it was the Romans who brought this refinement to Britain, although there appears to be no confirmed evidence; just when lavender was reintroduced as a cultivated plant is a matter of conjecture. Monastic gardens afforded it living room and plant treatises of the thirteenth and fourteenth centuries included "llafant" and "lavyndull." It is indigenous to the Mediterranean regions, hardy through temperate winters, and is a cottage-garden plant as well as a plant of commerce in Europe. Parkinson said in 1629: "Lavender groweth in Spain abundantly, in many places wilde, and little regarded, that many have gone, and abiden there to distill the oyl thereof, whereof great quantity now commeth over from thence unto us; and also in Languedock and Provence in France." Perhaps not to be dismissed as a plant associated only with perfume, its former and revived use in relieving nervous headaches and calming hysteria recalls William Turner's explanation of its name: the plant utilized to wash men's heads "which had any deceses therein."

Europe's main lavender-growing regions now are in the south, especially in southern France, though less today than formerly. In the late nineteenth and early twentieth centuries, it was a peasant industry, the mobile stills being taken from village to village during July, and the peasants carrying their lavender harvest from the thin-soiled slopes. In England, 100 years ago, the three main centers of cultivation were at Mitcham, Surrey, at the Potter and Moores farm, at Hitchin where the Ransom family cultivated extensive acres, and in Norfolk, especially in the vicinity of Heacham for the Yardley concern. And at that time, the best lavender water, manufactured from lavender grown on Mr. Ransom's farm in Hertfordshire, contained (according to Mr. Perks, his manager) English oil of lavender, rectified spirit, and rose water. Today, highly complicated formulas include many other ingredients like attar of rose, musk, neroli, and French rose absolute.

For drying, the flower spikes should be harvested before the flowers themselves are open, cutting the stalks with a really sharp knife. In England, July is usually the month when cutting can be done, but this means the bees are deprived of their precious harvest. In gardens where lavender is grown to attract bees, or for decorative effect, the choice must be made. The flower spikes dry easily, either laid in flat boxes, spread on paper in a warm spare room, or hung in bunches in a garden shed or dry porch; once dry, they can be rubbed free of the flower stem. Gloves should be worn for this operation and a smog mask made, because lavender is a strong sneeze-inducer. Domestic animals and birds should be removed for several hours from the part of the house where the rubbing is being done.

Probably the best known of the London street cries were those of the lavender sellers:

> Here's your sweet lavender, sixteen
> sprigs a penny,
> Which you'll find my ladies, will
> smell as sweet as any.

and

> Lavender, sweet blooming Lavender
> Six bunches a penny today
> Lavender, sweet blooming Lavender
> Ladies buy it while you may.

One of the fourteen paintings representing the cries of London, by Francis Wheatley, R.A., has been immortalized by the Yardleys of London who adopted it as their trade mark for all lavender products in 1913. Porcelain figures were also modeled based on the painting of the lady and two children bearing their baskets of lavender spikes for sale.

Lavenders tend to exhaust themselves in their profusion of bloom and are not a long-term proposition for garden display, despite being shrubby. A hard clipping back (but not into the wood) immediately after flowering helps to delay degeneration, but they can be propagated easily from cuttings, so that maintaining a supply of plants should never be difficult. Of the lower-growing kinds, the compact forms of *Lavendula spica* are best: 'Munstead Dwarf,' 'Hidcote,' 'Twickle Purple,' and *L. vera*, less silver of leaf but the small plant grown for the production of oil of lavender, and thus the strongest candidate for the herb garden. Of the taller growing bushes, *spica* itself, generally agreed to be "Old English," or "Mitcham," and the forms "Grappenhall" and "Dutch" are best. White-flowered compact cultivars are available, as are the pink-flowered 'Rosea' (rather a washed-out lilac in some situations) and the French lavender, *L.·stoechas*. This last-named species is early flowering and not hardy but the one to choose as a pot plant for garden room or light hall. It will grow indoors for Easter, with rounded spikes of deep purple flowers.

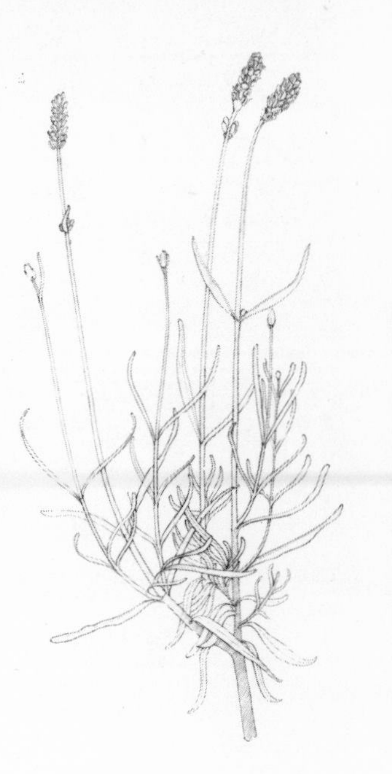

LICORICE

Glycyrrhiza glabra
LEGUMINOSAE

The flexible and fibrous roots of the licorice, bright yellow internally and sweet in flavor, are the valuable and effectual parts of the plant. The ancient world knew of its curative properties, and the name is from the Greek *glukus*, "sweet," and *rhiza*, "a root." Both the root and an extract are used in medicine; the British Pharmacopoeia stipulates that the root must be peeled, though some official authorities accept the unpeeled root.

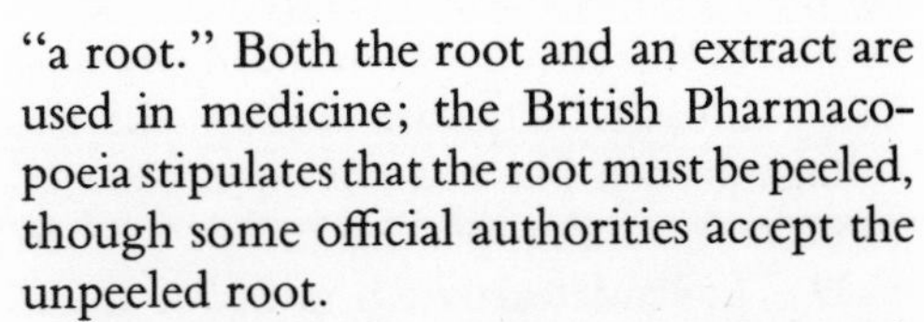

The French call it *la douce reglisse*, and

peasants may still sometimes be seen in the mountainous regions of southwest France digging down and carefully disentangling the reddish filament roots leading to the blonde tap root.

Its medicinal properties are emollient, demulcent, and pectoral; it forms the basis of many standard cough mixtures and throat pastilles. If the roots are chopped into tiny pieces, they can be used for a decoction which is sweet but refreshing and slightly laxative in action. Licorice alleviates bronchial congestion and throat discomfort and is used in France as a lotion in the treatment of inflamed eyelids. Its sweet, strong flavor is employed to mask the bitterness of other medicines, and it has occasionally been used as an ingredient of stout and the heavier beers.

To include licorice in the herb garden, especially in a representative collection, deep, crumbly stone-free soil is needed and must be cultivated to a depth of 2 or 2½ feet, to allow straight roots to develop. The root pieces, 3 or 4 inches in length with eyes, or pieces of the red underground stems of the same length, are planted in March or April 2 or 3 inches deep. Hope then for a dry, warm spring! Ideally, shoots (or canes) that form are cut down to soil level each November of the first two years; the third autumn the roots will be mature and can be lifted. However, damp winter climates do not normally allow for this unless the soil is rich and well drained. Large polythene cloches will afford some protection if necessary, or the plants may be lifted and the more mature roots used, the pinkish fibrous ones being stored in a dry frost-proof place and replanted the following March. However, the best roots are always those from plants left to develop for three years without disturbance. Once the roots are lifted and scrubbed clean, dry them in the sun or in a warm cupboard. They can be cut into pieces and stored almost immediately.

LILY-OF-THE-VALLEY

Convallaria majalis
LILIACEAE

No flower amid the garden fairer grows
Than the sweet lily of the lowly vale
The Queen of flowers

KEATS

Confined generally to woods in the temperate regions of Europe, the lily-of-the-valley flourishes on calcareous soils, and where it is cultivated, it luxuriates in shaded corners and borders that never face the high sun. The pale green radical leaves grow in pairs and enfold the flower stalk. The joy of a bed of May lilies, as they are popularly called, is exceeded only by the intense sweetness of their perfume. The tiny rounded bells of white flowers hang down around the stem.

Regarded as the symbol of a return to happiness, the plant is associated with purity and gentleness. The effective medicinal element is convallatoxin, a digitalis-like drug that similarly acts upon the heart; it can be extracted from all parts of the plant which, unlike many, is richest in its product during the flowering period. Unlike digitalin, however, convallatoxin is nonpoisonous. In herbal practice, an infusion is considered to be a good remedy for the restoration of speech following cardiac arrest, and, curiously, a tisane of flower and leaves is said to soothe a sore tongue.

Over the centuries, the lily-of-the-valley has come to be associated with spring festivals and Whitsuntide. An old custom in the vicinity of Hanover in West Germany was for people to go to the woods to gather bunches on Whit Monday, and it came to be called May bloom, *Maiglöckchen*. In France, especially in Normandy and the *bois* of Ile de France, similar festivals are held amid picnics and carnivals. The famous carnival near Rambouillet, when floats and carts are decorated with flower spikes in unbelievably elaborate ways, is held each year early in May. In many European countries, this dainty little flower is also customarily presented to ladies on the first day of May.

Nicholas Culpeper declares the usefulness of lily-of-the-valley in a variety of treatments for widely differing ills, and he agrees that distilled water of the flowers in wine "restores lost speech, helps the palsy, and is excellently good in the apoplexy; comforts the heart and vital spiritual." There is a remarkable consistency about its provincial names, the variations falling between lily and May: "May lily," "wood lily," "lily-conval," "conval-lily," "mugwet" (a Middle English corruption of the French *muguet*), and "valleys."

LIME

Tilia europaea
TILIACEAE

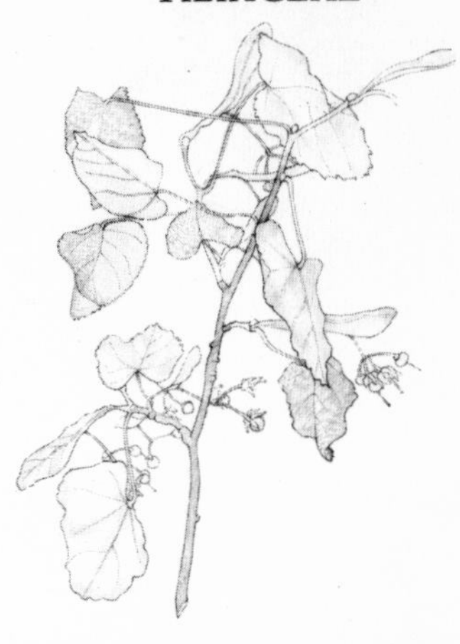

The fragrant lime flowers with their long yellow bracts give off a heavy and strongly fragrant perfume in June; when dried, they provide an excellent tisane, or lime flower tea. The French call it *tilleul*, their name for the tree itself. Together with peppermint and chamomile tea, it is among the most popular of tisanes, and it is useful for calming the nerves, relieving headaches, and aiding digestion. Alternatively (where large quantities are available!) the infusion can be added to warm baths, helping to relieve nervous headaches and encouraging relaxation.

The flowers should be collected in June and July before they have faded and dried outside in the shade, spread on sheets of paper or cloth. *T. europaea* is a tall tree with an oval crown, elegant and decorative of form but not a garden tree unless it is already well established. Limes were imported by the thousand into Britain in the seventeenth century from Flanders—mainly to be planted for avenues and arbors.

LOVAGE

Ligusticum officinale
UMBELLIFERAE

A very old-fashioned plant of cultivation, lovage resembles an overgrown celery/angelica, sometimes reaching six feet and bearing its tribe's great dish-telescope-like form of flowerhead. In Culpeper's succinct turn of phrase—"It is usually planted in gardens, where, if it be suffered, it groweth large." A powerful herb of the sun, it was formerly used as a drug, the brown seeds and leaves being macerated and infused and employed to clear the digestive organs and enliven the appetite. Its yeast-like aroma is suggestive of present-day tonic foods containing brewer's yeast, and its culinary use is to enrich soups, mayonnaise, and sauces. The leaves may be eaten as salad; they are dark green and widely spreading, deeply divided like the celery and angelica to which they are closely related. The stems, like angelica, may be candied but the flavor is inferior. In Slavic countries the seed is sprinkled over loaves of bread before baking.

Scottish lovage, *L. scoticum*, is a native plant of the rocky Northumbrian coast extending northwards along the sea-battered eastern coast of Scotland. It is also found in Donegal and other exposed localities of Eire and appears again across the North Sea in Scandinavia. Altogether a coarser-growing herb, it redeems itself by sometimes unfurling pink flowers. As a pot herb, the leaves provide the yeast-like flavor. The seeds of this plant are better known in America for embellishing baking.

Sow the seed of both species as soon as it ripens to ensure a high-percentage germination, for its viability is low. Once established, a plant will flourish for several years and may be successfully divided in winter, each division bearing a shoot bud. A plant for the back of the herb border, or the furthest corner from the house, one of its main uses is to give perspective to the garden. Culpeper was so right in his assessment: one plant may be more than enough!

LUNGWORT

Pulmonaria officinalis
BORAGINACEAE

The lung wort, long cultivated in the garden and sometimes becoming naturalized, is certainly a native European plant and is thought to have been introduced to Britain centuries ago. There are records of its having been used as a pot herb—the leaves may be added to salads—but its specific name affirms its medicinal importance in years gone by. Certainly it contains a mucilaginous juice which was considered to be effective in the relief of pulmonary congestion, but there is little proof of this effectiveness. Pulmonaria is always quoted as a stock example for the Doctrine of Signatures, the creamy white blotches on the leaf supposedly resembling tiny lungs, but its country names seem more to stress its appearance than its properties. Culpeper, who preached the gospel of the Doctrine of Signatures most vehemently, records lungwort as a "kind of moss that groweth on sundry sorts of trees . . . an excellent remedy boiled in beer for broken-winded horses"; and one senses that here he was in fact writing about a plant other than pulmonaria. The Latin name is *pulmo*, "lung," but the majority of its vernacular and old names cling closely to religious associations and its appearance. "Children of Israel," "sage of Bethlehem," "spotted Mary," "spotted virgin," "Mary's milk drops," "lady's milk sile" (or stain) are all descriptive of the blotched leaves; "Jerusalem cowslip" refers to the shape of the flowers, and the double names—"Joseph and Mary," "soldiers and sailors," "Adam and Eve," "bottles-of-all-sorts"—are descriptive of the colors of the flowers particularly when the two colors appear at the same time on a plant: a deep pink at first, gradually changing to bright blue.

An attractive perennial, the lungwort makes for good effect in early May in the herb border, managing to reach about a foot in stature, though the stems spread a little. Once the flowers fade, the variability of the leaves becomes more evident, and a good mat of foliage remains through the summer to add interest. The form of *P. saccharta* that is most in demand for garden interest is the cultivar "Mrs. Moon," the blotches on the leaves are more pronounced, and the whimsical color change (from deep pink to blue) suggest that Mrs. Moon may well have been a quick-change variety artiste.

An infusion made from the fresh leaves gathered early in mid-season, or from dried leaves at other times, and strained (because the leaves are hairy) has been used in the treatment of whooping cough and to clear chest colds.

MADDER

Rubia tinctorum
RUBIACEAE

Formerly grown in England to some extent for its value as a dye plant, it is sometimes to be found as a casual, though many botanists consider it little more than a form of *Rubia peregrina,* wild madder. Dyer's madder is obtained from the root, and there is evidence that it was known from earliest times, as cloth dyed with it has been found on Egyptian mummies. Dioscorides refers to its cultivation in Caria, and Pliny calls it *Rubia.* A native plant of Mediterranean regions and western Europe, it was cultivated in the past in France and Holland (and in medieval times, to a lesser extent in southern England) for the wool trade which dominated the commerce of northern Europe during the fourteenth century, centering on Flanders. The soil there was eminently suited to the cultivation of both woad and madder, the standard dyes of the period. Teasels were also grown in the same localities to raise the surface texture of the cloth. Large quantities of madder root continued to be imported into England mainly from Smyrna and Italy, until in 1868, the dye alizarin was made synthetically.

Gerard speaks of it in his lists of 1597 as being in cultivation in numerous gardens in London and draws attention to its supposed virtues in his *Herbal*, but medicinally it has never been in general use. Its most remarkable property, and one which has been used to enable physiologists to study the way in which bone develops, is that it will color the bones of animals or the claws and beaks of birds fed upon the root.

A plant of untidy, lax growth, it closely resembles cleavers, goosegrass, and bed-straws to which it is a near relative. The flowers are yellowish-green, and the leaves have a more conspicuous network of pale green veins on the underside than has the true wild madder, *R. peregrina*, of southern and southwest England.

MALLOW

Malva spp.
and *Althaea officinalis*
MALVACEAE

The delicately penciled markings of the flowers of the mallows repay close inspection: The etched lines on the sheen of the petal are exquisite. A native tribe of central and northern Europe, with the exception of the Hebrides and Scandinavia, the mallows have been introduced into North America. In the herb garden, the plants are primarily of decorative value, the deeply divided leaves and upstanding stem displaying the rose-colored flowers so well.

The marsh mallow, *Althea officinalis,* is also of interest as a medicinal herb for its mucilaginous quality, useful in the relief of bronchitis and other pulmonary complaints. The fleshy tap roots yield juice which, with sugar, can be made into candy for the relief of throat and chest disorders and is sometimes also used in confectionery. The leaves, harvested prior to the plant flowering and dried, are an ingredient of herbal tobacco, and an infusion makes gargle for the relief of sore throats. Dried flowers can be used in the same way.

The name is derived from the Greek *altheo*, "to cure." A local plant where it does occur in Britain, and when it has been introduced into North America, it can appear in the herb garden as hollyhock (*Althaea rosea*) to stand sentinel at the back of the border. "Hoc" is the Anglo-Saxon word for mallow; and while the medicinal properties of the other members of the malva species are not as effective as those of *Althaea officinalis,* they have sometimes been substituted for it.

MARIGOLD

Calendula officinalis
COMPOSITAE

The marigold of the old herbalists was a single flower, orange probably with a darker eye, or pale yellow or even apricot in color. Today, the pot marigold of gardens is a double-flowered plant, a foolproof annual that can be relied upon to bloom even under the most unfavorable of growing conditions. The word "marigold" in the seventies is coming to mean French marigold or African marigold. The popularity of these plants (*Tagetes* spp.) has increased during the past twenty years, and the hybridists have produced a fantastic range of named cultivars; but it is the pot marigold that belongs in the herb garden. It too has been updated, on both sides of the Atlantic, and is now available in a fairly extensive color range in such new cultivars as 'Geisha Girl,' 'Orange Coronet,' 'Pacific Beauty,' and a single-flowered 'Nova'—more reminiscent of the old-fashioned pot marigold. It has been said that once marigolds are introduced into a garden, they will stay forever; but do not expect these new forms to repeat the quality and color of their parents. The Latin generic name, *Calendula*, suggests that the flower may be found in bloom somewhere in every month of the year—almost as surely as the gorse (*Ulex europaeus*).

Marigolds are sometimes called Mary buds, recalling the Virgin Mary, but has remarkably few vernacular names for a flower so long grown and loved in cottage gardens. It does not exist in the wild state in the British Isles, and on the isolated occasions it is seen, apparently wild, it is only an escape from cultivation. The name "Mary buds" is recorded in Shakespeare's *Cymbeline*:

> Hark! Hark! The lark at heaven's gate
> sings

And Phoebus 'gins arise
His steeds to water at those springs
On chalic'd flowers that lies;
And winking Mary Buds begin
To ope their golden eyes.

and again, in *The Winter's Tale,* he emphasizes the habit of the marigold to close in the evening and open with daylight:

The marigold, that goes to bed with the sun,
And with him rises weeping

suggesting the drops of morning dew that hang around the folded orange petals.

For the kitchen, the calendula is useful only in imparting its color. The petals should be pulled from the flower and dropped into broth or added to rice to which they impart a good yellow color, long used as a substitute for the expensive saffron; dried or fresh, the effect is the same. To dry petals, spread them on paper in a warm ventilated room away from direct sunlight, and the color, on which both flavor and dye depend, will be retained. Calendulin is not unlike carotin for its coloring properties, but the flavor produced from the volatile oil is more bitter. Of old, marigold ointment was a household remedy for the treatment of wounds and ulcers and other skin eruptions.

MARJORAM

Origanum spp.
LABIATAE

A plant from mountainous regions, marjoram is entirely aromatic in all its parts. The aroma is strong, pungent and distinctive. The scent is retained on drying and for this reason, it was used in the past for strewing, for herb pillows, pomanders, and sweet bags, but always with discretion, lest it overwhelm the delicacy of perfume of the other plants used with it. Similarly, when it is used as a flavoring in cooking it is added with immense care.

Its Greek name, which means "joy of the mountains," is from *oros*, "mountain," and *garnos*, "joy" or "happiness." But it should not be considered an alpine plant—far from it, for it covers the northern hillsides bordering the Mediterranean, tolerating the shallow soils and emitting its fragrance into the warm air for most of the summer months. The Greek appellation denotes its symbolic use as a herb of happiness. It was formed into garlands to crown brides and bridegrooms to ensure their continued happiness, and it was also planted upon graves to dominate the environment of the departed and ensure their contentment.

Of the species, *Origanum vulgare* is British, growing wild in many parts and partial to dry chalky soils. It can be used for making tea, and Culpeper tells us that between it "and adders there is a deadly antipathy." The "French" or "port" marjoram, *O. onites* (sometimes referred to as winter-marjoram), a native of southern France, is best for the herb garden, if it is for culinary use. It is highly aromatic and stronger but less bitter than the British kind and is a perennial, a somewhat sprawling plant with "puffs" of growth upwards. Long stems hold the flowers well away from the lower growth, which is about two feet in height; the plant bears purplish flowerheads at the end of July and in August. It also tends to form "runners," as the sprawling stems form roots where they trail on the soil.

In contrast, the "sweet," "knotted," or "garden" marjoram (*Origanum marjorana*) is more compact of habit, bears smaller, grayer leaves and fine ruddy, brittle stems. It is a tender plant and is usually grown as an annual. Seed can be sown in February or March in frames or under glass, or out of doors in April. Gerard knew it as a plant that had a marvellous sweet smell but that "it perisheth at the first approach of Winter." The flowers are a dusty white, clustering in knots—hence its English name; they bloom earlier than those of the pot marjoram, in June and early July, emitting (together with the leaves), a sweet pungent scent. It is rightly named sweet marjoram; and when a recipe calls for oregano, it can be used. Treated as an annual or half-hardy annual and planted out or thinned out in early May (according to how the seed was sown) it will be ready for use in mid-June. Like those of most culinary herbs, the leaves are sweetest when taken just before the plant flowers. It is possible to pot a plant for use in the kitchen during the winter, but the best way to provide this luxury is to sow the seed under glass in August or September and keep the herb as a kitchen pot plant. Its use as a pot plant was known in the seventeenth and eighteenth centuries, and Parkinson wrote that it was a plant "to please outward senses in nosegays and in windows of houses."

What would appear to be a slight variation of sweet marjoram is *O. dictamnus,* the organy or dittany of Crete (syn. *Amaracus dictamnus*) grown especially in the United States. Some catalogues also list *O. microphyllum,* a native of Crete, as closely resembling *O. marjorana* and providing flavor in the same way. It forms a small mound some fifteen inches in height and is another of the marjorams that can be put to good use as a pot plant.

In Greek mythology there is the story of Amaracus, a Greek youth at the court of the Cinyres (kings of Cyprus), who accidentally dropped a vessel containing perfume. His terror on realizing the magnitude of his crime rendered him unconscious, but he was spared punishment because the gods, in their mercy and understanding, transformed him into a sweet-smelling plant which bore his name.

Culpeper's reference to the antipathy of adders to the herb may originate in the legend that the tortoise ate origanum before going to fight with the serpent. The sly serpent, on one occasion, removed the marjoram, depriving the tortoise of his precautionary defence. It seems quite likely then, that there was in the misty past some association of marjoram and snake, but nowhere is marjoram listed as effective against snake bites. Its use in pharmacy is probably limited to oil of marjoram, for perfumery.

As a culinary herb, its inclusion in *bouquet garni* makes it of common use; and because it dries well, maintaining both its flavor and aroma, it can be stored and used dry. It is used most frequently to flavor egg dishes, potatoes, mushrooms, milk puddings (use sparingly), and as an accompaniment to meat. A good flavoring with lamb or pork, it also enhances the taste of liver in sausages and pâtés, and in Poland it is included in *Kielbasa* (Polish sausage).

A warm, sunny, well-drained position is preferable for its cultivation, and the perennial species can be perpetuated by cuttings taken before flowering time. A compost of peat and sand makes a good rooting medium, but one of the no-soil composts is also convenient. Alternatively, the plants may be divided in the spring and replanted with some moisture-retentive compost around the roots to help them establish themselves. Normally, no watering is necessary in the ensuing weeks, unless the spring is particularly dry or warm.

MEADOW-SWEET

Filipendula ulmaria
ROSACEAE

Meadowsweet has chosen the damp woods, fens. wet rock ledges, and river brinks of Europe as its home. It ranges from arctic Russia and Iceland in the north to latitude 40° in the south, drawing an imaginary line across central Spain and central Italy and wandering east over temperate Asia to Mongolia. Known in North America as "English meadow-sweet," it has been cultivated in old-fashioned gardens and is a naturalized escape in the eastern regions of the continent. The American native *F. rubra* (syns. *Ulmaria rubra, Spiraea lobata*) known as "Queen of the Prairie" is cultivated in European gardens for its deep pink flowers. "Queen of the Meadow" is one of the country names in Britain and a translation of the old *Regina prati*. Bridewort is another common name for all the meadow-sweets, from the old custom of strewing houses for wedding festivals with the sweet-scented spiraeas, as they were called then. Michael Drayton, writing of his Warwickshire countryside says:

Among these strewing kinds some
other wild that grow

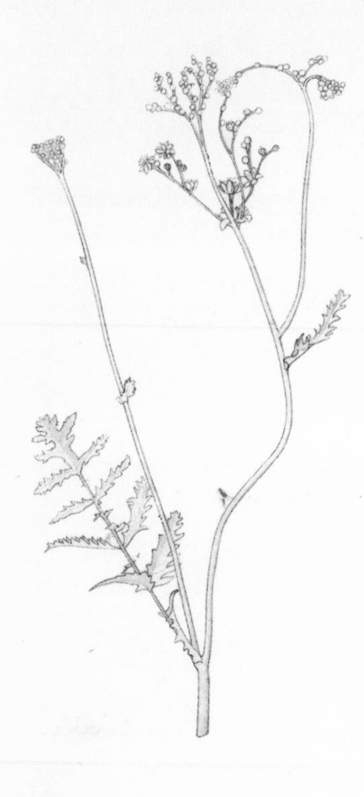

MEADOWSWEET

> As burnet, all abroad and meadowsweet they throw.

Gerard says: "The leaves and floures of Meadowsweet farre excelle all other strowing herbs for to decke up houses . . . for the smell thereof makes the heart merrie and joyful and delighteth the senses."

The frothy blossoms can be found throughout high summer, from mid-June to mid-September, and smell rather heavily of almond; the foliage is scented, too, with the same perfume. The aroma is rather heavy and sickly to some, but in spite of this, the dried flowerheads have been used among linen and in wardrobes. The heaviness of the perfume has led to the belief that it has soporific powers and could be associated with death; therefore, in some districts, in common with the heavily scented hawthorn blossom, it is considered unlucky to bring it into the house. In rural practice, the flowering tops were dried and used for a tisane said to relieve a head cold. The gypsies allow this tea to cool and store it as a refreshing drink to be sweetened with honey in hot weather. Its action is slightly binding, and it can be used in the treatment of diarrhea and colic; it is mild enough even for children to take.

In the herb garden, filipendula is a good plant to introduce in the damper corners, or along the margins of streams. The rhizomatous rootstock revels in dampish soils, unlike the wild *F. vulgaris* which chooses the thin, dry, limestone soils and because of its tuberous root is called dropwort.

The Scottish poet, Thomas Campbell, wrote in the eighteenth century:

> To nod from banks, from whence depend
> Rich cymes of fragrant Meadow-sweet;
> Alas! those creamy clusters lend
> A charm where death and ardour meet!

Campbell could not have foreseen that in 1827, a French chemist in his search for the active medicinal element of the willow—which had been used since the day of Dioscorides—succeeded in isolating and identifying salicin though he did not extract it from the willow (Salix) but from the Queen of the Meadow. The plant was known at that time as *Spiraea ulmaria,* but is now *Fipendula ulmaria.*

For eighteen hundred years, peasants and housewives all over Europe had made decoctions and infusions of willow for the relief of the pains of decaying teeth, gout, rheumatism, and earache. Dioscorides had identified *Salix alba,* the white willow, as the efficacious plant, despite the fact that at least *S. babylonica* and *S. fraxilis* were known to him; but it fell to the humble meadowsweet or *Reine des près,* as the French call it, to first reveal the secret of salicin.

In 1838, salicylic acid was discovered and is still widely used in the treatment of athlete's foot, corns, warts, and skin eruptions; later in this chain of research, acetylsalicylic acid or aspirin was produced in Germany in 1899 and named after the German *Spirnsaure,* or meadowsweet, in recognition that the original donor of salicin was *Spiraea ulmaria.* What medicine has a more universal use than aspirin? Research into the composition of essential oil in the sweet-smelling inflorescence of *Filipendula ulmaria* is being carried out at the present time at the University of Leningrad; and the presence of salicylic acid has been confirmed in the inflorescence, together with heliotropin, vanillin aldehyde, and three new compounds, at present unnamed.

MELILOT, COMMON

Melilotus officinalis
PAPILIONACEAE

Melilot is mainly found naturalized along railffiay embankments and waste ground of a gravel or sandy nature, forming a sturdy plant of conical form and reaching three feet or so in height. Its delicately textured foliage is bright green and reminiscent of laburnum leaves, as are the yellow flowers, though they are held in an upstanding, one-sided raceme. Seed collected from the wild in September can be sown immediately, mimicking the plant's own sowing mechanism at the end of the season when its small pods fall to the ground complete with one or two ripened seeds.

The name melilotus is from *mel,* "honey," ad *lotus,* "the lotus flower," denoting its great attraction for bees during its long flowering season from June to August. Formerly known as melilot trefoil, it was grown as a fodder crop like clover, sanforn, and lucerne, but the latter have superseded it. Upon drying, it emits a strong aroma of new mown hay and retains the scent very well because of the coumarin content of the plant, which is also found in meadowsweet and woodruff, both of which have good drying properties and were used as strewing plants. Scattered among clothes and linen, melilot acts as a moth deterrent.

A tisane relieves flatulence, and its action is to stimulate portal circulation. The tisane may be stored, reheated, and employed as a fomentation in the external treatment of tumors—a use to which Galen is reputed to have put it, giving the plant its tag, "plaster" or "plaister" clover. Occasionally, it is called "King's clover," recalling that it is said to have sprung from the blood of the lion slain by the Emperor Hadrian in the first century.

MIGNONETTE

Reseda odorata
RESEDACEAE

A perennial, usually treated as an annual, mignonette has a Victorian aura and was much cultivated 100 years ago, particularly for the metropolitan markets. It was introduced into England in the middle of the eighteenth century for the garden of the Apothecaries at Chelsea, now known as the Chelsea Physic Garden. The seed came from Leyden as a gift to Philip Millar, and he first described it in his *Dictionary* in 1752 as of "a dull colour" but having "a high ambrosial scent." Its lack of flamboyance is amply compensated by the strong, sweet musk fragrance, and it was for this alone that it became commonly grown in window boxes and on balconies. One writer of the day says "we have frequently found the perfume of the mignonette so powerful in some of the better streets that we have considered it sufficient to protect the inhabitants from those effluvia which bring disorders with them in the air." The name "little darling" is frequently quoted as being a translation of the French *mignonette,* but as the French know the plant by its Latin name *Reseda,* it is far more likely that the prosaic "little darling" was a corruption of "Frenchman's darling" to which Cowper refers when he says:

> . . . the sashed fronted with a range of
> orange, myrtle,
> or the fragrant reek of the Frenchman's
> darling.

Mignonette seems to have been injected into our language from the Spanish *minoneta*. Its other name of *herbe d'amour* or love herb is from the superstition that good fortune will accompany the lover who rolls three times in a bed of mignonette.

MIGNONETTE

Napoleon is said to have collected seeds of it during his Egyptian campaign and sent them as a gift to Josephine, a reputed gardener, who was at the time making extensive plant collections for her new garden at Malmaison. She introduced the vogue for using mignonette as a pot plant, and this use seems to have spread to every parlor and salon of Europe. In the vicinity of both London and Paris, the nursery trade in raising pots of mignonette for market thrived; Loudon recalls in his *Encyclopedia of Gardening* (1835 edition): "of mignonette, perhaps more pots are sold in and near the metropolis than of any other potted plant whatever, fifty years ago it was hardly known." He lists other pot plants and continues:

> All these and other sorts of plants in pots are also lent out by the market-florist to decorate private or public rooms on extraordinary occasions, but especially for those midnight assemblages called routs. This is the most lucrative part of the grower's business who generally receives half of the value of the plants let out, as many of them, and generally those of most value, are so injured by the heat as never to recover.

Though mignonette seems to have once been a somewhat straggling plant, its cultivation brought more robust and probably less aromatic forms. William Robinson, writing in *The Flower Garden* in 1889, says "of the red flowered sorts Victoria is the best." By 1910, varieties such as 'Golden Queen' and 'Golden Matchet' had anthers of a distinctly orange-gold, imparting a bright hue to the whole plant. Today, the seedsmen's catalogues offer us giant varieties with "better spike quality than the sweet scented" or sweet scented mixed. The small six-petaled flowers are curious in form. The two upper petals curve and have tiny spurs or filaments which make them appear deeply incised. The anthers are conspicuous, and half a century ago, when different forms were evolved, it was clearly the anther color that was distinctive. Double flowers have been known.

The tree mignonette, which is now seldom seen, was the same species but grown as a true perennial, and its cultivation depended greatly upon patient care. The immature flower spikes and lower shoots had to be removed in the first season—and sometimes even the second—to encourage growth. By protecting the plants from winter frosts, or by growing them under glass, the stems would eventually take on a woody consistency. Nurserymen who specialized in pot work would even stake the plants, removing the lowest shoots during the first and second seasons to produce a tree mignonette with a leg of one or two feet, bearing a head of blossom in its third year—in appearance, what would today be called a "standard."

Mignonette seed sown out of doors in April or May into firm ground, and thinned once the seedlings can be handled, will provide summer flowers. Autumn or winter sown seed will provide flowers earlier in the season, and this is a reliable way to ensure a supply of flowers for use in potpourri with the June rose and honeysuckle petals. Alternatively, seeds sown in February or March in seed pans or pots can be potted on, hardened off, and used as summer bedding in the herb garden, making an attractive plant for growing along the top of a dry wall or patio where the perfume can be enjoyed. It is a good bee plant and lasts well when used as a cut flower.

The wild mignonette, *Reseda lutea,* is a native plant to Great Britain, widely distributed as far north as Lancashire and County Durham. It is known in Jersey and in Ireland and Wales. The dyer's rocket, *Reseda luteola,* with a deeper tap root, displays a preference for calcareous soils and consequently is a more locally distributed plant. It has been introduced into America where it is known as an economic plant, having been long cultivated and used for the dye flavone, which colors cloth yellow, green, or blue, varying with the mordant used.

opposite Jasmine

MILKWORT

Polygala spp.
POLYGALACEAE

The milkworts range over the temperate regions of the Northern Hemisphere. They are humble trailing plants, quite hardy, some useful as rock garden adornment, but *P. vulgaris* is the common milkwort which Gerard says derives its name from its "vertues in procuring milke in the brests of nurses." It has also been carried in Rogation processions, hence its alternative common names of rogation flower or procession flower. "The maidens which use in the countries to walke the procession do make themselves garlands and nosegaies of the Milkwort." Dioscorides gave the plant its name from the Greek *polus* ("much") and *gala* ("milk") because of its supposed property of increasing milk.

A low-growing plant of the meadow and heath, it usually cowers among the grasses and is often passed by, despite its delicate blue, pink or white flowers, so closely resembling the gentian blue flowers of *P. serpyllifolia* (also, somewhat confusingly, called common milkwort). The semi-erect habit of *P. vulgaris* is typical of the genus, and for its neighbors it usually chooses the bedstraws and the harebells. It lives locally but in a gregarious way, usually on lime-free soils, throughout Britain and northern France and Belgium.

The American species, *P. senega,* known as milkwort or mountain flax, supposedly has ancient medical virtues, knowledge of which was passed by the North American Seneca Indians to an immigrant Scot, Dr. Tennant, through whose work it became popularized in treatment for asthma and rheumatism. The Meskwaki Indians use the root, sometimes called snake root, in a herbal tea as a cure-all for heart disorders, and Dr. Tennant's reports upon this use of the plant were sent back to England. It would appear that it captured the imagination of every quack and charlatan of the day and was an ingredient of many heal-all potions. As a lucky charm against dangers, the Chippewas carried it with them on their journeys. The roots, like those of several other plants known as snake root, were used fairly universally on the North American continent, as an antidote for snake bites, hence its common name of snakeroot—a vernacular name given to other plants for the same reason.

MINT

Mentha spp.
LABIATAE

The profusion of form and the variable characteristics of the mints make them confusing, but it is generally accepted that about six species are to be found in herb gardens, together with their various forms. It is a genus that not only hybridizes freely but has been accepted as a plant of cultivation from ancient times, so that a botanical boundary between cultivated forms and escape or naturalized types is a matter for conjecture.

The mints themselves revel in the confusion because many variations depend on environmental factors, and so problems of identification are extensive. But, by the examination of the essential oils, methods have been developed (using gas chromatography) to distinguish related plants.

The herbalists of the fourteenth and fifteenth centuries were certainly aware of the cleansing and refreshing properties of mint and its use as a masking flavor is of long standing. The plant is herbaceous and found in all temperate parts of the world, though the dampness of the maritime climates of the eastern American seaboard, Great Britain, and northern Europe enhance its aromatic properties. In the New Testament, St. Luke (11 : 42) refers to tithemint which the Jews were commanded to pay. The species now generally to be found in the Holy Land are the three used medicinally throughout the Ancient World, and they are still the main ones employed today in the preparation of pharmaceutical products: *Mentha* X *piperita* (peppermint), *M. spicata* (spearmint), and *M. pulegium* (pennyroyal). The generic name is derived from the Greek *mintha,* a word subsequently latinized to *mentha.* Pliny listed over forty uses for the herb.

Mentha X *piperita* (considered to be a hybrid between *aquatica,* the water mint, and *spicata,* but always identified as peppermint) is used to provide oil for both pharmaceuticals and confectionery. In fact,

the many hybrids of *M. spicata* are all widely cultivated in Europe for essential oils. A household remedy, peppermint tea, made by infusing a few dried or fresh leaves, is helpful to the digestion and is commonly used as a nightcap. The ordinary commercial variety is the stronger-odored black peppermint *(M.* X *piperita vulgaris),* with thicker purplish stems and darker leaves than the comparable white peppermint, *M.* X *piperita officinalis,* which is a more slender plant when grown under the same conditions. The stem of the peppermints is erect but usually branches two or three feet in height if left uncut. The leaves are distinctly stalked and are about two inches in length, while the whorled clusters of reddish flowers in August nestle in the axils of the upper leaves. English peppermint oil is far superior to that produced elsewhere. One ton of leaves will provide between eight and ten pounds of oil. Most of the oil-producing glands are found on the underside of the leaves. Commercially, it is put to a wide variety of uses in the manufacture of toothpastes, digestive paliatives, confectionery, and the liqueur, *crème-de-menthe*.

Mentha X *piperita citrata*—again usually simplified to *M. citrata*—is the eau-de-Cologne mint (and bergamot mint of the herb catalogues) and has the power to enhance the perfume of any plant growing near it. The pineapple, orange, and lemon mints are slight variations of this form, and the most pronounced difference is in the aroma. The surface-growing runners of the plant take on a splendid purple which often looks metallic. The main use for this particular collection is in *potpourri* or in sachets and herb pillows. They dry rather more easily than the common horsemint and do not shatter so readily.

The various aromatic nuances are important in the southern states of America for the making of the true juleps; in Virginia, during the temperance crusade of the 1930s, mint beds were supposed to be uprooted.

Mentha spicata (spearmint), in some references given as *M. viridis,* is a lower-growing plant than peppermint and is distinguished by an absence of leaf stalks. The overall height of the plant is not more than two feet; frequently, it attains no more than eighteen inches. The flowers are in terminal spikes of lilac pink, and it is probably the most commonly grown of all the mints, hence its all-purpose name of "garden mint." It is also known as "pea mint," "fish mint" (although the culinary practice of serving mint as an accompaniment to fish has long since fallen into disfavor), "spire mint" (an allusion to its form), "green lamb mint" (the plant is of a light green color, and the leaves make the best mint sauce to serve with roast lamb), and "our Lady's mint."

Mentha pulegium (pennyroyal) is seen in two distinct forms: the commonly-grown creeping form with flower spikes only a few inches high, and in contrast, the upright form which may attain a foot in height. Very strong in flavor, the herb is not used for culinary purposes nowadays but is an officinal plant. As an inhalant in the treatment of heavy colds, it acquired the name "lung mint." Its ancient use was to remove staleness and purify the casks of drinking water carried for months at sea. It is known also as "flea mint," from its old use as an insecticide, when crushed leaves set among bedding and clothing would suffocate fleas. The Latin name is derived from *pulex,* "a flea."

Pennyroyal can be used to form a lawn, especially in shaded situations, in a way similar to that described for chamomile. The pieces must be divided, each with a root, set out six to nine inches apart, and planted fairly deeply with a dibber. It is best to sprinkle a little moisture-retentive compost in the hole and consolidate it around the root of the plant to encourage the formation of a good root system. This plant is also useful for running among paving stones and should be planted in a similar way if employed for this purpose, so that a good deep root-run can be established.

Mentha arvensis (cornmint) is a plant native to Great Britain and so called because it appeared as a weed of arable land, preferring drier conditions than most other mints. Looking through country floras of the early twentieth century, it is interesting to note repeated reference to it as a weed of corn. The flavor of this mint is a little rank in comparison with its refined relatives, but *M. arvensis piperascens* (Japanese mint) provides menthol.

Mentha aquatica (watermint) is a native of the British Isles in swampy areas and marshes and thrives in fens and soggy woodland areas. Its natural habitat can be simulated in the garden by constructing moisture gardens. It is a strongly scented plant, often taking on a reddish tinge and carrying terminal heads of lilac flowers.

Mentha suaveolens was formerly called *M. rotundifolia.* As the older name implies, this is the round-leaved mint, but happily the one which has received the accolade for its decorative qualities during the past twenty years. Bowles' mint was thought to be a hybrid of *rotundifolia* and *suaveolens,* but now that the examination of the essential oils has helped the taxonomist it has been established that 'Bowles' Variety' is *M. spicata* X *M. suaveolens.* This form is excellent in both foliage and flavor, and fortunately is not subject to attack from the fungus mint rust. Sometimes this plant is labelled apple mint and in the United States, if the leaves are variegated it is known as pineapple mint. The leaves are softer in texture, more rounded in form than other garden mints, and slightly hairy. It dries well and can be relied upon to retain a fairly good green color. It is this variety of which the late A. E. Bowles, a plantsman of considerable authority, said that the leaves made mint sauce *par excellence.* Mr. Bowles built up a fine collection of bulbous and economically interesting plants in his garden at Bulls Cross, Enfield, Middlesex, England. The garden is now in the possession of the London School of Pharmacy.

Other common names for this plant are "wooly mint," "monk's herb," and the variegated-leaved form is known in some places as "pineapple mint," certainly in America; but there is still varietal confusion in England, for the labeling in reputable botanic gardens disagrees.

The foregoing list makes no attempt at completeness, but for the herb garden, the tiny *Mentha requienii* is the plant to encourage between the gaps of paving stones. Its creeping stems soon spread and its strong fragrance is enhanced by crushing underfoot. Its catalogue name is Spanish mint, probably because it was introduced into the British Isles at the time of the defeat of the Armada. In the United States, its vernacular name is "Corsican mint." The Spanish mint is probably the smallest-leaved cultivated plant, competing only with *Helxine solierolii* with which it may be confused until the leaves are crushed.

Folklore seems surprisingly free of superstitions about mint—curious for a plant so easily cultivated and so universally employed through the centuries. Mint is a symbol of virtue, clearly alluding to its cleansing properties, and the Greeks added it to their bath water in much the same manner that pine essence is used today.

The mints, unlike other members of their natural order, prefer a fairly moist soil, or at least a moist root-run, but must have good light; otherwise, they become etiolated. A mint bed is easy enough to establish but difficult to confine; and for a good quality crop, it should be cleared and replanted in fresh ground every third year. Rooted divisions, rooted cuttings, or so-called Irishman's cuttings, should be put in along a shallow trench in either spring or autumn. Some moisture retentive material, like well-rooted compost or moistened horticultural peat, should be incorporated to help establish the plants. If they are started in autumn, tread over the bed and around the plants in spring to firm the soil that has been lifted by the action of frost; a firmed soil will encourage fresh root formation. Gather the long shoots as required, or the leaves separately throughout the summer; but once the plants have reached the flowering stage in July or August, the leaves should not be used from those shoots, as they become tough and the aroma is somewhat stale. Shoots harvested for drying should be cut early in the summer and certainly before the plants flower. The soft leaves of all the mints dry well but need special care to maintain a good color, otherwise they deteriorate to an unattractive dull black.

Once a mint bed is established, weeding presents a problem, particularly if other plants with running roots like nettle and buttercup invade the beds. The mints themselves do not respect territory. They never like the place that has been selected for them but will move off to the adjacent land very quickly. To prevent this emigration, sink an old bucket or zinc bath from which the base has been removed and plant the mint within its confines. Plastic or galvanized utensils can be used; the plastic stands up to the three seasons before a new bed needs to be found. The practice of moving mints every third year is primarily to reduce the likelihood of attack by the soil-borne fungus spores of mint rust. Modern fungicides can control the disease, but the old practice is still recommended; otherwise, the mint bed becomes impossible to weed and too tight for a good crop.

Mint may be forced to provide an early crop, in either a greenhouse or cold frame. Rooted pieces are planted in October in moisture-retentive compost, in boxes or beds made up under the staging of the greenhouse. The young shoots can be cut as they reach two or three inches in height.

MULLEIN

Verbascum thapsus
SCROPHULARIACEAE

Architectural in stature and striking in appearance, the mullein or blanket weed, as it is popularly known, is an interesting plant with which to dominate the plan of the herb garden. A group can form a centre piece: stately, spire-like, and almost ethereal despite its solidity. Alternatively, it may form a good back-drop, colorful and light, especially if some of the modern cultivars with pink, rose or salmon-colored flowers are introduced. The thick, white, felty foliage, which forms a stout-based rosette and then sparsely ascends the sturdy stems, not only gives it its vernacular names (blanket weed, beggar's blanket, blanket leaf, velvet dock, feltwort, flannel weed, our Lord's flannel, fluffweed, hare's bear, old man's flannel, rag paper) but provides the therapeutic value of the plant. It is mucilaginous and has been used since ancient times in the treatment of pulmonary congestion, even for cattle, and is still considered an effective remedy for coughs and colds.

A stout perennial, it bears spires of yellow flowers in July and August, each flower with clear orange stamens. During the first year, the large rosettes are formed and cannot always be transplanted successfully; therefore it is best to plant out the seedlings where they are required to bloom. The second season, the pale stalk rises from the center and is of such rigidity that the popular names of "Jacob's staff," "Jupiter's staff," "Peter's staff," shepherd's staff," seem appropriate; "Aaron's rod" is the common name given to a smaller species found on chalklands, *Verbascum nigrum*.

Economically, its torch-like appearance has suggested the use to which it has been put for many years: to supply a torch light. The stalks used to be dipped in suet or wax to burn "whether at funerals or for private uses," and it is known as the candlewick plant, for the silky down of its leaves was used to form wicks and tinder before wicks and lamps were in general use. They ignite readily and burn slowly. The vernacular name of "hag-taper" is from the Anglo-Saxon *hege* or *haga,* "a hedge," denoting the usual habitat of the plant, where its tapering growth looked like candles or torches as they stood in the hedges to light the harvest-home procession.

In France, its local name is *bouillon blanc* ("white soup"), the French forever alluding to gastronomic delights, but it is also the *herbe de St. Fiacre,* a little-known patron of gardeners whose saint's day is August 30.

An immigrant in America, native of southern Europe originally but now ranging over the whole of Europe and North Africa, *Verbascum thapsus* is thought to take its name first from Pliny as a corruption of *barbascum* ("with beards") and *thapsus* from a Sicilian town in whose environs it grew. It is thought that the seed "stowed away" among the ballast of sailing ships, to colonize the New World.

MYRTLE

Myrtus communis
MYRTACEAE

The common myrtle is one of the few hundred species of the genus which extend over temperate and subtropical regions of the world. It is hardy in favored situations out of doors: it must be protected from cold winds and early morning sunshine; but it is a true evergreen, which used to be far more popularly grown than it is today. In living memory in Britain, it was customary for a sprig of myrtle to be among the orange blossom of bridal bouquets and for a bridesmaid to plant the sprig in some sheltered spot. In this way, the myrtle bushes of some country gardens have flourished for as many years as a friend's marriage. The long association with weddings probably alludes to the mythological symbolism of myrtle as an emblem of love. Venus wore a wreath of it when Paris gave her the golden apple, and the Graces, who attended her, were adorned with chaplets of the same fragrant plant.

Virgil alludes to its fragrance: "and thee O Myrtle, next in dignity to the Laurel; for thus arranged you mingle sweet perfumes." The Greeks hold it as an emblem of authority, and its evergreen foliage formed wreaths for victors' heads. To Jews it represents justice.

Milton, in describing the bower of Paradise, says:

> The roof of thickest covert was in
> woven shade
> Laurel and Myrtle, and what higher
> grew
> of firm and fragrant leaf; . . .

When the Alhambra, the ancient palace and fortress of the Moorish monarchs of Granada in southern Spain was built, one of the courts was named Court of the Myrtles, *Patio de los Arrayanes.* Some references describe it as *Patio de la Alberca* (Court of the Blessing or Court of the Pond). It is described as about 140 feet long and 27 feet broad, a large goldfish pond running the length of the court, and set in a marble pavement, with myrtles planted in avenues on either side. The aroma was enjoyed in the galleries of the court in that warm climate.

The foliage is fragrant when crushed, the aromatic volatile oil being released; myrtol, a constituent, has been given, on sugar, in the treatment of tuberculosis and bronchiectasis and similar conditions. It is for perfumery, however, that its properties have been valued most; and both leaves and flowers are included in potpourri.

There is risk in cultivation in some colder districts, but the protection of a wall or sheltered corner may ensure success. The foliage is damaged by cold winds and turns brown. In North America's colder regions, myrtle must be treated like rosemary and given some winter protection in greenhouse, plant room, or sheltered porch. The many-stamened white flowers bloom in June, and the variety 'Tarentina' is compact of form, with smaller leaves, and is sometimes listed as 'Jenny Reitenbach.' The fruits of *Myrtus ugni (Eugenea ugni)* are the Peruvian guava, an edible fruit.

NASTURTIUM

Tropaeolum majus
TROPAEOLACEAE

A colorful annual, the garden nasturtium is a misnomer because it bears the Latin generic name for watercress *(Nasturtium officinale),* but its gaily painted, long-spurred flowers and round, flat leaves are among the first plants children learn to identify.

A native of Peru and the West Indies, its seed was introduced to England in 1597 when it was sent to John Gerard. Its ease of cultivation coupled with its somewhat exotic appearance ensured immediate popularity, and Parkinson called it "Yellow Larked Spurr." It was already known as

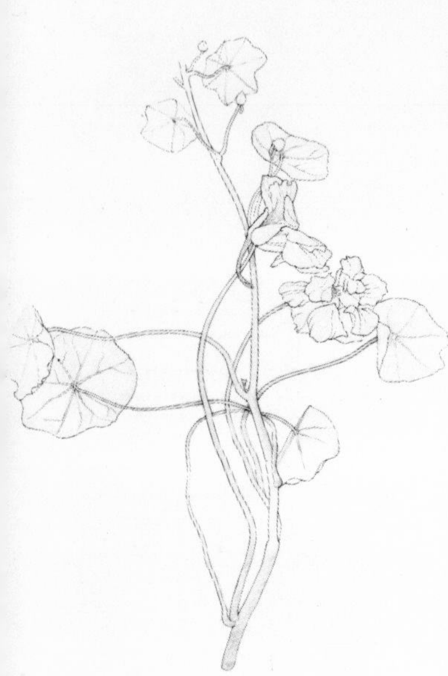

Indian cress, which suggests that it was eaten in the sixteenth century, probably more frequently than today.

The plant popularly grown at that time was not the species we grow today. *Majus* came to Europe about a hundred years later, but both are trailing plants—and how they can be relied upon to trail, especially if July is a damp month! The double-flowered form first came from Italy in the mid-eighteenth century, and with the plethora of new plants that were arriving, not very much attention seems to have been paid to it. It was not really until the Gleam Hybrids of the mid-twentieth century, which combined double flowers with scent, that the nasturtium reached a new height of popularity. The "scent" of the flower was inbred from plants found in a garden in California. Since then, work has progressed on both sides of the Atlantic to produce a race of garden nasturtiums that hold their helmet-like flowers of glowing orange or yellow or apricot above the ground-masking smooth, green leaves. Strains with smaller leaves have been produced, dwarf plants, non-trailing varieties, and a host of lovely scented blooms, semi-double and ranging from palest apricot to dark cherry red. The nutritive value of the plant is in its pleasant pungency, especially useful in diets devoid of salt and other seasonings. The vitamin C content is high, as in watercress, and both have anti-scorbutic properties. The nasturtium was used in treatment for general debility following influenza.

In addition to the seed being used as a condiment, it can provide a substitute for capers in caper sauce—the sauce then strictly becoming a nasturtium sauce, particularly appetizing when served with boiled beetroot as a winter vegetable. The seeds can be used in pickles, or can be dried and ground in a pepper mill. The leaves of nasturtium should be added to the salad bowl, with discretion, or may simply be crushed and rubbed around the inside of the bowl. Chopped leaves can be added to cream cheese, like chives, or can be sprinkled on a tomato salad with pleasing results.

NETTLE, STINGING

Urtica dioica
URTICACEAE

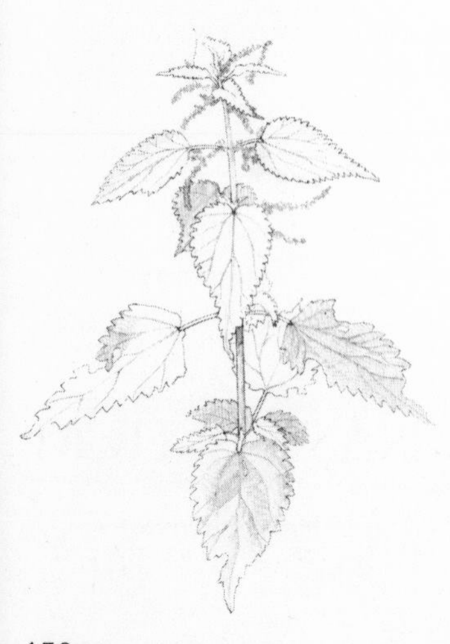

One would be a crank to plant nettles deliberately in a herb garden, but in a representative collection, they beg inclusion for their ancient medicinal and nutritive value and for the folklore that surrounds them. The plants can be confined to made-up beds, grown in old bath tubs, or the clumps constantly clipped back to restrict their running growth. Ideally, they prefer sandy and light soils, but in nature they are ubiquitous and are generally regarded as an ugly weed. The paraquat weed-killers and others generally in use against annual and perennial weeds have little or no effect on the nettle, and so stronger herbicides that are effective against brushwoods have to be used. It is a tenacious weed, its underground stems running far and wide.

Nettles are believed to have been introduced into the British Isles by the Romans, who were warned of the dampness and chilliness of the northern latitudes and are said to have chastised themselves with nettle shoots in order to increase circulation and help keep themselves warm. This is a practice which seems to have lasted through the centuries, particularly in the thrashing of afflicted joints with nettle shoots to relieve rheumatism. The possible improvement in condition results, no doubt, from the increased flow of blood. The high content of iron and silicic acid in young, spring nettle shoots explains the effectiveness of the tonic of nettle tea which has been made for many years—effectively though not tastily—in the preparation of saline tea and diabetic diets. As the leaves are dried, the change in chemical content robs them of their power to sting. They also become harmless when boiling water is poured over them.

Young nettle shoots make a good spinach-like vegetable, especially when combined with a few sorrel leaves. The spring shoots are best; but if the crop is cut back, new basal shoots will form (as every gardener knows!), and these can be harvested for food. (Gloves must be worn, and a knife or scissors used for the reaping.)

In medieval flower symbolism, the nettle stands for envy, and in Scandinavian mythology, they are sacred to the god Thor, which probably accounts for the ancient practice of throwing nettles on the fire during a thunderstorm to protect the home from being destroyed by lightning.

It is not surprising that so common a weed should have numerous folklore associations. A charm to reduce fevers was to grasp a nettle and tear it up by the roots while saying the names of the victim and his parents. One of its local names, "devil's apron," was given because it was believed that it had the power to protect the Evil One. Other local names are "naughty man's plaything," "scaddie," and "tanging nettle." When carried about the person, it was believed to give courage to the bearer and drive away fear in times of danger.

The name is from the Latin *uro*, "I burn," and the specific name refers to the dioecious character of the plant. It is the alternate host for some funguses and is beloved of some of our most attractive butterflies; it is, in fact, the main food of the peacock, small tortoiseshell, and red admiral caterpillars.

The domestic uses of the plant in former times seem legion. The dried leaves when used as packing for fruit will retain the bloom on the fruit. Nettle juice combed through the hair was believed to combat baldness; a bunch of shoots tied together and hung in the pantry would keep flies away; and the fibrous roots and stems have been utilized in the making of cloth and paper. The leaves, with the addition of a little common salt, can curdle milk and can be put to use as a substitute for rennet.

Economically, the value of dried nettle leaves appear to be recognized by poultry keepers; and once boiling water is poured over them, deadening the "sting," mash is added, and the nettle is said to enhance the appearance of the plumage of the bird as well as to stimulate egg-laying.

NIPPLEWORT

Lapsana communis
COMPOSITAE

Most hedgerows have their complement of nipplewort, a plant native to Britain and spread insignificantly over the temperate and Arctic zones. In North America it is an introduction, inhabiting waste ground and showing, as it does in Europe, a preference for sandy soil. The small yellow flowers bloom about eighteen inches above the thin, egg-shaped, hairy leaves, which were formerly eaten as salad. The flowerheads close in mid-afternoon and do not open at all in dull weather.

Dioscorides named it *Lapsana,* apparently meaning "charlock" though only the color of the flower is similar to the common charlock. In its colloquial names, we find the clue to its use in the past, as a plant for the treatment of the nipples of nursing mothers and the udders of cattle. Also called ballagan, bolgan-leaves (literally "swelling leaves," *Bolgan* being Celtic for "swelling"), its bruised leaves were used in the treatment of ulcers around the nipples.

ONION

Allium spp.
LILIACEAE

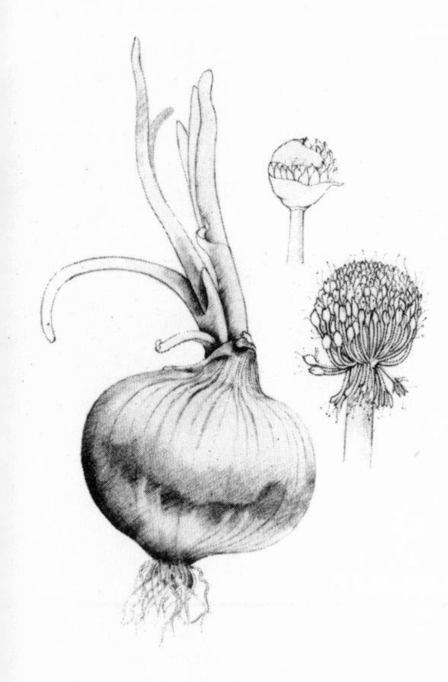

All the onions, or *Allium* species, have the curious habit of developing a "bulb" consisting of layers of colorless leaves which, botanically, are really a swollen stem base. This base is enclosed in a protective skin, which is impervious to water and protects the fleshy layers from bruising. One of the oldest cultivated vegetables, it is a native of Asia, but its form was so widely adopted by the Egyptians in their design and religious belief that it has come to be associated most closely with that country. It was undoubtedly part of the very culture of the ancient world and is recorded in Indian, Chinese, Arabian, Greek, and Roman references. The onion of our gardens is *Allium cepa*.

An intriguing form of *Allium cepa* is the tree onion, a hardy perennial with a swollen base from which spring stems carrying clusters of small onions or "sets" at intervals, intermingled with white flowers. The bulblet or sets may be planted to perpetuate the stock.

Apart from the onion's powerful aroma and flavor which, when cooked, enhance all other flavors, the whole tribe contains phosphorus and sulphurous elements and has an ancient reputation for its cleansing properties and effectiveness in clearing head colds and phlegm. Culpeper reminds us that "roasted under the embers and eaten with honey or sugar, they much conduce to relieve an inveterate cough and expectorate tough phlegm." In the Middle Ages they were believed to draw putrefaction to them. One remedy was to hollow out an onion, fill the center with black treacle, roast the onion and, after removing the outer skin, mash the hot black paste for use as a poultice. This seems to have been a country practice. As recently as the 1920s, black treacle poultices, usually made with white flour or bread, were still successfully used in breaking carbuncles.

The Welsh onion, *Allium fistulosum*, is believed to originate from eastern Asia but was unknown to the ancient world; it may have been introduced into Europe through Russia in the Middle Ages. The tubular leaves are mild in flavor and may be used for flavoring in the same manner as spring onions. An evergreen perennial, clumps can be lifted, some taken for use, and the remainder replanted. (*See also* Chives.)

The native British species of allium are the garlics (*q.v.*) and *Allium ursinum*, ramsons, so called because the odor is said to pertain to bears. The word "garlic" has its origins in the Anglo-Saxon *gar* ("spear") and *leac* ("leek"). Ramsons form large colonies in localities where they are often detectable by their smell long before they are in sight; damp woods and shady places harbor them. The white starry flowers bloom in July and bear strong resemblance to those of the lily-of-the-valley. Country names abound but do not vary widely: "Hog's garlick," "buckrams," "rams," "ramaden," "ramsey," "rommy," and "stink plant" are all commonly encountered; the old rhyme says:

> Eat leeks in Lide [March] and ramsies in May
> And all the year after physicians may play.

PARSLEY

Petroselinum crispum
UMBELLIFERAE

Like the rue, parsley is a plant of cultivation, known to the ancient world as a harbinger of death. None the less, through the ages, the demand for its presence in the kitchen garden has remained constant. The saying goes that where parsley flourishes "Missus is Master." It is probably the best known of all such garnishes and a rich source of iron and vitamins A, B, and C. Parsley tea is a remedy for rheumatism, a cleanser of the complexion, and an antifermentive.

It is a hardy biennial, usually flowering and going to seed in the spring or early summer after sowing; but the flowering stems may be removed if the seed is not required. In really warm, dry summers, the plants, in common with most of their umbelliferous relatives, will bolt the first season. As a pot plant, window box tenant, or in the attractive jars designed for it, fresh parsley can be readily available for the kitchen through all kinds of weather. The secret of getting a high percentage of germination, both in the open garden and in containers, is to sow fresh seed and pour boiling water onto the soil immediately prior to sowing. Out of doors in Britain, there is little point in sowing seed before the end of May, by which time the soil will have warmed up to encourage the seed in its lazy germination.

Oil of parsley contains apiol and is a nonvolatile liquid with a distinct odor and flavor, and it yields "parsley camphor" on being cooled to a low temperature. It is perhaps as well that parsley from the freezer is so drab of appearance that its use is not widespread. Dried, it will not always retain a good color, but it does retain its flavor and is useful in casseroles and broths.

Greek mythology endows parsley, and its seed, with the most gloomy and sinister associations. It supposedly sprang forth from the blood of Archemorus, the forerunner of death, and was used in ceremonies dedicated to Persephone, the heart and soul of the earth. Parsley's excursions to Hades seem of commuter-like regularity, and there is an old superstition that the seed takes from a month to six weeks to germinate because it goes nine times to the Devil and back before breaking into leaf!

Gerard knew the curly leaved form, which is commonly grown, and the plain or fern-leaved parsley, which is today sometimes erroneously called French parsley. The preference for the tightly curled, almost distorted-leaved forms offered in seedsmen's catalogues reflects the demand and proves the point that this plant, whose name means "rock," is regarded as the garnish *par excellence* of the table. Varieties —or more precisely cultivars—which are winter-hardy are 'Moss Curled,' 'Exhibition,' 'Imperial Curled,' and 'Giant Curled' all readily available.

The parsnip-rooted or Hamburg parsley has, according to the seedmen's description, "plain foliage" which is fern-like and tasty; the root is lifted for use as a winter vegetable. In texture, this root resembles the parsnip but has a more interesting flavor. A native of southern Europe—Turkey, Sardinia, and Greece—and of Lebanon, it is to be found locally as an escape from cultivation over most of the temperate zone, but the deeply distorted leaf character does not persist. Fool's parsley, *Aethusa cynapium,* is a native plant of the Caucasus and Algeria and a weed of cultivated ground in Britain, especially in the south; it contains the poisonous coniine. It is a European immigrant to North America where it inhabits waste ground and rubbish dumps from Nova Scotia to New Jersey and westward. It is well-named "fool's parsley," and in America it is known as "dog's poison." The leaves are glossy, somewhat bluish-green, and, when bruised, do not exude the familiar parsley odor.

The vernacular "parsley" is a tag for a range of wild plants, all umbelliferous: cow parsley, *Anthriscus sylvestris*; hedge parsley, *Torilis arvensis*; knotted hedge parsley, *T. nodosa*; stone parsley, *Sison amomum*; and the bur parsleys, *Caucalis lappula* and *C. latifolia.* Tracing the history of its cultivation, one finds it as a form of the same plant as celery, the latter known as marsh selinon, and parsley known as mountain or rock selinon, *Petrosilium,* which later underwent an unexplained change to *Petroselinum,* from the Greek "rock" or "stone"—*petros* and *selinon*— "parsley". The Middle English name was *petersilie.*

Through the process of anglicization, the plant has been variously recorded as "percil," "percelle," "perseli," "persele," "perseley," and "parsley"; it has also been tossed from one genus to another and has been recorded under a number of aliases; but it is now fixed clearly and firmly in its own right as *Petroselinum.*

PARSLEY PIERT

(*See* LADY'S-MANTLE.)

PASQUE FLOWER

Pulsatilla vulgaris
RANUNCULACEAE

A very rare British native, the pasque flower is said to flourish only where the blood of Danes has fallen. Where it does occur, it is a closely local plant, although its seed is suited for dispersal by wind, and seemingly congenial conditions abound. It is to be found in colonies on dry calcareous, grassy slopes from the South Downs to the Yorkshire limestones on the eastern side of England. Cultivated in a rock garden, or in troughs or pots, it is an endearing, shaggy plant, glistening silver in the sunshine; its lilac-blue flowers coincide with Easter, hence its common name. The link with Easter is probably of some antiquity and more accurately relating to the pre-Christian dawn-goddess Easter, for it appears to have been a cult plant of the Danes and in the southeast of England is locally known as "Dane's flower." Gerard claims to have christened it "pasque flower." Previously, it was known and cultivated as *Anemone pulsatilla* and is indeed classified as such in many authoritative books, but it differs in some botanical detail from the anemones. The name *Pulsatilla* was first given to that genus by Mattioli, and it possibly means "shaking in the wind." Another anemone elevated to generic status is *A. hepatica,* now known as *Hepatica triloba,* an almost stemless little plant sometimes puzzlingly called American liverwort in Britain. Gerard misplaced its classification. Confused by its three-lobed leaves, he deemed it a trefoil.

The medicinal properties of the anemones as antispasmodic and sedative are strongest in the pasque flower; and it is particularly suitable for "highly emotional people who are given to extremes of pleasure and misery and who change their moods with the wind," Mrs. Leyel records. The toxic principle is an acid—anemonium—which, like the acrid oil anemonel, has been used in the past to provide a bright green dye for the coloring of Easter egg shells.

The hairiness of the pulsatillas makes them shrink from the dampness of winter, and other than really sharp drainage they need good protection. The generic name may not just allude to the sensitivity of the plants in the breeze but may well indicate that the drying effect of the wind is beneficial to them in ridding their silky calyces and foliage of excess moisture.

The European mountain plant, *A. apennina,* is naturalized in some localities as an escape from cultivation and is an excellent plant to introduce into the herb garden, where it can be naturalized in drifts under a tree or in a shaded corner at the base of a hedge. Called the blue anemone, its pools of blue and white appear with the first sunshine of the spring. Its black rhizomatous root contains the same active principles as the pasque flower.

PELARGONIUM

Pelargonium spp.
GERANIACEAE

For nearly 100 years, many pelargoniums have been called "geraniums," but the bedding plants of the gardens of northern Europe and the cascading plants of the cliffs of the Mediterranean coasts, as well as many house plants, are true pelargoniums. Of special significance to the grower of herbs are the scented-leaved pelargoniums: *P. abrotanifolium,* which smells of southernwood (*Artemisia abrotanum*); *P. acetosa,* tasting like sorrel and edible as a salad flavoring; *P. crispum,* strongly lemon-scented; and *P. quercifolium,* the oak-leaved pelargonium (or oak-leaved geranium) better known as the house plant, scented oak. The verbena-scented *P. radula,* the rose-scented *P. graveolens* and also *P.* X *fragrans,* the nutmeg-scented geranium, are all excellent conservatory or house plants, and their leaves may be added, with discretion, to potpourri or sachets to be put in wardrobes or cupboards. The whole genus is rich in essential oils, and some species have elaborately showy flowers as well as the rich scent—although most of the spicy ones bear small flowers; therefore, in an indoor herb collection or as pot plants they are of prime importance.

PELLITORY-OF-THE-WALL

Parietaria diffusa
(syn. *P. officinalis*)
URTICACEAE

No plant seems more at home in ruins and old brick walls than pellitory-of-the-wall; it is essentially rupestral and addicted to heights. Its brittle red stems and deep green leaves hide minute flower clusters, shyly tucked in the axils of the leaves. So shy are they that when they are discovered and touched, their stamens display a reflex action jerking inwards away from the intruder, and in so doing, dispelling their pollen. Under the dominion of Mercury, the plant is very rich in potassium nitrate, as are most deep-green leafy vegetables, and was used of old to alleviate constipation, flatulence, and "stomach vapours," which modern-day nutritionists know are due to potassium deficiency.

Culpeper knew all this and went to some length to extol the plant's virtues. Tucked away among his advice is the one operative sentence, "The juice held awhile in the mouth easeth pains in the teeth." This appears to have been the reason why many cottagers cultivated pellitory. A piece of cleansed root, bitten over the offending tooth, draws the pain away—no doubt by some astringent action. Another everyday remedy was to form poultices which, together with mallow and boiled wheat bran or bean flour, were applied hot to bruised sinews and tendons or strained muscles, or even used in this way to dissolve the congealed blood of bruises and take away discoloration. Gerard recorded that in medieval days it was employed in the treatment of broken limbs.

The country names are "peniterry," "wallwort," "perietary," "peletin" and "Billie boatie," the last presumably because of the jingle:

> Peniterry, Peniterry, that grows by the wall
> Save me from a whipping; or I pull you, roots and all

The Latin name is from *paries,* "wall," from which came perritory, and more recently the r's have been replaced by l's, corrupting the English name to pellitory. Lichwort is another name which merely recognizes the fact that, like the lichens, it adheres to walls.

PERIWINKLE

Vinca major
Vinca minor
APOCYNACEAE

A herb of Venus, periwinkle was said to bind people together, and indeed its habit of growth is binding, forming a really tough ground-cover plant and, in days gone by, used to bind or stem the flow of blood. Today it is an accepted treatment of herbalists for diabetics, and research work is being done on its powers against fiercer diseases. As many as thirty-five alkalis have been isolated from it.

Thought to have been introduced at the time of the Roman occupation of Britain, *Vinca minor* is to be seen sometimes in copses and light oak-hornbeam-ash woods throughout England, and in Europe south from Denmark. Its ancient name of pervink appears in writings on sacrifices and on criminals condemned to the gallows; in Italy, its appellations *fiore di morte* and *mortine* signify its use as a crown for the head of a dead infant. The leaves of the periwinkle have astringent properties; ointments made from them can be used in the treatment of ulcerated skin, bleeding haemorrhoids, and eruptions and irritation of the scalp. A tisane or gargle made from crushed or chopped leaves alleviates throat ulcers.

There is a white-flowered form; indeed several garden forms are extant, and Culpeper records, "some of a dark reddish purple colour," but today and for a century gone by, its flowers have been known as blue. I have a dainty double-

flowered form in my own garden but it seems not to have grown as rampantly as the single-flowered form which Margaret Brownlow described as accurately as "blue wheel-like flowers." There is also a slower-growing, variegated-leaved form of this evergreen.

Its reputation in the past for warding off evil spirits accounts for its English name of sorcerer's violet and its French name *violette des sorciers*. Other French names are *pervenche* and *pucellage*.

Cultivation is simple, and once planted the periwinkle is difficult to eradicate—the binding qualities of its roots can be exploited by the gardener to stabilize banks of earth and to cover hedge banks and slopes. It does not seed in the British Isles but is easily propagated by pulling up some of the running shoots which will root quickly in a moist site.

Since it falls under the influence of Venus, one would expect the periwinkle to represent the love charm, and indeed it does. Its use in aphrodisiac's has been recorded since the fourteenth century—further confirmation of its binding qualities. Bacon tells us that bands of periwinkle stem tied around a limb would prevent or relieve cramp. Chaucer describes it well:

> Parvenke is an erbe grene of colour,
> In tyme of May he beryth blo flour,
> His stalkys ain so feynt and feye
> Yet never more gloweth he hey
> On the ground he runneth and growe
> As doth the erbe that hath turnhow
> The lef is thicke, schinende and styf
> As is the grene ivy lef . . .

Miss Mitford writing in *Our Village*, in the first half of the nineteenth century, says of the periwinkle:

> Ah, here is the hedge along which the periwinkle wreathes and twines so profusely, with its evergreen leaves shining like the myrtle, and its starry blue flowers. It is seldom found wild in this part of England; but when we do meet it, it is so abundant and so welcome—the very robin red-breast of flowers—a winter friend. Unless in those unfrequent frosts which destroy all vegetation, it blossoms from September to June, surviving the last lingering crane's bill, forerunning the earliest primrose, hardier even than the mountain daisy, peeping out from beneath the snow, looking at itself in the ice, smiling through the tempests of life . . . and yet welcoming and enjoying the sunbeams. Oh, to be like that flower!

POPPY

Papaver spp.
PAPAVERACEAE

The brilliant red petals of the field or corn poppy, *Papaver rhoeas*, an abundant weed of fields and waste places, are still sometimes used as a coloring agent in medicine. The latex contains a red chrystallizable coloring matter, laudanine, and an alkaloid, rhoeadine. In the ancient world it was generally believed that red poppies growing in the corn improved the quality of the grain harvest and they were offered together with the symbolic corn to Ceres. Ceres is said to have been neglectful of her crops because of weariness and so the great God of Sleep, Somnus, created the poppy to induce her to rest. The name *Papaver* is from the Latin *pappa* or *papa* which in the Middle English became *pappe*, a breast, probably because of the soporific milky fluid that exudes from the plant—said to have been administered to fractious infants. The Anglo-Saxon name *popig* became *popi* in Old and Middle English. These garnets of the corn harvest are no longer so plentiful among the crops since the advent of chemical herbicides, but the red poppy is still a universal plant—some say native of the British Isles, and certainly native of Europe. It has been introduced into North America, New Zealand and Australia and is the parent of the Shirley Poppies, so immediately popular as garden plants at the turn of the century and now still offered in such annual varieties as 'Pierrot' and 'Shirley Double'. The forerunner of these were forms known to William Robinson's generation as carnation, picotee and ranunculus poppies and in the *English Flower Garden*, Robinson says,

"These varieties possess almost every shade of colour except blue and yellow; some are self coloured while others are beautifully variegated." They are known too as French and German poppies.

The fleeting flowers of *P. rhoeas* with their silken petals spring up so quickly on barren land and recently disturbed soil—their seed is said to germinate within twenty-four hours—that the battle-torn fields and desolate farms of Flanders were robed in red after one season of calm following the Battle of Waterloo and again after the First World War. The flower was thus chosen as the emblem of remembrance of war dead. The French call it *coquelicot* from the verb *coquiller*, to crumble, because of its crushed petals that unfold so quickly and perfectly. The plant itself is a token of sleep. In the Netherlands it is *Klaproos*.

The poppy's volatile nature—appearing quickly, brilliant, falling and yet leaving behind innumerable seed, earns it the Latin name of *rhoes*, given to it by L'Obel in the sixteenth century; the name means "a flow" or "falling off" and is descriptive of both the latex and the falling petals.

The English vernacular names are numerous: "cockrose" (because the flowers unfold at cock crow)—compare the French *coquelicot*—"soldiers," "canker," "canker rose," "headache," and "redweed," the last from the English farmer's opinion of it as a weed of arable crops.

The capsule or poppy head is known to every school child, and the pepperpot action by which it sprinkles its hundreds of seeds is early knowledge. The tiny gray-black seeds are used in confectionery and as decoration for bread and biscuits. The seeds of the field poppies may be collected and used in this way.

It was in North America that *P. orientale,* the oriental poppy, was found by the French botanist Tournefort; seed was sent back to Paris and arrived in England via the Netherlands early in the eighteenth century. Through two more centuries, it was cultivated as a garden plant before the now famous color breaks appeared and were developed by the nurseryman, Amos Perry, at Enfield in Middlesex, England.

The poppy of commerce, and one over which wars have been waged and governments have conferred, is *P. somniferum,* the opium poppy, or *pavot* of France. Employed for medicinal purposes, the plant has been cultivated on a commercial scale in England in both the Mitcham district of Surrey and in Lincolnshire. It was formerly called *P. album* because of the white flower and grayish appearance of the whole plant, as if clothed in its own dreamy opiate. After flowering, the capsules are left to dry, and those that dry well to a pale buff color are the most remunerative; but the crop can be a precarious one.

In various parts of the world, the incision made in the capsules to drain off the precious drug, differs in shape and position, but the end product is opium. This incision has to be precise and should not penetrate the wall to the seed cavity. The juice flows out as a creamy-colored liquid with a narcotic smell and dries to a brown color; when of a gummy consistency, it may be scraped off with a knife and collected. *P. somniferum* is the oldest species in cultivation. A plant of immense antiquity, hailing possibly from the Middle East but known around the Mediterranean in medieval times; it was long grown about monastic settlements. A few plants were developed as varying garden forms as far back as the days of Elizabeth I. "John silver-pin, fair without and foul within" is how it was described. Gerard recommends the seed as a confection "to season bread with" or serve at table "with other junketting dishes . . . and is delightful to be eaten." The seeds themselves contain no opiate but provide oil. Gerard was aware of the drastic effect of the capsule, for he said: "It mitigateth all kinds of paines, but it leaveth behinde it oftentimes a mischiefe woorse than the disease it selfe . . . opium somewhat too plentifully eaten doth also bring death." As a hot fomentation, poppy heads are used even today to soothe sprained joints, toothaches and neuralgia.

Dioscorides knew of the opiate juices from the poppy and differentiated between that of the herb and that of the capsule, the latter being superior in effect. The use

of opium as a narcotic drug is said to have been introduced across the ancient trade routes to China by the Arabs in the thirteenth century and, three centuries later, opium smoking, which was to become a scourge in China, had become a common practice. The importation of opium into China was prohibited in 1729 by Emperor Yung Cheng. This ban, and other restrictions on trade, led to a war with Great Britain, the Opium War of 1839–1842, and ultimately to the growth of home production of the opium poppy. This is turn began to reverse the trend, and China tended to export opium.

Early in the present century, a world conference was held in Shanghai to control world production of and trade in opium. Today the main commercial opium-producing country is Turkey.

PURSLANE

Portulaca oleracea
PORTULACACEAE

The only species of a tropical and subtropical genus to inhabit the Old World is purslane; it cannot be claimed as a native of Europe but is believed to have been introduced in cultivation. It is a long-established culinary herb which, combined with sorrel, is a component of the French soup *bonne femme*. The true purslane is *P. oleracea sativa* and there is an excellent golden-leaved form, golden purslane, which is a delightful addition to the herb garden for its effectiveness of leaf. Both the gold and the green-leaved are first-class salad plants, imparting coolness and a succulence seldom found among salad plants. In the Netherlands, it is much cultivated as a salad crop, and the thick mid-ribs or stems can be pickled in vinegar for winter use, served with caraway seed for added flavor.

Culpeper spelled it quaintly as "purslaine" and recommends the cooling effect of the whole plant as a blood cleanser. The seed, he says, "is more effectual than the herb" and, bruised and boiled in wine, could be administered with safety to children as a vermifuge. He goes on in his forthright way to asset its healing powers: "The juice is used with oil of roses for the same causes [crick of the neck], or for blastings by lightning and burnings by gunpowder . . . to allay the heat in all other sores or hurts." He also recommends it as a cure for a ruptured navel in infants. Seed sown early in the year produces a good succulent crop, though it requires more water than many other herbs. A damp border, some shade, or the edge of a pool, all make happy homes for this annual plant.

PYRETHRUM

Pyrethrum coccineum
COMPOSITAE

The name pyrethrum comes from the Greek *pyr*, "fire," no doubt because some of the genus were used medicinally to allay fevers, notably *P. parthenium*, now known as *Chrysanthemum parthenium*, or feverfew (*q.v.*). In the decorative herb garden *P. roseum*, a native of Persia and the Caucasus, and its numerous hybrid forms and cultivars can be added to give color in May, when the daisy-like flowers of both single and double forms appear in a wide range of color.

The insecticide "pyrethrum" is derived from the flowerheads of *Chrysanthemum cinerariifolium*. The main centre of commercial cultivation is Kenya. Pyrethrum formulations are valued for their harmlessness to man and domestic animals; food crops sprayed with this type of insecticide can be harvested, washed, and used with impunity within a day or two.

RHUBARB

Rheum officinalis
POLYGONACEAE

Medicinal rhubarb is one of the oldest plants of cultivation and was described in the Chinese herbal *Pen-King* (believed to date from 2700 B.C.), but it does not appear to have found its way into Western Europe until very much later. Dioscorides knew of it in the first century as a commodity and said "it grows in places beyond the Bospherus from whence also it is brought"; its use probably became known to the Greek and Romans around the third century B.C. Considered to be a native of Tibet and known to successive generations of Europeans as a commodity that came from the East, its place in monastic gardens was taken by one of the docks then called monk's rhubarb, *Rumex alpinus*, which the cultivators of the Middle Ages believed to be rhubarb. Gerard, at the turn of the sixteenth century, grew a rhubarb in his garden, and he called in *Rhababarum monachorum* (again monk's rhubarb), indicating it to be an inhabitant of the monastic garden. However, the root of the true official plant, crossing the vast areas of Russia, became a valuable article of commerce after the trade negotiations with China in 1653 were completed; by 1704, the rhubarb trade became the monopoly of the Russian Government—hence "Russian" or "Crown" rhubarb. Up to that time, it had been supplied as "East Indian" rhubarb, routed via Alexandria. The Arabs had adulterated the roots, and so the Russian source began to provide the superior commodity, selling in Europe in the sixteenth century for ten times the price of cinnamon and four times that of saffron.

Culpeper may have known of the culinary rhubarb of our gardens, for he describes three plants: patience or monk's rhubarb (probably *Rumex alpinus*), great round-leaved dock or bastard rhubarb, and rhubarb or rapentick—though with some confusion! The latter is most likely to have been the present-day *Rheum rhaponticum*. It is generally accepted that this culinary rhubarb, known to Americans as pie plant or tart rhubarb, has only been used in Western Europe in comparatively modern times.

Rhubarb was known in the botanic garden at Padua in 1612 and grown in other botanic centres in Europe, probably as *Rhaponticum verum* or *Rhaponticum thracicium*. When Khan visited the Chelsea Physic Garden in 1728, he recorded that "Mr. Miller told me that in a place where *Rhababarum verum* had stood for ten years he has this season had it moved from there to another place. . . ." This plant is likely to have been the one the apothecaries used, for rhubarb was a commodity of their trade in fairly common usage by the seventeenth century. Several seeds were obtained from the botanic garden at Venice by Dr. Matthew Lister, physician to Charles I, who gave them to John Parkinson, and it is believed that the first plants of what is now *Rheum rhaponticum* flourished in his garden.

Rheum palmatum made an exciting entry into western cultivation, for the Chinese had traded only the dried roots and kept the seed to themselves. In the middle of the eighteenth century, Dr. Mouncey, who was the chief physician to the court of the Tzar of Russia, and brother-in-law to Sir Alexander Dick, President of the Royal College of Physicians, Edinburgh, Scotland, was persuaded by the Edinburgh contingent to attempt to smuggle a box of seed out of China. With the full support of the Tzar and the help of the Russian Medical Service in Asia, seed arrived at the Royal Botanical Garden, St. Petersburg. When Dr. Mouncey retired to Edinburgh, in 1762, he brought the seed to Scotland. It was distributed to influential landowners and members of the Royal College of Physicians at Edinburgh. The Royal Society of Arts awarded a medal to Dr. Mouncey for his services; and as a source of seed was now available, the Society encouraged the cultivation of this plant by offering further awards. One of the first recipients was Sir Alexander Dick himself and, remarkably, awards were made to an apothecary, William Hayward of Bodicote (a village just south of Banbury in Oxfordshire, England)—a silver medal in 1789 and a gold in 1794. John Ball of Williton, Somerset, England, received three gold medals from the Royal Society for the cultivation of the same plant.

The true official rhubarb, *Rheum officinalis,* was not cultivated in Europe until nearly a century later. It was then introduced into France as the true Tibetan rhubarb. Monsieur Dabry, the French consul at Hankow, obtained plants from some French missionaries and despatched them to Monsieur Soubeiran, secretary at the Société d'Acclimatation in Paris. For some years, plants of this species were cultivated at the physic garden of the Faculty of Medicine in Paris, from which plants were distributed to various centers in Europe, including the Royal Botanic Garden at Kew (where they flowered first in 1873) and to Mr. Hanbury's garden at Clapham, London. It seems that Hanbury sent crowns to Mr. Usher (see page 213) who cultivated it for medicinal use, and reported that three years after planting, the crowns showed no tendency to produce stems but had increased in bulk, weighing about thirteen pounds.

The root of the official plant is one of the constituents of the famous Gregory's Powder, which is composed of two parts rhubarb, six parts magnesia, and one part ginger; the latter averts colic, which the rhubarb alone is apt to cause. Used mainly as a purgative and as a stimulant to the digestive tract, acting upon the liver in the production of bile, it is especially useful for clearing the system after an unsuitable diet. It was also used as an old-fashioned remedy to persuade infants to be weaned, because it made the mother's milk slightly bitter.

Cultivation of the official plant is similar to that of the culinary sort. The crowns are left for some years before being lifted; the roots are then washed, peeled, and dried. Other more decorative forms may be introduced into the herb garden, *R. alexandrea* being the most elusive of flower, but the pale yellow bracts of the flowering spike are worth waiting for. *R. palmatum* produces red flowers on six-feet-high cylindrical stems and decorative foliage. Its attractively jagged, deep-indented leaves are even better in the form *tanguiticum*.

ROSE

Rosa gallica officinalis
ROSACEAE

It is debatable if many forms of rose were grown in private gardens before Elizabethan days; Gerard listed only fourteen kinds, and as a collector of plants, he must have been familiar with the genus. Prior to Gerard's lifetime, roses had been used for strewing and are certainly depicted in numerous illustrations of medieval gardens, obviously included for their astonishing beauty and perfume. Parkinson, a few years later, had added ten more kinds to Gerard's list, and as both men were connoisseurs of plants, one can conclude with certainty that far fewer roses were known generally in the Europe of the day.

Of rose water, which used to be prepared by various tedious distillation processes, Culpeper says: "Red rose water is well known, and of a similar use on all occasions, and better than damask rose water; being cooling and cordial, refreshing, quickening the weak and faint spirits, used either in meats or broths, to wash the temples, to smell at the nose, or to smell the sweet vapours out of a perfume pot, or cast into a hot fire shovel."

In the thirteenth century the town of Provins, about seventy-five kilometers south east of Paris, became the center of rose-growing for the production of petals. The industry prospered, reaching its height in the seventeenth century, when perfumes, conserves, confections, and powders were produced in profusion. The trade had begun with the discovery that a certain variety of the "red rose" had the miraculous property of retaining its perfume upon drying, and even when reduced to a powder.

Whether it was simply that well-directed work resulted in a flourishing industry—a virtual monopoly, with the main street of Provins famous for its apothecaries' establishments by 1600—or whether the rose enjoyed the environment there and flourished well under cultivation, is not

opposite Juniper berries

known, but the variety of rose used became known as the Apothecary's rose, *Rosa gallica officinalis*. Graham Thomas records in his book *The Old Shrub Roses* that the records of the town of Provins show "that in 1310 the town was able to offer presents of conserves and dried Roses to the Archbishop of Sens on his solemn entry, to Charles VII and Joan of Arc in 1429, to Henry II in 1556, to Louis XV in 1725, and to the Emperor Napoleon I in 1814." By the middle of the nineteenth century, France had exported 36,000 kilos of Provins rose petals to America.

Since the seventeenth century, this rose has had various names in England, but it is most authoritatively referred to as the red damask rose, probably because it was believed, quite rightly, to have originated in Damascus. The true red apothecary's rose also reached Europe from Damascus—believed to have been introduced by Thibaut IV, King of Navarre in the thirteenth century, and to have provided the very beginning of the great rose perfumery and confection industry which was to flourish for the following six centuries. France did not have the entire monopoly of this trade; it was carried on elsewhere to a lesser extent, although interesting records do exist.

In England, the main cultivation of the rose for cosmetic purposes (such as the production of rose water) was in the hands of the Potter and Moore concern of Mitcham, Surrey, though rosaries or rose gardens are known to have existed in London in the early seventeenth century, very probably for the production of dried rose petals. One such garden was formed near Tottenham Marsh around 1615–1618, on land that was in the possession of George Chapman and his wife Susan as "customerie tenants." The holding was known as Asplins, "with a Barne Stable Cowhouse garden and backside, to the same belonging and also one Crofte of land called Hencrofts now converted into a Garden of Roses." Tenants of adjoining land owned the Little Fielde "with a small garden of roses at the east end thereof" and "one Close of pasture with a little Garden of Roses at ye west end thereof called ye long fielde adjoining to ye demeasne on the lands called Hardings on the northe part, the said Marsh Lane on the east, a parcell of Mockings farme called great field on the south."

That roses were not only known to the Romans but used by them as perfume comes as no surprise; among the products they made from the rose were *hedysmata,* a solid unguent, *stymmata,* a liquid perfume; and *diapasmata,* a powdered perfume.

Attar of rose came from the East, and in the sixteenth century, when the first attempts to make medicines palatable were undertaken, among the primary substances to be employed was oil of rose. It was included in the *Pharmacopoeia Collegii Regalis Londinium Medicorum* of 1720, and the 1746 edition insists that *Rosa Damascenarum* be used, a practice perpetuated in the London Pharmacopoeia to the present day.

The rose has not only been used to make medicine more pleasant: Its virtues are many and varied. In the Balkans, its purgative properties are recognized; in central Europe it is known for its carminative effect; and an established herbal practice is the use of rose petals and rose hips in the treatment of pulmonary disorders. Throughout the ages, red roses have always been in demand both for cosmetics and medicine, but white rose petals, for some unaccountable reason, seem to be preferred for the preparation of an eyewash.

Rose hips are the fruits of the wild rose, *Rosa canina,* its many forms difficult to distinguish, and to a lesser extent of the sweetbriar *R. rubiginosa.* Rose hip syrup, which is commercially produced, has a high vitamin C content; the hips used with their seeds are diuretic.

To make a tea from rose hips, they should preferably be gathered after the first frost has touched them, when they will be slightly soft to the touch. If they must be collected earlier, choose those that are fully mature, plump, and a good color. They should be crushed with a pestle or heavy rolling pin or ground in a domestic grinder. Do not bring rose hips into con-

tact with any metal except stainless steel, for they will lose their color and the precious store of vitamin C will be depleted. The tea is made by soaking 4 tablespoonfuls of the crushed hips in 5 pints of water for 24 hours. Then simmer gently for half an hour, but do not boil. Strain and store the liquid in covered earthenware jars or darkened bottles. When required for use, boil the quantity needed, adding dried rose hips and discarding them before drinking. Sweeten with honey.

ROSEMARY

Rosmarinus officinalis
LABIATAE

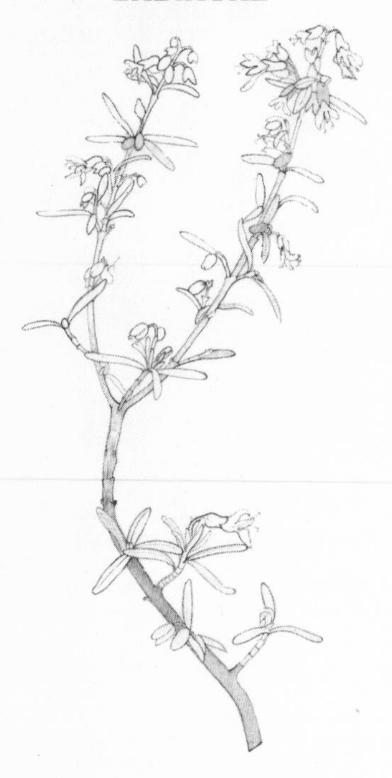

Rosemary, symbol of fidelity and remembrance, is a common enough plant of the Mediterranean coastland, where it flourishes. Grazing animals avoid it because of the pungency of its leaves, but it is beloved of bees. Legend and folklore embellish this plant's past probably more than any other's; and its aromatic and medicinal uses are both of ancient repute. Greek scholars wore garlands fashioned from rosemary to stimulate their brains and aid memory. This gave rise to its old Latin name of *Coronarium*. Shakespeare's reference in *Hamlet* derives from this ancient belief:

> There's Rosemary, that's for
> Remembrance.

A native of the sea-blown cliffs of Greece, Italy, France, and Spain, its misty blue flowers account for the names "rose of the sea" or "sea mist." Its legendary origin is in the steep, barren cliffs of Sicily. When the Evil Woman of Etna cast jealous spells over the island, destroying love and peace and causing mandrake, henbane, and belladonna to grow, fixing their roots so firmly into the ground that only evil could spring from the land, the people despaired, and the surrounding sea grew turbulent in anger. So great was the Woman of Etna's power, that she quelled the ocean's rage, but as the last wave crashed upon the cliffs, a maiden was drawn back into the swirling waters crying "Remember, remember." With these words, where her fingers grappled helplessly with the wet rocks, a beautiful plant burst forth—the rosemary. Another of the numerous legends, calling it "dew of the sea," records that it never exceeds man in height, never exceeds Christ's thirty-three years in age, and always has to lift its eyes to man. This is said to account for its uplifting and tonic effect.

Reputed to have been brought to England before the Norman Conquest, and no doubt reintroduced about the sixteenth century, the cultivated forms known in Britain and northern Europe are inferior in medicinal quality (according to a French authority) to the wild forms found in the *Midi*. The famous Hungary water, first used to cure Elizabeth, Queen of Hungary, of dropsy, was rosemary wine, or spirit of rosemary, as we make it today: dried leaves soaked in white wine, allowed to draw for a week, and then filtered into bottles. Culpeper recorded that the decoction in wine removes "cold distillations of rheums in the eyes and other cold diseases of the head and brain as giddiness or swimmings, drowsiness or dullness of the mind and senses. . . ." In the first century Dioscorides and Galen knew of its value.

Oil of rosemary, now used in hair tonics, can be made by simply soaking tops and leaves in a good vegetable oil for a week in the sun, to help to draw the essential oils, and then filtering off the liquid; but Culpeper gives an engaging recipe made by "insolation"—extracting the oil from the flowers. Rosemary has been highly valued for centuries for its splendidly perfumed oil, which the plant gives generously. There is no need to crush the leaves; just brushing the hand over the shoots will cause the scent to cling to the skin. It is mainly grown commercially in the district of Nîmes in Provence and in Spain, but it is no longer cultivated on a large scale in Britain.

The French believe that, while southern climes produce a rosemary superior in medicinal qualities, plants cultivated in the north provide a better condiment. To use a sprig of rosemary in the cooking of meat is an old custom; and it was well-known as a garnish for the boar's head at Christmas, which we read of as decorated with "Baies and Rosemaries." Its use generally in the preparation of meat dishes has gained great favor in the last decade.

Rosemary was also introduced into garlands decorating the halls for Christmas festivities. The words of the old carol remind us: "The Bore's Head in hande bring I with garlands gay of rosemarie."

In Europe, rosemary is universally the herb of remembrance, used for this reason in various ways at both weddings and funerals. The old *Chanson de Malbouk* says: *"A l'entour de sa tombe romarin l'on planta"* and there, as in some northern localities until the early years of this century, a sprig was placed in the folded hands of the corpse, since rosemary is the longest-lasting sweet-smelling evergreen. Its use as a herb of remembrance has recently been revived, and it is sold in Britain on November 11th when the dead of two World Wars are commemorated.

As a love token, its powers of recollecting happy moments are symbolized in wedding bouquets; and in Victorian days a gilded sprig was carried in bridesmaids' bouquets. It is the rosemary which is addressed by the soldier in a Polish song telling of his secret love and his hopes that his sweetheart will reciprocate his feelings: *"O mój Rosmarynie rozwijaj sie"* (Oh, my Rosemary, flourish!).

Many more qualities are attributed to this plant, which is also an appealing garden decoration. The hoary gray of its flowers may sometimes appear almost lilac-blue, probably indicative of the soil-type but reminiscent of the favorite legend about the rosemary: when the Holy Mother was escaping with the baby Jesus, she rested near a bush and threw her cloak over it, and ever since the rosemary, which until that time had white flowers, has borne flowers of blue to match her cloak. The Spanish name *romero,* pilgrim's plant, is said to derive from this legend. A fourteenth-century manuscript says:

The herbe is callit Rosmaryn
of vertu that is good and fyne
But alle the vertues tell I ne cane
Ne I trowe no erthely man.

In the garden, select a sunny spot for the rosemary if it is to thrive, and let it show off its blue flowers by not crowding it, as sometimes it adopts a relaxed habit. There is a more upright form of 'Miss Jessup,' introduced by A. E. Bowles, which displays a more golden-green foliage and pale blue flowers but is still very strongly aromatic. Not quite as hardy, 'Miss Jessup' tends to show her dislike of biting cold winds by rusting, but it normally recovers by May when the flowers come on the previous year's wood. In North America, rosemary is not hardy in areas where the ground freezes deeply in winter and must be taken in for shelter.

There is a white-flowered form of *R. officinalis, 'Albus',* usually not quite as robust, but misty in appearance, almost as if it were seen at a distance of many centuries. From Corsica and Sicily, where the rosemary supposedly originated, the distinctive form 'Benenden Blue,' with bright blue flowers, was introduced some forty years ago. One sometimes sees 'Tuscan Blue,' another bright-flowered form. As an informal hedge, the evergreen rosemary is a constant delight, its only drawback being its loose-limbed habit; but because of this, it can have a remarkably decorative effect when scaling steep banks.

Propagation is from cuttings taken, in July, of the nonflowering shoots of the current year's growth. A few cuttings struck in a pot or window box in sandy compost or a no-soil cutting compost will provide sprigs in the kitchen throughout the winter. Rooted cuttings can be planted out into their permanent quarters the following spring.

RUE

Ruta graveolens
RUTACEAE

Speak not—whisper not;
Here bloweth thyme and bergamot
Softly on the evening hour,
Secret herbs their spices shower
Dark-spiked rosemary and myrrh,
Lean stalked, purple lavender;
Hides within the bosom, too,
All her sorrows, bitter rue

WALTER DE LA MARE
from *The Sunken Garden*

A hardy evergreen perennial from the Mediterranean regions, the rue was almost certainly introduced into Britain by the Romans, although it was not much grown before the fourteenth century. It may have been reintroduced then and has since been cultivated as a garden plant, for it does not appear in the wild state. Give it a dry situation and it will flourish happily, probably not making showy new growth too readily, but thus ensuring its winter survival. The deeply cut foliage has a fernlike quality best observed in the form 'Jackmans Blue,' where the blue-green of the leaf is emphasized. The yellow flowers are insignificant but are used in an eye lotion. Shrubby in growth but low in stature, it reaches about three feet in height and benefits from close pruning in April to provide good leafy shoots. Plants of *Rutaceae* may not be imported into the United States (as a preventive measure against a disease of citrus trees), but seed is available.

Rue is so closely linked with the treatment of the eyes that the Romans seemed to believe in its powers to bestow second sight; however, it is as a preserver and restorer of sight that it is best known. Milton says:

Then purged with Euphrasy and Rue
The visual nerve, for he had much to see

Euphrasy or euphrasia is the common eyebright, long eaten as a source of vitamin A, to keep the eyes in good condition and ward off night-blindness. Craftsmen who depended upon their sight, engravers, painters, and wood-carvers, used rue regularly as a draught, Pliny tells us, to preserve their eyesight and relieve eyestrain. In present-day herbalism, it is used in the treatment of eye strain, when the flexor tendons have been overworked. A leaf chewed is reputed to relieve the headache over the brow that results from eyestrain.

When John Evelyn wrote his *Discourse on Sallets* in 1699, which he addressed to his patron, the Right Honourable John, Lord Somers of Evesham, he says that rue and coriander were among the sallet herbs not in favor for salads, but that "Galen was accustomed to eat [it] raw and by itself with eyl, and salt . . . of great vertue against infection. Pliny, I remember reports it to be of such effect for the preservation of sight that painters of his time, us'd to devour a great quantity of it. And it is still by the Italians frequently mingled in their sallets." More recently its action, through its essential principle rutin, has been recognized as probably effective in the treatment of abnormal blood pressure. A tisane can be made of fresh leaves, but it must be swamped with some sweetener, such as licorice or molasses, to mask the bitterness. The leaves used to be given to poultry to relieve croup. Medicinally it is regarded as a stimulant and antispasmodic; Turner refers to its effects when eaten: "It quickeneth the sight, stirs up the spirits and sharpeneth the wit." Rue was regarded an effective antipestilential, between the fifteenth and the eighteenth centuries. It was one of the ingredients of the Vinegar of the Four Thieves, a potent concoction which was supposed to have protected the thieves who invented it from the plague, enabling them to enter and rob plague-infested households.

In July 1760, a rumor in the City of London that the plague had broken out at St Thomas's Hospital sent the price of rue and wormwood rocketing in Covent Garden Market: the following day the price had risen by 40 percent! The governing body of the hospital published in public journals a denial of the outbreak. The signatures include four physicians, three surgeons, and "George Whitfield, apothecary to the said hospital." Rue was strewn against pestilence in many public places, traditionally, in the law courts against jail fever; for this reason it is a constituent of the nosegay carried by judges in the law courts. Its claim to inclusion in these traditional collections of herbs was by no means its sweet smell. Its aroma is unpleasant, to put it mildly, and is variously described as musty, stale, and mousey. Unexpectedly, this decorative sub-shrub, so garden-worthy and related to the glamorous myrrh and the sweet-flowered citrus trees, is dull in every way except for its beautiful foliage.

Traditionally, it is the herb given to Ulysses by Mercury to overcome the charms of Circe, as an antidote for her potion and a preserver of chastity. This may be why it became known as the herb of grace. The name "rue," from the Latin *ruta,* has entered our language via Old French and has come to mean "regret" or "repent": hence the vernacular name "herb of repentance." The use of a bunch of rue stems to sprinkle holy water in preparation for High Mass also emphasizes the association of rue with repentance.

SAFFRON

Crocus sativus
IRIDACEAE

A bulbous plant, the true saffron crocus was a product of the ancient world, long cultivated in Persia and Kashmir and supposedly introduced into China at the time of the Mongol invasion. It was known to the Greeks and Romans—Homer and Hippocrates refer to it. There are records of its cultivation by the Arabs in Spain in A.D. 961, and a tenth-century English leech book includes it as a medicinal plant. It would appear that it fell out of cultivation in Europe and was reintroduced at the time of the Crusades. An ingredient of many ancient medicines which seem to have been palliatives for an astonishingly wide variety of ailments, saffron was also largely employed in the culinary arts to provide both flavor and color.

Saffron was highly prized and is highly concentrated—one grain of saffron is made up of the dried stigmas of nine flowers—and it is not surprising that the charlatans of bygone days sought to adulterate saffron for financial gain. Legislation against this practice led to one Johst Findeker being burned, together with his adulterated saffron, in the marketplace at Nuremberg in 1444; and twelve years later, two men and a woman were buried alive, convicted of the same crime. These penalties were pronounced under legislation controlled by "Saffron Inspectors."

In the Middle Ages, not only were the medicinal powers of saffron renowned, but it furnished an effective substitute for gold in illuminated manuscripts, burnished upon tinfoil. Its main use in England has been to color confectionery, and it is still used for that purpose, notably in Cornwall. However, with the increasing interest in international cooking during the past twenty-five years, the use of saffron as a coloring agent for rice in *paellas* and similar dishes has increased. Pure cake saffron is made from the dried stigmas of *Crocus sativus,* taken from the flowers in September and October in the early morning as the blooms open and laid on paper in a layer some two or three inches in depth. A cloth, board, and weight are laid on top, and heat is applied to make the saffron sweat. The "cake" thus formed should be brittle. Pliny says: "If a man lay his hands upon it he shall hear it crack as if it were brittle and ready to burst." This product is cake saffron, as opposed to the dried stigmas which are known as hay saffron.

Many centuries ago, and at vast expense, the streets of Rome were sprinkled with saffron for Nero's entry into the city. As a token of honor and high birth, the golden dye imparted by saffron was used for royal robes; and in ancient Ireland the "lein-croich" or saffron-dyed shirt was worn as recently as the seventeenth century by individuals of high Celtic rank. Saffron Walden in Essex, England, takes its name from the area where the plants were extensively cultivated commercially; and one would like to believe the romantic legend that a corm was smuggled into England by a pilgrim who had hollowed out the head of his palmer's staff for the purpose, and that he did this "with venture of his life." Whether the story is true or false, the arms of Saffron Walden bear three crocus flowers, and the cultivation of saffron was carried on there from the reign of Edward III until its gradual decline in the middle of the eighteenth century. English saffron was considered to be of the best quality in the world (in spite of the English climate and the plants' need for sunshine!); old English herbals frequently refer to the merriment that follows a dose of saffron, Tournefort even reporting a death from laughter resulting from the effect. Supplies are now imported. The autumn crocus, whose flowers bloom alone with the leaves following in the spring, is sometimes referred to as meadow saffron, but it is not the species from which the valuable product comes.

SAGE

Salvia officinalis
LABIATAE

From ancient times the sage has been associated with longevity and strength; its healing and fortifying properties were highly esteemed by ancient physicians. An Arabian proverb runs: "How can a man die who has sage in his garden?" Gerard notes it as a herb of the brain and memory, and it has been used since ancient times as a shield against diminution of the senses and to retard the processes of declining faculties and failing memory. Used by the apothecary and cook alike, it is remarkable how closely the expected pungent dry aroma matches the appearance of the leaves. There are no problems about drying sage leaves; whole shoots retain their shape, color, and pungency. Especially valuable as a digestive, sage is not only used widely in countries where oil is commonly employed in the preparation of food, but also in conjunction with pork or venison and other rich meats. As an ingredient of sage and onion stuffing for poultry and game, in *bouquet garni,* gravies, and sauces, its effect is to counteract the richness of the whole dish. A sage leaf added to a savory flan made of, say, eggs, onions, and cheese, gives a warm flavor; and leaves added to beers in brewing provide delicious herb beer.

Sage tea has been popular in many countries of Europe; and the Chinese preferred it to their own tea: At one period they carried on a barter trade with Dutch merchants, exchanging as much as three times the weight of their own tea for the sage. Sage tea can be made simply by pouring 1 pint boiling water on to 1 ounce of the dried leaves; but the old-fashioned way of making it is more elaborate, resulting in a pleasant drink that is cooling for feverish conditions and acts as a blood purifier. To $\frac{1}{2}$ ounce dried sage leaves, add the juice of a lemon, or $\frac{1}{4}$ ounce grated lemon rind, and a spoonful of honey. Pour over this a quart of boiling water, and allow it to stand for half an hour before straining for use. The Jamaicans make this cooling drink, using lime instead of lemon, as a treatment against the delirium of fevers. In France, a maceration of sage leaves and port is given "*aux femmes qui vont prochainement accoucher.*"

As a flavoring agent, it is still commonly used in the preparation of Derby sage cheese. The whole cheese takes on a green marbled appearance, and the tang of sage tempers the richness of the cheese. As a deodorizer or air purifier, the leaves may be "burned" in a scoop or chestnut roaster, and will dispel quite strong cooking smells and domestic animal odors or freshen the sick room. Further, sage has for a long time been used as a tooth powder, not only to cleanse but to whiten stained teeth; quite recently, it has been used after smoking or after drinking red wines to remove stains.

The name *Salvia* is from the Latin *salveo*, "I am well," a reassertion of the health-giving qualities; and the colloquial corruption of the name became *sange* in old French and *sauge* in Old English. A shrubby plant, native of thin-soiled slopes of the sunny Mediterranean regions of southern Europe, sage shows some preference for chalky soils and is tolerant of drought. An evergreen, its flowers vary from pink to mauve and white; in common with most other herbs, the essential oils and properties are strongest just prior to flowering. The broad-leaved form or English sage does not flower in Britain and is superior in flavor and quality to other sages, since all its energies are directed towards the foliage; it is by far the best plant to cultivate for culinary purposes.

All the sages tend to look very weary of life in the garden after four or five years; it is best to replace them either by seed, for the narrow-leafed form, or by cuttings taken in summer, for the broad-leaved or colored-leaved kind. The red-leaved sage, *S. officinalis 'Purpurascens,'* has dark purple leaves suffused with a bloom like a Victoria plum. It can be useful as a bedding plant and has the great advantage of taking happily to clipping. It is not as hardy as *S. officinalis.* A variegated form, probably the one which Gerard called "painted sage" is *'Tricolor.'* The fresh growth is splashed with green, carmine, and cream. The variegation is forever changing, both from season to season and from plant to plant.

SAMPHIRE, ROCK

Crithmum maritimum
UMBELLIFERAE

Samphire is a maritime plant native to the British coastal areas from Ayr to Cornwall and eastward to Kent and Suffolk. It likes sandy gravel or shale-like rock where the drainage is sharp. It is akin to fennel, a resemblance Gerard noted in his description: "It has a stalk divided into many small spraies or sprigs on the top where of grow spoky tufts of white floures, like tufts of Fennl." Culpeper also noted the similarity, describing how after the white flowers "come large seed bigger than fennel seed yet somewhat like it." Culpeper assigned it to Jupiter and said it "was in former times . . . used more than now it is; the more is the pity . . . If people would have sauce to their meat, they may well take some for profit as well as for pleasure."

Rich in iodine, and washed by the sea, samphire can be eaten as a pickle or vegetable. The root is white and long; the leaves, which have a pleasant spicy taste, add wholesome nourishment when added to salad. An earlier name for samphire was crest marine, and this was the name used when it was cried in the streets and markets of London. The unwitting, however, were often sold the flavorless golden samphire, *Inula crithmoides,* from the Isle of Sheppey. The true samphire, collected for the London markets mainly from the coast of Kent and Sussex, was referred to by Shakespeare in *King Lear*: "Halfway down hangs one that gathers samphire: dreadful trade."

Like many other maritime species, samphire is a fleshy plant, somewhat shrubby in stature, which helps it survive under the blast of the salt wind and spittle of the sea. The leaves are several times divided, succulent, and tasty. The seed is oblong, like barley, whence its name is derived via the Greek *crithe.* In France it is called *St. Pierre,* and the English "samphire" is a phonetic corruption. Provincial names include "camphire," "crestmarine," "sea fennel" (Culpeper's and Gerard's fault!), "pierce-stone" and "rock samphire" (alluding to its habitat). It may be grown successfully in moist beds or sinks, or even pots in the garden, but needs dressing with barilla.

Kahn describes in great detail (1748) how samphire was gathered from the low-lying banks of the Thames, below Gravesend. "English women pluck this herb at this season [August 3] and pickle it . . . It is well washed in cold vinegar, one stalk and plant after another, that all the dust and dirt that has clung to it might be rinsed off." He continues to describe how it was put into a large crock and covered with vinegar, and after standing for two to four weeks, was boiled up with spices. Alternatively, it was boiled before the steeping with clove pinks, ginger, pepper, mace, and allspice. To prevent mildew from developing on the surface of the liquid in the crock, a "cap" was made thus:

> They then cut a clean linen cloth to the size round and diameter of the jar inside, and then another linen cloth of the same size, hem them round the edges to a round bag, fill it with ground mustard so that it is only as thick as the blade of a knife; then not only sew up the hole through which the mustard was put in, also sew a quilted network of cross lines upon the fact . . . that it might lie even.

The neck of the jar was then covered by a large chamois leather and tied tightly to exclude air. "They are used in the autumn and winter season with steak and other food, in the same way as pickled walnuts or cucumbers."

SAVORY

Satureja spp.
LABIATAE

There are two distinct forms of savory, the winter savory, a perennial (*S. montana*), and summer savory, and annual (*S. hortensis*); the former has a stronger flavor and is more popular for cultivation. Both are deeply aromatic because of the presence of a volatile oil, the main constituent of which is caracol. Savory is used medicinally in an infusion for the relief of some digestive troubles, and the bruised fresh leaf will reduce the effect of wasp stings.

Its action upon the digestive tract may account for its main culinary use, which is as a flavoring, in the form of a condiment, for the less easily digestible foods. Sprinkled on cucumber, turnips, or parsnips, it enhances their own flavor (provided that it is used with restraint, for its effect is strong). If a leaf is boiled in the water with Brussels sprouts or cabbage, the unpleasant cooking smell can be prevented; as a constituent of *Sauerkraut* it will banish the odor and improve the finished flavor.

Summer savory is usually sown out of doors in April. A small sowing is all that is necessary, for the crop is strong-growing. Savory is best used only as a garnish, or in sauces and stuffings, and as a flavoring for beans—as mint is used to flavor the cooking pot for peas. Winter savory requires less work, as the crop can stand for five years before it needs replacing; and two or three crops of leaves a season can be taken from it without detriment to the crown. It forms a shrubby growth and is slow growing.

Savory is a native of Mediterranean regions, and both species had culinary associations in antiquity. The Romans used the chopped leaves to make a savory sauce, as mint sauce is made today; and the palates of olden days no doubt appreciated the hot pungency.

SEAWEEDS

Fucaceae
Laminariaceae
Gigartinalis

There are forty-two families of seaweed in British waters, but only three are of any commercial significance. Their inclusion here is justified by their use in former times as drug plants and as sources of food. Contemporary work on seaweed extractions is highly progressive. The seaweed's link with the Roman occupation of South Wales is probably a genuine one, considering that laver bread is made from an extract of seaweed. The dark brown jelly is produced from *Porphyra umbilicalis* or *laver*, the Latin for "water plant." Its attractive rosy purple color fades quickly to olive green and grows even darker as it dries and becomes brittle. In South Wales and Ireland it is boiled until tender and then floured and fried, or coated in oatmeal and fried. Once picked, washed, and boiled, it produces a brown jelly which is sold on market stalls in the Swansea and Cardiff areas, notably at Neath and Llanelly. It can be warmed, flavored with vinegar or lemon, and served on toast. The plant is cultivated in Japan, on bundles of bamboo shoots dropped off-shore. Once the growth has established itself, the bundles are lifted and maintained in brackish water, and the seaweed is later harvested.

The Romans were probably the first to employ seaweed as a fertilizer for land; since the sixteenth century, it has been used in Scotland as a manure, especially for potato crops, spread over the land in a six-inch deep layer. The difficulty of harvesting it and its bulk are probably the drawbacks which have prevented its being used more extensively. In Guernsey, it is partially composted before use on potato crops, and in Brittany it is collected for use as a top dressing for asparagus beds. It has thus been a known source of organic fertilizer at least from Roman times, though until the end of World War II, it had not been considered economically. Only when other sources of bulky organic fertilizer became difficult to obtain were its virtues reassessed, and it is now on the market in the form of soil conditioners.

Seaweed is the richest known natural source of iodine, a name derived from the Greek for "violet-colored." (Pliny referred to seaweed as a dye plant used in Crete, producing a color so fast that it could never be removed from wool.) Iodine was discovered by accident in 1812 by a French chemist, B. Courtois, while investigating the products of kelp or burnt seaweed; and in 1815, Gay-Lussac proved it to be an element.

Street sellers of the lowlands of Scotland cried "Who'll buy dulse and tang?" and seaweed used to be chewed, prior to the habit of chewing tobacco or gum! Before it was known to contain iodine, and before the therapeutic value of iodine was known, it was used as a "sweetener of the blood" and as a preventive of glandular infections. Its use in medicine from that time on is another story; but during the present century the production of alginates from seaweed has become highly commercialized, and Scottish seaweed is now more widely used in this way than it ever was as an organic fertilizer. Alginates of seaweed origin are used in pharmacy to form emulsions, barrier creams, and hand creams and for thickening toothpastes. They are used in confectionery as emulsifying and binding agents in jellies, cream fillings, and ice cream and in dentistry for impression powders. The modern vinyl wallpapers are coated with alginates of seaweed origin, and in America, carrageenan (an extract of red seaweed of carragheen type) is employed as a stabilizing agent for cocoa in the manufacture of chocolate and milk drinks.

That seaweed can provide a gelatinous and palatable substance has been known for centuries to the Celts, and red Irish moss or carrageen (*Chondrus crispus*), which grows abundantly along rocky coasts of the Atlantic in both Ireland and North America, is coming back into favor with the increasing popularity of health foods.

It can be purchased dried, but when softened in water it emits a sea-fresh odor. A century ago, it could be purchased only from apothecaries' shops, dried and blended; it could be stored in this form for years. Considered as a light and nourishing diet for invalids, it became quite fashionable, and the price rose accordingly. To make a cream-like cold pudding or *blanc mange*, a cupful of dulce or carrageen is softened in water and then boiled. The water is strained off and added to an equal measure of milk. Sugar, cinnamon, nutmeg, or lemon may be added, according to taste. It can be molded and sets as it cools. Apparently the Icelanders used to prepare it in the same way, but mixed in rye flour and served as "cakes" with fish.

There is much scope for research into the curative properties of seaweed; progress is being made in this direction, and the wider uses of seaweed are becoming known in all parts of the world. Generally it has been accepted as a natural source of relief for rheumatism; the hydrolized extract can be added to hot baths. Kelp was the basis of a nostrum known as "Anti-Fat," which was marketed in 1880 as a slimming treatment; and today health farms encourage seaweed baths as a toning device to the entire system and as a remedy for obesity. Japan has led the world for many years in exploiting the seaweed resources of the ocean; but government-sponsored laboratories are in existence now in many countries, and investigation into the pharmaceutical uses and industrial applications of seaweed is continuing with increasing interest. There are factories in Britain, France, Portugal, Spain, Morocco, Norway, Canada, and the United States for the production of alginates from seaweed, and several marine laboratories in such far-flung places as Tasmania, India, and Chile have extended their range of study to include the health-giving properties and commercial value of the various seaweeds of their coasts. To use carrageen—which is readily obtainable from health food shops for therapeutic

benefit—a recipe given in *Gardening Illustrated*, July 1881, cannot be bettered:

> Steep $\frac{1}{4}$ oz. of moss in cold water for a few minutes; then take it out, shaking the water from each sprig, and boil it in a quart of new or unskimmed milk till it attains the consistency of warm jelly. Strain it and sweeten with sugar, honey or eryngo root. Should milk disagree with the stomach, the same portion of water may be used instead.

In *Green Medicine*, Margaret B. Kreig says:

> Since the dawn of history man has attempted to find medicinal uses for the comparatively few marine plants he could obtain. In the most ancient Chinese writings, species of seaweed were prescribed for dropsy, abscesses and cancer. Primitive tribesmen in the South Seas and in America made seaweed extracts to treat skin diseases, stomach disorders and inflammations. The use of seaweed for goiter has been very widespread: Peruvian Indians, high in the Andes, chew on compressed 'goiter sticks'. Among the Irish, Chinese, and Japanese, who today use mineral-rich seaweeds in their diet, goiter and other deficiency diseases are practically unknown. (The iodine used in medicine now comes largely from the nitrate mines of Chile, and brines in the United States and Japan.) The Indians of Sitka, Alaska, make ingenious use of the tube-like stripes of bull kelp as an instrument for treating earache: the thin end is placed in the ear, and the bulb put on a hot, wet stone, thereby allowing steam to enter and soothe the auditory canal.

The Reverend David Landsborough in the preface to his highly respected standard work on seaweeds (*A Popular History of British Sea-Weeds*, 1851) records that seaweed in the Channel Islands was called "vraic," probably a corruption of the French *varec*:

> The seasons for cutting and collecting used to be appointed by law . . . when the Vraicking season has come, if a family be not sufficiently numerous for the work they are joined . . . and though a time of labour it is a season of merriment, the Vraicking cakes made from flour, milk and sugar are plentifully taken of . . . It makes a hot if not cheerful fire, scarcely any other fuel is used in these islands: a little wood, though rarely, is mixed with it, and it is only on feast days and family festivals that a coal fire is lighted in the best parlour.

SELF-HEAL

Prunella vulgaris
LABIATAE

The ubiquitous selfheal, lax in growth but bearing distinctive terminal flower clusters, unlike its relatives is a native plant of North America, Europe, and Asia. Universal in its distribution, it has been dubbed a universal healer and a panacea for numerous ailments. It was Linnaeus who changed its original name of *Brunella* to the softer-sounding *Prunella*, the name originating from the German *die Brüen*, "quinsy," the painful throat complaint. Parkinson records that "This is generally called prunella or brunella from the Germans who call it brunellen because it cureth the disease which they call *die Brüen* (or *die Bräune*) common to soldiers in campe, but especially in garrison, which is an inflammation of the mouth, throat and tongue." Its use in present-day herbalism is not only as a tonic and an astringent but as a gargle made by infusing the fresh herb in May, when it is most potent, with boiling water.

For country workers, self-heal was probably always growing near at hand and was the quickest styptic available. Gerard recommends making a paste or salve by bruising the herb on a plate with a knife. By the Doctrine of Signatures, the corolla being in the form of a sickle or billhook, it was used as a hedgers' styptic, usually growing at his feet, available to staunch his cuts.

"Heart of the earth" seems to be a common name for it on both sides of the Atlantic. In the past, farmers on both continents have believed that where prunella grows on thin soil, it exhausts the substance of the soil. Other vernacular names in England are "hook-heal," "Prince's feather," "herb carpenter" (yarrow bears the same name sometimes, and for the same reason—as a vulnerary), "London bottles," "brunel," "allheal," and "brown wort." In America it sometimes appears as "blue curls," a name shared with another labiate, *Trichostemma dichotamum*.

SOAPWORT

Saponaria officinalis
CARYOPHYLLACEAE

Probably introduced to the British Isles by the Romans, who knew saponaria for its water-softening properties, this plant can be invasive in the garden where it finds congenial conditions. It must be happy to thrive and will then really flourish, creeping along by its rhizomatous roots. Always found near habitation, it has lived up to its name of bouncing Bet on both sides of the Atlantic, because it really does seem to enjoy life and vitality. Children love the foam the leaves make when agitated in water, and the suds that ensure have long been used as a natural detergent; but more recently, as a result of long and patient work, Lady Meade-Fetherstonhaugh has evolved a method of restoring fabrics by utilizing the leaves of saponaria. Her work at Uppark in Hampshire, England, is quite remarkable, and how it came about is described delightfully in her book *Uppark and its People*. Tapestries and priceless fabrics from all over Europe are now sent to England to be restored by the process developed over a generation's work using this "Stygian mass of weeds, red and dripping." Vernacular names, with the exception of "wild sweet William" (which safely slots it into the right natural order), allude to its soap-producing properties: "soapwort," "fuller's herb," "crow soap," "latherwort," and "soaproot."

Some medicinal value of a minor order is indicated by the country name "bruisewort," denoting that the crushed leaves are useful as a decoction for bathing bumps and bruises to disperse congealed blood. Mrs. Grieve in *A Modern Herbal* claims that it was used by apothecaries in the treatment of the stubborn veneral diseases. Culpeper calls it bruisewort or soapwort and after describing its bruise and open wound-healing qualities says "[some people] extol it [as] an absolute cure in the French pox, more than either sarsaparilla, quiaacum or China can do; which, how true it is, I leave others to judge."

SOLOMON'S SEAL

Polygonatum spp.
LILIACEAE

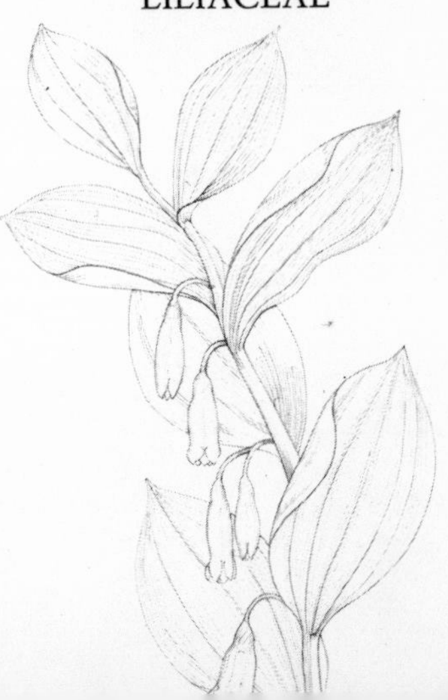

The species indigenous to Britain and native of Europe from the Iberian Peninsula to Finland is *Polygonatum multiflorum*, and this is the species which has been grown in gardens for many generations. The true official plant is *P. officinalis*, a British native of limestone woodland, very local in extent, probably now only to be found in four or five counties, but also in localized areas of Europe and extending to North Africa, the western Himalayas, and China.

It is from the edible roots that a mucilaginous dressing was made for broken bones in days gone by, and Gerard also suggests that the root could be pulverized and used to brew ale which "soddereth and gleweth together the bones in very short space but very strongly, yea, although the bones be but slenderly and unhandsomely placed and wrapped up." This is a reminder of the limitations of orthopaedic skill of the sixteenth and seventeenth centuries, when such plants as Solomon's seal and comfrey were employed as plasters.

The name "polygonatum" was used by Dioscorides and is descriptive of the form of the rhizome, from *poly*, "many," *gonu*, "knee joints." The rhizome is of a zigzag formation—the scars of cut or broken rhizomes bearing impressions like some ancient seal marks, which has been said to account for the plant's vernacular name, though the word "seal" is also a reminder of the plant's use in the past.

A delightful addition to a cooler part of

the herb border, the fresh green leaves are borne along the arching stems before the flowers appear and are exquisite in themselves. By the time the dangling white flower bells are strung beneath them, they have forfeited much of their youthful bloom.

SORREL

Rumex acetosa
POLYGONACEAE

Sorrel is generally distributed over the whole of Europe, temperate Asia, Greenland, and North America as a weed of verges and meadows. Its beauty is often overlooked, but it stands erect and graceful competing with the meadow grasses, the leaves gently clasping the stem at the base. The flowers are like red grain, and the blood red suffusion of the plant when seen against the light is a striking feature. The form cultivated in herb and kitchen gardens is habitually referred to as French sorrel, because the leaves are a little browner than those of the natural plants. Some lists refer to *R. scutatus* as French sorrel or buckler-leaved sorrel, but this species, an introduced plant to both America and Britain, is of flaccid growth, and is not found nearly as prolifically. Margaret Brownlow confirmed that the French sorrel of our gardens is in fact a good and long-cultivated form of *R. acetosa*.

As a salad herb, or sandwich filler, the tangy flavor of the leaves seems to be appreciated more by the French than anyone else. In years gone by, the plant was eaten far more, both fresh and as a cooked green vegetable or in soups, as the French still enjoy it. As green sauce, it had a considerable vogue in the sixteenth and seventeenth centuries. This sauce was prepared by mashing leaves with sugar and adding vinegar in much the same way that we make mint sauce; and it was used as an accompaniment to cold meat. The sharpness of flavor is from its tartaric acid and a potassium salt; the juice of the leaves can have the same action upon milk as rennet, forming a junket. Used widely in the past as a flavoring for cold meats, sausages, and brawns, the acidity of the sorrel helped to tenderize the meat.

Officially the action is diuretic, refrigerant, and antiscorbutic. Taken as an infusion, or as whey, it is a safe herb in the hands of the amateur.

The vernacular names associate it with the cuckoo, which is said to strengthen its voice with the herb: "cuckoo's meat," "cuckoo sorrow" (a corruption of sorrel); other names are "sour sud" (referring to its effect upon milk), "green sauce," and "ver juice."

SPIKENARD

Inula conyza
COMPOSITAE

"Spikenard," along with a descriptive term, is a name applied to several plants. Ploughman's spikenard is a native of calcareous soils of Europe, parts of Asia and of Algeria. The basal leaves form a rosette not unlike that of a young foxglove; but on developing, the branched stems rise somewhat coarsely, but erect, to bear loose heads of dingy yellow flowers in July. A plant of barren soils, it is perhaps odd that it is associated with a ploughman. Gerard says "In English we call it cinnamon roote . . . by reason of the sweete aromaticall savour which this roote containneth and yeldeth." Another vernacular name in Britain is fleawort (not to be confused with the erigerons) because when hung up in a room it drives away fleas and gnats. Spikenard is a Middle English name taken from the Latin *spica nardi,* an aromatic substance employed in ancient times in the preparation of a variety of perfumed salves and oils used in the East. (*See also* American Spikenard.)

ST. JOHN'S WORT

Hypericum spp.
HYPERICACEAE

The St. John's worts are native to the temperate regions of Europe, North Africa, and western Asia and are generally spread over the whole of the North American continent as naturalized plants. As always, the "simple" form is the best to use for herbal practice; and *H. perforatum* is the one usually grown in herb gardens, but for show *H. calycinum* (rose of Sharon) and *H. androsaemum* (tutsan) are often introduced. The name "tutsan" is universally used, coming from the French *toute saine*.

Small bunches of hypericum have been hung under the eaves or in windows of European peasant homes, particularly in the mountainous regions, on the eve of St. John's Day, June 24, in the firm belief that evil spirits will be discouraged and spells averted. The story runs that the dew on the plant that morning will preserve the eyes from disease. This superstition led to the plant being collected and used in combination with oil as a balm for every wound. Leaves boiled in wine were also put to that use; and by the Doctrine of Signatures, the spots, almost transparent and perforated on the leaves, were said to represent wounds. In fact, essential oil is contained within these glands, which probably protects the plant from the ravages of cattle.

Its name in the Middle Ages was *Fuga Daemonum*; and Stowe in his *Survey of London* catalogues *Hypericum perforatum* as a plant used to drive away witches. Like most bitter herbs it stimulates the action of the kidneys and is diuretic. One of its old names is "save," dating from the twelfth century when it was used as an all-healing plant for sword wounds. Its other country names in Britain are "balm of warriors' wounds," "penny John," "touch-and-heal," and "cammock."

SUNFLOWER

Helianthus annuus
COMPOSITAE

The most conspicuous of the horde of sunflowers is the giant annual plant native of North America, from Minnesota, North Dakota, and Idaho to Missouri, Texas, and California; under cultivation, the sunflower produces plants of gigantic dimensions. Even fishermen's tales are outstripped by the stories of some of the traveling botanists of the past concerning the height and vastness of flower size of the sunflower, a plant immortalized by the Inca civilization in their traditional design and in painting far more recently by Van Gogh. It appears that the Indians on the eastern shores of Lake Huron were cultivating this plant about four centuries ago when the early settlers in Canada came upon them; and seeing the one plant provide so much of economic value, the settlers were quick to start cultivating it themselves. Seed must have been sent home; and Gerard, writing in the last decade of the sixteenth century, says: "This great floure is in shape like to the Comomil floure, beset round about with a pale or border of goodly yellow leaves." The disc he describes as "of unshorn velvet or some curious cloath wrought with the needle."

The stalks provided the North American Indians and the early settlers with fibers for rough textiles, the leaves with fodder, the flowers with a yellow dye, and the seeds a valuable source of oil and food. The seed is beloved of swine, poultry, game, and parrots, and it makes good cattle cake. For human consumption the seed can be added to home-baked bread, scattered on salads and breakfast cereals, or nibbled with drinks. In honey sandwiches, they are deliciously nutty; the seed is rich in protein and edible oil. In the lower regions of the Carpathian mountains and in eastern Europe generally, every peasant's cottage has giant sunflowers standing alongside it in summer. Poultry are assured of winter food during the snows, for each flower-head produces up to 2,000 seeds. The people of these rural communities may also believe the old gypsy lore that if sunflowers grow near the wall of your house, dampness will never present any problems.

The Romanies gather the flower buds just before they break, and they boil them in salted water for use as a vegetable, served with butter; Gerard must have known of this practice, for he calls them "exceeding pleasant meate." Sunflower tea, infused from the freshly picked leaves and flowers, acts as a febrifuge and can be used instead of quinine, another gypsy practice.

The name "helianthus" is from the Greek *helios,* "sun," and *anthos,* "flower." A further species, *H. tuberosus,* provides the Jerusalem artichoke of the garden—native to North America and there known as "Canada potato," "earth apple," and "girasole." *Girasole,* the Italian for sunflower, has been corrupted over the years to "Jerusalem," and we know that the English settlers in Virginia grew "rootes of several kindes, Potatoes, Sparagus (strictly not a root), Carrots and Hartichokes." The true or globe artichoke is formed by the unopened heads of *Cynara scolymus,* a native of southern Europe.

Tubers of the Jerusalem artichoke, which were acquired by John Goodyer of Mapledurham in Hampshire, England, were probably among the first to be imported from North America. Goodyer is generally credited with having distributed the plant in England, for one of the plants brought him "a peck of roots." When Gerard's *Herbal* was revised by Johnson, the description of the Jerusalem artichoke and its cultivation was contributed by John Goodyer.

As a garden decoration, the scale of both plants must be considered with some care, for their immense proportions can coarsen the whole garden design and overpower the daintier plants. Sunflowers are also gross feeders, robbing the soil of much plant food material. However, representative helianthus cultivars could be planted in the herb border, especially if the object of a collection is to represent economic plants. The 'Autumn Beauty' range, or the more recent 'Sunburst,' of manageable proportions, add a bold color effect, the flowers ranging from pale yellow to orange and maroon, each zoned with a darker band, and the discs purple-blue to black.

Crosne, *Stachys affinis,* sometimes referred to in older writing, is a vegetable of Chinese origin, harvested and used in winter when there is little else fresh from the garden. It was imported into France and cultivated by M. Pailleux de Crosnes, hence its name. It is rather vaguely described as a cross between the Jerusalem artichoke, *Helianthus tuberosus,* and the globe artichoke, *Cynara scolymus,* and is marketed as Chinese artichoke. The tubers contain starch, and blacken on exposure to air as does the cut surface of a potato. They are formed late in the season and grow in a necklace-like string.

SWEET CICELY

Myrrhis odorata
UMBELLIFERAE

A doubtful British native, this is certainly a European plant, known to the ancient world and by them given the name *Myrrhis.* Strangely, its scent is not a strong one; some find it reminiscent of lovage, but it is supposedly more closely allied to anise, for its real sweetness lies in the sugary taste of its leaves. The foliage is the plant's crowning glory, filmy and lacy, deeply divided, and highlighted with white flecks; the stem holds it elegantly along its whole height. It is topped by umbels of white flowers in early summer, which are succeeded by brownish-black fruits, flavorful and worthy of collection. Sweet Cicely can be introduced into the herb garden as a salad plant or for its good tap root, which may be used as a vegetable. In the southern mountainous regions of Europe, where it produces a better root than in the cooler temperate regions, the roots are eaten with a vinaigrette and are said to "comfort the heart of them that are dull and without courage." Herbal remedies include this plant in treatments for coughs and pleurisy; and the sugary essence of the leaves has been considered, in the past, as an aphrodisiac. The seeds may be used as flavoring; macerated with beeswax, they also make a good household polish for oak floors.

The vernacular names often confuse the sweet Cicely with other umbelliferous plants; and the name of "Roman plant" suggests either some recognition of its introduction by the Romans or that it was of great economic importance to the Roman civilization. The country names are "cow chervil," "smooth Cicely," "sweet fern," "British myrrh," and "shepherd's needle."

TANSY

Tanacetum vulgare
COMPOSITAE

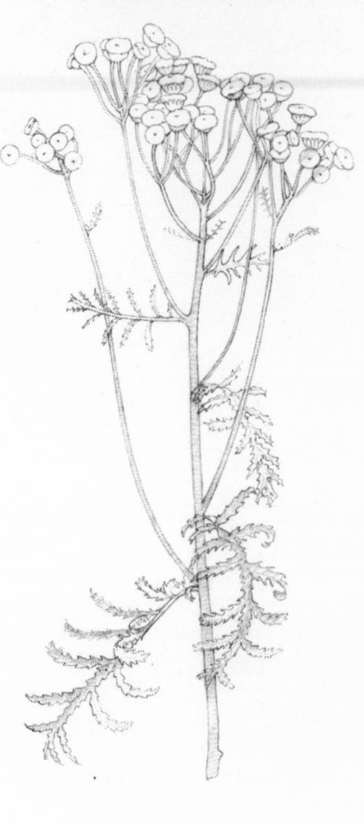

Flourishing best on good garden soil, the tansy is a plant native to the British Isles, Europe, the Caucasus, and on into Siberia; reading from nineteenth-century books, it seems to have been considered a wild plant of river banks. Paxton in his *Horticultural Register* of 1833 describes it as "growing plentifully" on the banks of the river Derwent, and the sandy banks of many other rivers. Anne Pratt, who wrote charmingly but without great authority at the end of the last century, describes it as a plant "of our river-sides, as on those of the Avon about Clifton, but never in such abundance as on the borders of the Rhine where its large masses may be seen plainly while sailing up that noble river." Clapham, Tutin, and Warburg describe it as an inhabitant of roadsides, hedgerows and waste places. It does indeed seem that on moisture-retentive soil the plant marches with even greater energy across the garden, within a season or two of being introduced. This is a plant to include with some reservation, for it will never stay in one place but will travel by means of its spreading stolons which lie close to the soil surface. The origin of the name "tansy" seems obscure, but there is general conjecture that it derives from the Greek *athanatos,* "immortal," or *thanatos,* "death," It was Pliny who named it *Tanacetum,* suggesting that it is impossible to eradicate completely once it has a foothold.

Tansy pudding, formerly eaten in celebration of the festival of Easter, commemorates the bitter herbs which the Israelites used to eat with the paschal lamb. The "pudding" varies from one source to another, sometimes appearing as a bread or dough cake, and at other times as almost a rich mousse of brandy, eggs, cream, and sugar.

The plant has terminal corymbs of hard, yellow flowers typical of their natural order but devoid of ray florets, and so appearing slightly convex like buttons; this explains one of its country names—"buttons" or "butter buttons." Other vernacular names reflect its history—"English cost" proves its close relationship to *Tanacetum balsamita,* costmary or alecost *(q.v.)* an introduced plant. "Giner plant" refers to its strong pungent flavor, but "Joynsons Remedy Cheese" must be a local name given by an apothecary anxious to patent his whey, to which chopped tansy leaves had been added as an anthelmintic.

Tansy tea used to be given to sickly children when fasting and was considered to be diuretic; but its use has been discouraged, and tansy leaves cannot be sold for tea in the United States because they are considered to be of a poisonous nature. As a fomentation, it has been used as a hot application for the reduction of swelling on joints affected by sprains and rheumatism.

Dawn McLeod in *A Book of Herbes* draws attention to tansy, the one plant she was able to include in her guide to each of the four sections of the herb garden at the American Museum in Britain, at Claverton Manor, Bath. The four categories there are culinary, medicinal, fragrant, and dye-plants, and it is curious to note that almost a century previously, Anne Pratt was recording the profusion with which the plant canopied the river banks in that district of England.

TARRAGON

Artemisia dracunculus
COMPOSITAE

An aristocrat of the herb garden, tarragon, like parsley, has survived the centuries on its culinary claims alone. Medical history is devoid of the herb in official use; no mystical virtues are attributed to it nor is legend woven into its history. How proudly it stands on its own merits. There are two forms, the French tarragon (estragon) colloquially known as *herbe au dragon,* growing some three feet in height with

TARRAGON

slender stalks, and the taller Russian tarragon *A. dracumculoides,* hardier but with less flavor. French tarragon is more widely cultivated, and its use in cooking is increasing, but it does not set seed and must be divided frequently, preferably in spring, to prevent deterioration from age. It revels in a dry soil, especially one with ample drainage in autumn, for dampness about its feet at the end of the season may affect its ability to withstand the winter. Protection during severe weather can be afforded by a generous mulch of leaf mould, bracken, or horticultural peat around the crowns of the plants. In short the French tarragon, native of Mediterranean climes, is less adaptable to the damper climate than the Russian tarragon which comes from Siberia. The forms differ in leaf texture, too. Those of the French plant are smooth and dark green, the Russian less glossy and paler in color.

Usually the leaves are used fresh, as something of the unique quality of its flavor escapes on drying. The leaves are taken from midsummer to Michaelmas and used to temper the coolness of salads, adding warmth without overpowering flavor. For tarragon vinegar, the shoots are probably used most, and it is the herb most popularly employed in this way. In the past, vinegars were made of rosemary, barberry, and gilliflower (pinks) in the same manner, that is, by covering leaves with good wine vinegar and allowing it to stand for three days before straining through cloth (today, woven nylon is most suitable); then it must be bottled and tightly corked. The soaked leaves may be retained and used in sauces to be served with fish. Tarragon vinegar is the vinegar used in true tartare sauce.

The names "dragon's herb" and "dragon's mugwort"—for remember the tarragon is an artemisia, a sister to wormwood and absinth—have been given to this herb because of its supposed ability to combat venomous stings.

THISTLE

Silybum marianum
Carduus benedictus
COMPOSITAE

The milk thistle, *Silybum marianum,* is a striking plant, with its deeply jagged, polished leaves painted with trails of creamy white. Very easy of cultivation, it is an introduced plant in Britain, central Europe as far north as Denmark, and in both South and North America. It is a native of the Caucasus and near East. A plant for the front of the border, where its leaves may be admired, the flowering stem should be removed.

St. Benedict's thistle, or Holy thistle, *Carduus benedictus,* has a pronounced wing to the stem, and its main medicinal value is as a tonic. Either a tisane or a vinegar—or even a wine—made from the leaves encourages profuse perspiration and alleviates the congestion of a head cold or helps to allay a fever.

THORN-APPLE

Datura stramonium
SOLANACEAE

The Jamestown weed or Jimson weed makes a contribution to modern medicine, but it has a history of doubtful integrity involving numerous magico-medicinal rituals. The American Indians called it "white man's plant," and it is believed to have arrived on the North American continent with the Jamestown settlers. Europeans, on the other hand, believe it to have been introduced to their continent probably from the Americas and/or Asia. Datura is given as a vernacular name in the East Indies, stemming from the Hindu, *dhatura*; *stromium* is an ancient botanic name for the thorn-apple or medicine. A lethal narcotic alkaloid present in the seeds is indestructible by either boiling or drying, and the entire plant houses poison. It is listed in Part I of the British Poison List. The action is narcotic, producing in extreme cases hallucinatory effects of terrifying intensity, and it is employed by South American Indians to induce stupor and cast out devils. Fading sight, resulting from the effects of the thorn-apple, figures in fable and legend. Its country names are

opposite Greater periwinkle

"devil's apple," "devil's trumpet," and "thorn-apple," because the leathery little fruits resemble hard green apples in førm and bear thorns similar to the Spanish chestnut fruits *(Castanea sativa)*. Gerard received some seed, for he refers to "seeds I received of the Right Honourable Lord Edward Zouch, which he brought from Constantinople."

Occasionally to be found naturalized in waste places in Britain, and exciting much attention on discovery, this datura is one to be wary of. An annual plant, with stiff side stems immediately radiating from it, the contorted convolvulus-like flowers bloom in August and September and are creamy green. It is said to have been used by the priests of Apollo at Delphi to inspire their prophecies, and this practice is to some extent also carried out by South American tribes of the present day who use the same genus for divination. A relative of tobacco *(Nicotiana)*, the dried leaves of the thorn-apple form a constituent of herbal tobacco, especially recommended in the relief of asthmatical conditions.

More decorative species are used in the conservatory or as house plants. *Datura suaveolens*, with white elongated convolvulus-like flowers, is known as "angel's trumpet"; *D. chlorantha*, and its cultivar 'Golden Queen,' is another shrubby species making an arresting conservatory specimen, with yellow double flowers which look like one trumpet inside another.

THYME

Thymus vulgaris (et al.)
LABIATAE

Thymus vulgaris, the common thyme, garden thyme, or black thyme, is of primary importance in the culinary arts, and for this reason the one most commonly cultivated as a pot herb. A constituent of *bouquet garni*, it should always be used in small quantities, otherwise the pungent flavor masks the more delicate effects of other herbs. For centuries it has been used in herb butters, herb vinegars (along with other herbs), salads, soups, butter sauces with fish, and as an addition to potted meats. Distilled, it is common thyme that provides the oil of thyme so effective as an antiseptic in gargles and mouthwashes because of the thymol content. It is a native of Mediterranean regions, always thriving where rosemary and lavender do, and enjoys full sunshine, rewarding it with a strong aroma, especially when crushed. The variegated-leaved form *T.* v Variegatus adds light and shade to a patch of thyme in the garden, as does Aureus, the golden form, though it is less hardy. Layering is a reliable method of propagation for these variegated sorts and should be done in high summer; the rooted layers will then be ready to plant out the following spring. The general habit of the common thymes is to form hummocks about nine inches across.

Another favorite culinary thyme is somewhat smaller than *vulgaris* but is known for its strong lemon scent: *Thymus* X *citriodorus*. It is variously known as German thyme and winter thyme and has rich green evergreen foliage used in herb teas, herb butters, for sandwich and salad flavoring, and in poultry stuffings. Both this species and *T. vulgaris* are quickly propagated by dividing the plants in autumn or spring or from cuttings taken from nonflowering shoots during the late summer and autumn. The form "Silver Queen" is not quite as hardy as the type but is most attractive, displaying a creamy white variegation of the leaf. *T.* X *citriodorus* "Nyewoods" has even more intricate details of variegation on its tiny leaves; the leaves themselves, a pale greenish yellow, bear a green central stripe.

T. herba-barona from Corsica, so called because it was used in ancient times for rubbing over barons of beef before cooking—to impart a distinct caraway flavor, can be grown as a pot plant in the greenhouse or in the kitchen, as it appears not to like northern climates, and damp winters are just too much for it.

Another favorite thyme is *T. serpyllum*, the English or wild thyme, and is the native plant that Shakespeare referred to when he wrote "I know a bank whereon the wild thyme blows." To be found on heaths and in dry grassland and rocky places, its creeping stems that root so readily form a good carpeting effect when introduced into the garden and can be employed to enhance paving, banks, or stonework with excellent results; like other carpeting thymes, when left to itself it makes a reliable ground-cover and can spread over a considerable area. Introduce this species and its numerous forms for ornament and decoration, rather than for culinary use. Their combined tapestry effect at all seasons of the year is a worthy addition to the garden. The somewhat woolly green leaves and stems of *T. drucei* are to be found in the wild state in the British Isles and Europe and are considered to be synonymous with *pseudo-lanuginosus* and *lanuginosus,* though the leaves on close comparison appear somewhat darker. Of the various types of *T. serpyllum* offered by the nurseries, 'Pink Chintz' is probably one of the most popular, with its shell-pink flowers and gray-green leaves. The crimson-flowered 'Coccineum' is not quite so vigorous; 'Albus,' a white-flowered form with light green leaves is late in flowering, 'Russettings' has good deep pink flowers, and 'Annie Hall' displays the distinctive characteristic of holding her leaves small and close together; but all are good thymes for pavement gardens and carpeting effects, and they are tolerant of treading.

The old belief was that thyme was a donor of courage, a source of strength, and even a considered cure for shyness. The name is from the Greek, *thuo*, "I excite," or from *thumos*, "courage." Certainly its effect as a tisane or decoction is to calm the nerves, clear indigestion, and act upon the mucous membranes to clear the head, by the action of its tannins and resins, as well as the volatile oil of thymol The antiseptic properties of thyme are employed in the preparation of surgical gauze and other dressings and as an ingredient of liniments for wound treatment. It is incompatible with iodine. In France, especially, oil of thyme is used in herbal baths as an essence of therapeutic value.

TOBACCO PLANT

Nicotiana tabacum
SOLANACEAE

The tobacco of commerce is *Nicotiana tabacum,* and its numerous varieties and cultivars are grown for their huge leaves which when dried provide "a herb for smoking." Tobacco was first introduced into Europe from America in the 1560s, when seed was sent by Jean Nicot, a French consul in Portugal, to Catherine de Medici; it was not until 1586 that the use of the plant in the practice of smoking began. The seed that arrived in Europe was of *N. rustica,* and Jean Nicot is commemorated in the generic name. It is generally believed that Sir Walter Raleigh and his seamen, together with returning settlers from Virginia, introduced into England the habit of smoking tobacco. Some scepticism accompanied the arrival of the habit, but campaigns against it by church and state alike were gradually over-ruled, and 400 years later the use of tobacco is still a controversial topic. Gerard recorded wondrous hallucinatory results enjoyed by the "Priest and Inchanter of hot countries" after smoking tobacco, but as a botanist he was curious enough about the plant itself.

The ornamental species of nicotiana have long-tubed flowers carried well above the foliage, and most of them are wonderfully fragrant, especially at dusk and during hours of darkness. Nature has equipped them with this powerful scent to ensure fertilization by long-tongued moths.

VALERIAN

Valeriana officinalis
VALERIANACEAE

A native British perennial and lover of dampish soils, valerian has wandered over the whole of central Europe and ribbons the world eastward across temperate Asia, to Japan. The flowering stem attains some three feet in height, with pale pink blossoms carried in a loose head. (It must not be confused with the garden and naturalized plant of cliffs, railway embankments, and old walls, commonly referred to as valerian but which is in fact *Centranthus ruber*.)

The short rhizomatous rootstock is a dull brown in color, but its drab appearance belies its usefulness and potency. Its particular useful property is entirely due to the presence of a volatile oil in the root; when dried, it gives off an offensive odor which explains the names "phu," "phew," or "phu plant." However, if the roots are cut before drying, the odor will be reduced.

As a nervine, a very bitter and foul-smelling tonic is administered in the treatment of hysterical conditions, the volatile oil acting as a sedative and the active principle being valerianic acid. Tastes change with the passage of time, but it seems incredible to read in Turner's *Herbal,* 1568, that the roots were placed among linen and clothes as a perfume. "No broth, pottage or physical weat" was considered of value without it, according to Gerard, and it appears to have been employed in the kitchen mainly in the northern districts of England. The Anglo-Saxons certainly used the ash-like leaves as a salad herb.

The name "valerian" is probably from the Latin *valere,* "to be powerful" or "of well-being," and the relaxing of tension following a dose of the drug suggests that this use was known to the ancient world. Nard was an aromatic balsam used by the ancients, and we believe that the volatile oil of valerian was a constituent. Its use in perfumery together with spices and nectars has persisted through the centuries, and some people find it reminiscent of the sickly scent of heliotrope. Rats adore it, and the old rat-catchers used to carry pieces of the root as bait for vermin. The story runs that the Pied Pipe of Hamelin was no magic musician in reality but lodged pieces of valerian about his person to attract the pestilent rats and led them away in a state of frenzied search.

As a cultivated crop, valerian has been grown in England, mainly in Suffolk and Derbyshire where, in the vicinity of Chesterfield, the "Valerie growers" worked until World War II. Previously, it was grown commercially in northern Europe, in East Germany, and in Holland.

Rhizomes of economic size are obtained by maintaining a dampish rich soil with a plentiful supply of moisture-retentive humus, and by removing the immature flower heads to promote the growth of numerous strong basal leaves and consequently a sturdier root stalk. After the top growth has been cut away in September or October, the roots are lifted, shaken free of soil, washed and dried. Washing is usually carried out on racks by directing strong jets from a hose on to the roots. Cutting the rhizomes facilitates drying and although the smell at this stage is distressingly unpleasant, the dried root is finally less offensive.

In a rich dampish corner of the herb garden a single clump of plants is an attractive addition to a representative drug collection, but the day will soon come when the clump needs dividing, if only for renovation!

VERATRUM

Veratrum viride
LILIACEAE

An interesting plant, quite arresting in appearance, the false hellebore or American white hellebore has dense terminal spikes of green flowers that increase in depth of color with maturity. An unusual resident of the perennial border, it hails from the swamps and wet low-lying meadows of America.

The leaves are pleated, folding towards the base and clasping the stem with parasol-like firmness. It rises in stately splendour up to six feet in a damp, warm environment, while its black roots are narcotic and poisonous. The name from *vere,* "truly," and *ater,* "black," is descriptive of the roots of the whole genus. *Veratrum album,* a

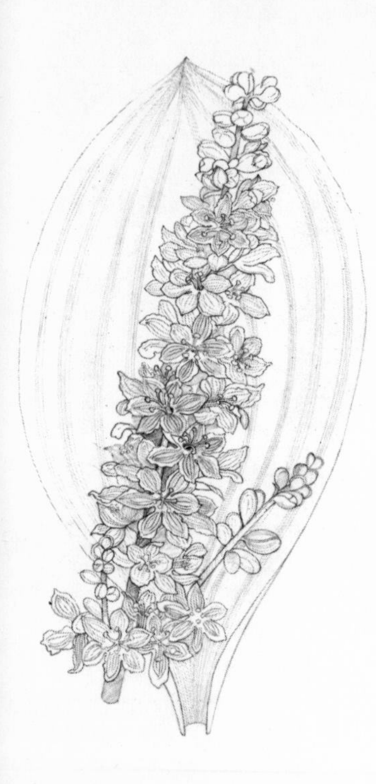

North African relative, has to look up to its American relatives, *V. viride* and *V. californicum,* but it is *viride* that takes pride of place in the herb garden for architectural effect.

In America it is "American poke," "itch-weed" or "green-hellebore." It is said to have been a weapon of sorcerers and in folk medicine was used as a counter-irritant while, as an American Indian potion, veratrum figured in rites held to prove the stamina of Indian youths. As a reducing agent for blood-pressure it is used in treating some toxemias of pregnancy and other conditions, and pharmacological research work is progressing into the further uses to which *V. viride* and the European *V. album* can be put.

Early in the year in America and Europe the leaves burst forth. In the melting snows of the Alps and Tatra Mountains, where it is called *Ciemierzyca Zielona,* the cowherds trample it down and cattle give it a wide berth—its very thrusting arrogance displays its poisonous powers. Leaf by leaf it rises, each neatly folded and pleated as the leaf blades shimmer a blue-green. Homeopathy teaches us that the plant that heals may also poison and such is the dual purpose in Nature of the veratrums or false hellebores.

As border plants they are not averse to some shade but need good deep soil. A group forms a remarkable eye-catcher in the herb border. Propagation is from seed or by division of the roots in spring, when care should be exercised in handling them in spite of the fact that they are at that time of year at their least potent.

VERBENA, LEMON

Lippia citriodora
VERBENACEAE

A deciduous shrub, slender of habit, grown for its lemon-scented leaves, the lemon verbena is the vervain of the pharmacy. From its native Chile it arrived in Europe in the eighteenth century and though little known is a delightfully friendly plant to have about the doorway or balcony. In August it bears filmy spikes of mauve flowers, and unlike many other fragrant plants, the leaves hold their scent best if harvested at this time. Normally the oils are richest in the foliage immediately prior to flowering, but as a plant the lemon verbena in its elegance exhibits its whole being at one time. Use the leaves dried to make sachets for wardrobes, or add them to potpourri.

A refreshing tisane may also be prepared from fresh or dried leaves. It is considered effective for the relief of heartburn and as an antispasmodic; a French herbal stresses that: "Il semble toutefois qu'il ne faille pas accorder un bien grand crédit à ces vertues et que l'usage fréquent de cette infusion soit plutôt à déconseiller." Used sparingly, the chopped leaves may be added to poultry and game stuffings or to impart a lemon flavour to desserts. As a garden plant only its habit of having "given up the ghost" in winter and quite late into the spring can be held against it—the leaves flush rather late and the twigs look too dormant too long, but waiting is always rewarded by the fresh green of the summer foliage. It is during this spring death that pruning should be carried out by removing unwanted or bruised branches and cutting back to good wood to maintain its shape. In the United States it is another of the plants that needs to be taken in for the winter in case the ground freezes.

VERVAIN

Verbena officinalis
VERBENACEAE

And hard by then again the holy
Vervain finds
Which he about his head that hath the
megrim binds.

MICHAEL DRAYTON

"Herb-of-the-cross" or "holy vervain" are country names on both sides of the Atlantic for this somewhat insignificant verbena with pale lilac flowers. The jingle runs:

Hallowed be Thou, Vervain
As thou growest on the ground.

Superstition surrounds it, the Druids supposedly having gathered it only at certain phases of the moon, and as an amulet its powers have been valued in the past. Further, it was closely associated with altar worship and ceremonies by the Romans as *herba sacra* or *herba veneris*; Virgil says in one of his Eclogues:

> Bring running water, bind those altars
> round
> With fillets and with vervain strew
> the ground.

Its association with witchcraft, when vervain and rue were supposedly common ingredients of the cauldron, cannot be verified but it has been employed not only to ward off evil spirits but also bring magical powers to man. If a man would make a small incision in his hand and press a leaf of vervain into it, keys would turn when his hand touched them.

Reputations as love philtres and romantic associations are attached to numberless plants—if one wants to count petals any compositous plant will do, or any fluffy seed head can be pressed into use; but vervain picked by the bride herself on her wedding morning and added to her bouquet was believed to ensure her her husband's faithfulness and eternal love.

A European, local plant, it has emigrated to the North American continent, spreading on both the Atlantic and Pacific coasts, but has fast enjoyed its new found freedom and is generally distributed over waste areas right across the States. It has gained such names as "European vervain" (as opposed to the blue vervain), "simpler's joy," "herb-of-the-cross," "herbine," and "pigeon grass." "Pigeon's meat" is the name by which it is more commonly known in Britain—apparently pigeons are fond of it. Its medicinal properties are slight, though it is dubbed "simpler's joy" in many Victorian books on wild flowers in Britain and was certainly included in early editions of the British Pharmacopoeia—the 1837 edition advised its use, attached to a white satin ribbon as a necklace, effective against evil and as a disinfectant! Old writers have perpetuated its reputation as a charmed plant, and the Victorians seem to have accepted its reputation unquestioningly as a general prophylactic. Of high repute as a hair tonic it was an ingredient of one of the first proprietary hair preparations to be marketed, and is also considered by herbalists to be soothing as an eye wash, notably in scrofulous eye diseases. When Drayton was writing in the second half of the sixteenth century vervain was clearly regarded as offering relief from nervous tension and migraines.

VIOLET

Viola odorata
VIOLACEAE

With conviction, we can say that the sweet violet was a flower well known to the ancient world. Both the Greeks and Romans used it in a variety of ways as a symbol, as an economic plant, as an officinal plant, and as a cosmetic. Grecian ladies are said to have used the dye from the flowers to paint their eyelids. The Greeks called it *Ione,* because Io, a princess dearly beloved of Jupiter, was changed by him into a heifer, as a disguise to protect her from the jealousy of Juno. Jupiter provided violets for her to eat. What more convincing symbol of his constancy and protection could she have wished for? Perhaps this is why the flower has come to be regarded as indicative of constancy and was used, especially in the nineteenth century, to decorate love tokens, porcelain, and treasure boxes. Napoleon is said to have bestowed a nosegay of violets upon Josephine for each wedding anniversary, and when he was banished to Elba, he vowed to return with the violets in the spring. During his exile, the flower was adopted by his supporters as an emblem, its name serving as a password.

Perhaps one of the earliest uses of scented flowers on a patio is described by the younger Pliny. Telling of his new villa on the shores of the Tuscan sea, he says: "the gallery has a double row of windows on both sides . . . and one on each side toward the garden . . . before the gallery lies a terrace perfumed with violets."

The Greek and Romans seem to have

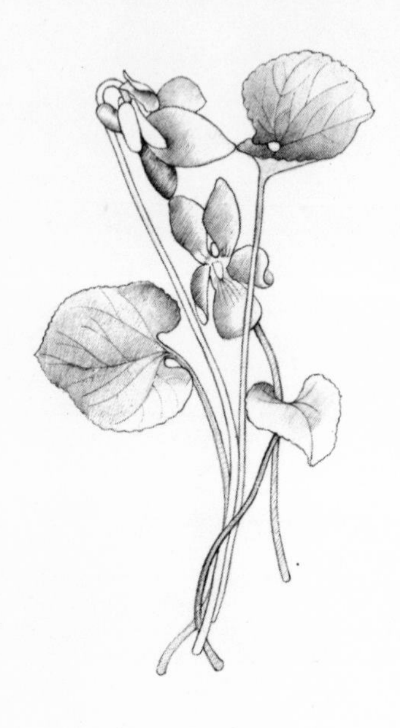

endowed the flower with such a variety of charms that there is little doubt that violets grew or were cultivated in some profusion in those thin Mediterranean soils. Athenians suffering from insomnia drank violet tea (as we would call it today). They took it for cardiac disorders and gout; and the leaves formed poultices and dressings for a variety of ulcers and wounds. Recent editions of the *Encyclopedia Britannica* still refer to the use of violets as a treatment for cancerous pustulations.

Culpeper believed them to be "a fine and pleasing plant of Venus, of a mild nature and in no way hurtful." He then went on to enumerate so many ways in which violets might be employed to relieve symptoms, that one wonders if he should not have left the statement unsupported! Clearly, throughout the last 2,000 years, violets have been employed as dressings for wounds and taken as relief for pulmonary complaints, disorders of the liver, spleen, bladder, as a cure for quinsy, and "the falling sickness" and to "purge the body of choleric humours." Culpeper tempts his readers with a seemingly delicious beverage:

> but the syrup of violets is of most use and of better effect being taken in some convenient liquor; and if a little of the juice or syrup of lemons be put to it, or a few drops of the oil of vitriol, it is made thereby the more powerful to cool the heat, and quench the thirst, and it giveth to the drink a claret-wine colour, and a fine tart relish, pleasing the taste.

Syrup of violets, for which quantities of the plant were cultivated near Stratford-upon-Avon in England, has a chemical property whereby its blue color is rendered red on contact with acids and green on contact with alkalis. Wine was made from violet flowers by the Romans, and, conversely, they wound garlands of the plant around their heads to ward off the effects of intoxication during prolonged drinking feasts.

During Charles II's reign "violet plate" was sold by apothecaries as a laxative, probably compounded from the roots of the plant, which also have a strong emetic action. It was at the time of the restoration that the favorite French "Vyolette" became a recipe to be used in England: Macerated, boiled violet flowers were used to impart color to rice flour which was mixed with warm milk and sweetened with honey or sugar. Sometimes one finds this sweet referred to as "violate paste" and it was largely consumed by "persons of quality" with some enthusiasm because it was supposedly endowed with health-giving properties. The Koran says that "the superiority of the extract of violets above all other extracts is as the superiority (of Mohamet) over the rest of men." And as an emblem of constancy, love and victory, this delightful little plant has survived many centuries.

Shakespeare's belief in the transference of souls into flower form was expressed when he made Laertes wish violets to spring from Ophelia's grave:

> Lay her to earth
> And from her fair and unpolluted flesh
> May violets spring

And again, on the theme of constancy, an old English sonnet says:

> Violet is for faithfulness
> Which in me shall abide
> Hoping likewise that from your heart
> You will not let it hide

But perhaps Tennyson expresses it best:

> From the meadows your walks have left so sweet
> That, whever a March wind sighs,
> He sets the Jewel print of your feet
> In violets blue as your eyes

The violet is still used in confectionery. Crystallized violets have for centuries been imported from France and can still be bought, though they are not too difficult to make at home and with a little patience and practice, reasonably successful results can be achieved. Pick the flower-heads from the stalk, wash them and drain, then wash in a solution of gum arabic and just enough rose water to spread the mixture. Dust them with fruit sugar (caster sugar) and dry them off on floured paper, or aluminium foil, in a very cool oven, or in the warming drawer of a domestic stove. (Another recipe to try with violets is given on page 63.)

A native herb and perennial, the violet has long procumbent stolons which, rooting at the ends, give the plant a prostrate habit; it spreads and survives the driest chalky soils and the severest winter frosts but when cultivated revels in a humus-rich soil where it can socialize with other low-growing plants. Its various local names are "apple-leaf," "bairnwort," "banwort," "blaver," "Bessy banwood," and "vilip."

There are three main methods by which violets are propagated—seed, division or from cuttings; the most usual method is to plant out-rooted runners, or divisions, in the spring or autumn in crumbly, humus-enriched soil. The plants will tolerate dryness, chalk, or damp conditions, but their flowering quality is dependent on the condition of the good soil prior to planting. Spring planting will often produce autumn flowers, especially in mild districts; and strictly speaking, the violet has two flowering periods, spring and autumn. At the time of planting runners, the dead leaves should be removed, and the plants should be firmed into the ground repeatedly for the first few weeks, and watered or syringed if weather conditions suggest it.

Winter flowering in Britain can be encouraged by growing the plants in cold frames, and provided frost can be kept out and some ventilation given, mildew will not affect the plants. Violets are hardy and really need fresh air and any winter sunshine that there is.

Propagation from seed is not of much value unless reliable seed is sown, and this should be done in boxes or pans in autumn. By the spring, the individual plants can be potted up—or put into frames or planted outside after hardening off. They will flower the same year. The so-called cuttings of violets more nearly resemble an "Irishman's cutting" than a runner of mint, for they consist virtually of detached pieces with a "heel" of rootlets. If they are struck in a sandy/humus cutting-compost in March, they too will provide flowers in September. The simple sweet violet can be used in the herb garden to edge borders, to form a decorative base to a centre piece, be it sundial or birdbath, or can be allowed to fall across low walls.

WALL GERMANDER

Teucrium chamaedrys
LABIATAE

A plant of shrubby growth, reaching about a foot in height and spreading by creeping rootstocks, the wall germander is not used in herbal practice today as it was in former times. A perennial of gardens, sometimes to be found naturalized in old walls, especially in western districts of England and Wales, its range extends over central and southern Europe and to Morocco and the Orient. The tufted growth is useful in walls, around garden seats, and in paving in the herb garden. The pinkish-purple flowers, two-lipped like so many of their race, and open in July and August, provide attractive companionship for the blue-flowered herbs like hyssop and borage. The shining green leaves have been used as an infusion or decoction in the treatment of gout and taken hot as a relief for colds and chest complaints.

A close relative, *Teucrium scorodonia,* is a common wild plant of the British Isles and is quite generally distributed throughout Europe. Its common name is wood sage, but considerable confusion reigns over its vernacular names, indicating that colloquially no one knows for certain which family it belongs to, and so it is treated like the vagrant it appears to be, popping up in a wide variety of localities. The name "wood sage" is reasonably universal, but "rock mint," "wood germander," "garlick sage," "mountain sage," and "ambrose" (or "ambroise") are all names one encounters. As a substitute for hops, it seems to have had a certain following, especially in Jersey where its name "ambroise" comes from; but on the whole it imparts a color that is too strong for beer. Highly aromatic, an infusion makes a reliable tonic and alleviates the twinges of rheumatism. The flowers are green to cream, again two-lipped and blooming in July and August. Culpeper recommends it for use in the care of ulcers and open wounds either as a lotion or "the powder thereof dried."

The Latin name *Teucrium* was given by Dioscorides to this range of plants, from Teucer, an ancient King of Troy, supposedly the first man to have used the germanders and the wood sages as a medicinal tonic. The specific name *scorodonia* is from the Greek *scorodon*, "garlic"; hence one of its country names, "garlic sage," though this is not descriptive of its aroma.

WATERCRESS

Nasturtium officinale
CRUCIFERAE

Lord, I confess too when I dine
  The Pulse is Thine,
And all those other Bits, that bee
  There plac'd by Thee;
The Worts, the Purslain, and the Messe
  of Watercresse
Which of Thy kindness thou has sent;
  And my content

Robert Herrick, writing from his Devonshire countryside in the seventeenth century, in his poem *"A Thanksgiving to God, for His House"* gives an indication that wild plants were then more widely used as food. From Asia, across the great wastes of Russia and throughout Europe, the creeping herb with dark green leaves and somewhat insignificant white flowers grows in streams, ditches, and slow-moving rivers. It has been introduced into North America and North Africa and has come to be regarded as a weed in New Zealand. There is at present in England a flourishing trade in watercress which started about 1808; the beds bordering canals, rivers, and many water conservation areas are used for the husbandry of this edible herb. Botanically, it is a hydrophyte growing submerged with its roots fixed upon the mud of the margin of its habitat; but it can be persuaded to grow on gravel beds over slow-running water or in moisture beds where it will flourish, existing, as so many true aquatics can, between a life on land and in the water. Usually, cuttings of non-flowering shoots are inserted from June to September in rows in the direction of the current. They quickly form roots, and a crop can be cut as soon as good, strong, fresh side-growth has started.

The generic name, *Nasturtium*, was given to it by Pliny and is derived from *nasus*, "nose," *tortus*, "twisted," presumably in reference to the peppery flavor of the plant which causes a sharp contraction of the mouth and nasal muscles. Pliny also recorded that it was used for brain disorders. High in vitamin C and iron content, it provides a good green salad plant, always in season. Nutritive value is lost by cooking, and bulk is reduced in the same way as when one boils spinach. Watercress butter, made from mixing chopped leaves into butter, is a tasty alternative to parsley butter and makes a good savory spread for sandwiches.

There is no doubt about its strength of growth, often prolifically trailing three or four feet under natural conditions; and if poor weather coincides with its short flowering season, and the bees are not inclined to leave the hive, long anthers bend towards the stigma to effect self-pollination.

Watercress was introduced into the United States by the early settlers and became a trailing weed of river estuaries. Provision for fresh food was made in various ways for the sailors and voyagers of the sixteenth century, and "cabin" passengers are believed to have taken watercress with them across the Atlantic and maintained it in water in a jar.

The vernacular names are all descriptive: "water grass," "well grass," "well-kerse," "water kerse," "billers," "brown cress," "stime carsons," "water crashes," "teng-tongue." A bronzed-leaved form, *N. officinale* × *N. microphyllum*, is a hybrid known and marketed as winter cress and is generally of more stunted growth.

WILLOW-HERB

Chamaenerion angustifolium
ONAGRACEAE

Rosebay willow-herb, formerly and still popularly known as *Epilobium angustifolium*, is a tall, showy perennial that has distinguished itself as nature's greatest beautifier of the mutilated earth. Following hard in the wake of the forester's axe, the heath fire, and the demolition contractors, it sends up dominant magenta spires to mask the ugliness. Botanists were provided with new and rewarding hunting grounds in the mid-forties in Europe after the devastation of bomb damage, for many plants colonized around ruined buildings, but none as readily or as attractively as the rosebay. A century ago, this species was a local plant scattered generally throughout the British Isles; but Clapham, Tutin, and Warburg ascribe its phenomenal spread, especially in southern districts of Britain, to the practice, which has increased since the 1920s, of clearing woodland and scrub for development. When steam locomotives charred the steep embankments beside their tracks the rosebay, or fireweed as it has come to be called, painted them a glowing pink within a season, and the fluffy seed was carried away in the wake of passing trains the same year to germinate further along the embankment. The plant is a native of waste places, slagheaps, and barren areas throughout Europe and parts of Asia and from the Atlantic seaboard to the Pacific Coast of America.

William Robinson in *The English Flower Garden* noted that "few are worthy of cultivation, the best being the showy crimson native *E. angustifolium* of which there is a pure white variety." He calls the plant "French bay" because the leaves strangely resemble in shape those of the bay tree. From time to time horticulturalists have endeavored to hybridize the epilobiums (and chamaenerions) and in 1934 and 1939 the Royal Horticultural Society gave Awards of Merit to two cultivars, both of which have been dropped from commerse because of their disagreeable habits. Whereas Robinson could extol their beauty by saying the plant "is magnificent when allowed to run wild in a rough shrubbery or copse, where it may bloom along with the foxgloves," few present-day gardeners want a plant too effusive and with the squatter habits of the willowherb. Considerable work has been carried out on hybridizing species of willowherb by H. C. Pugsley and at the University of Durham in an endeavour to find a sterile but garden-worthy race.

The rosebay must therefore be introduced with discretion into any herb garden, but the leaves can be used as a substitute for tea; in Russia, where it is known as kaporic tea, it is used fairly widely among peasants. An ale brewed from the leaves can be made especially intoxicating by the addition of the fungus, fly agaric (*Agaricus muscarious*). Medicinally, both leaves and roots are astringent; they can be used as an antispasmodic, demulcent, and tonic and have been used to alleviate the distress of asthma and whooping cough and to calm hiccoughs. The young shoots are edible as a vegetable and should be treated like asparagus. The name chamaenerion seems to have been bestowed and published by Clapham, Tutin, and Warburg in 1952 in their *Flora of the British Isles*, when the species was banished from the genus *Epilobium*, bestowed upon it in the mid-sixteenth century.

In America, it is the "great" or "spiked willowherb," "fireweed," and "wickup" or "wicopy," (the last two names seemingly onomatopoeic of hiccough). "Blood vine," another name, alludes to the reddish suffusion of stems and basal leaves, and "willowherb," "Persian willow," "tame withy" (not so tame!), all acknowledge the likeness of the leaves to those of the willow. "Blooming Sally," its Irish vernacular, is also no doubt corrupted from *Salix*, the willow.

WINTER-GREEN

Gaultheria procumbens
ERICACEAE

The wintergreen or partridge berry is a plant native of the sandy peat soils of southern Canada and the United States. The small, creeping evergreen plant is hardy in Britain where it provides good garden decoration and ground cover, with shining green leaves, waxy pink and white flowers, and conspicuous red berries which earn it its vernacular names of "partridge berry" (especially in England) or "deer berry" (both creatures enjoy the berries as a meal!). The leaves are sharply astringent and aromatic on account of the volatile oil, known as oil of wintergreen, and frequently made into wintergreen ointment, used as an embrocation to alleviate the stiffness, swelling, and pain of rheumatism. The presence of salicylic acid makes it useful in corn salves and foot powders. An infusion, using the leaves sparingly, makes mountain, or Salvador, tea; and the small shrub has thus come to be known in America as mountain tea, Jersey tea, or ground tea. The entire plant is aromatic, the berries particularly, with such names as "tea berry," "spruce berry," and "checkerberry."

The English vernacular names include "Canada tea" and "creeping wintergreen." As a cultivated plant of our gardens, it provides year-round interest for the rock garden or woodland and can be perpetuated by removal of the rooted offsets in spring.

WITCH HAZEL

Hamamelis virginiana
HAMAMELIDACEAE

Perhaps nowhere in the naming of wild plants can we trace as clearly the homesickness of the early old-world settlers in America, for when they found *Hamamelis virginiana*, its leaves and general growth reminded them so strongly of the coppiced hazel of Europe that they dubbed it a hazel. Imagine their surprise when in November the 'hazel' burst into bloom as if it were spring, and because they had already used small branches or sticks of the wood to locate water and endowed it with all the folklore aura of the common hazel at home, it had to be called "witch hazel."

The Indians made from it a decoction for soothing bruises and ulcers, and the cooling healing powers were quickly appreciated by the immigrants. Seed was introduced into England in the eighteenth century. The bark is gray, the flowers yellow, and the previous year's nuts hang on the bare branches at the same time; hence its Latin name *hama*, "together," *mela*, "fruit." The fruit is a blackish nut, containing white seeds which are edible and oily but do not often mature in Britain. Their explosive habit of ejecting seed has earned them the vernacular American name of "snapping hazelnut." When branches of the unopened flowers are taken indoors to open and provide floral decoration, the drying nuts frequently pop and shoot their seed about.

Used in pharmacy as "Pond's Extract," its demulcent properties are employed mainly in the treatment of skin inflammations, to allay internal bleeding after bruising, and to clear the effect of broken veins and ulcers. As an eye lotion, when suitably prepared, it relieves pain and hastens the clearing of "bloodshot eyes." Its astringent action is also used to stem bleeding, especially from the nose; the active principles for all these properties are tannin and gallic acid, obtained from both bark and leaves.

As a garden plant, *H. virginiana* reaches some twelve feet or so and is used to provide the stock for the slow-growing Japanese species, *H. mollis*, which is beloved of British gardeners for its February flowers, looking like yellow and brown frills on bare wood during the shortest days of the year.

WOODRUFF, SWEET

Asperula odorata
RUBIACEAE

A perennial herb, the woodruff has whorled leaves and white terminal star-like flowers. A native of Europe in general and locally abundant on damp calcareous or base-rich soil, it is also sometimes cultivated as a ground-cover plant in the wild garden and is very useful for this purpose, tolerating even city air. On drying, the leaves give out the sweet smell of new mown hay, and through the ages this property has ensured man's affection for the woodruff. Legend has it that it formed the virgin's bed; it has certainly been used in mattresses and herb pillows, and for hanging in wardrobes and linen cupboards, to pervade the warmth with its freshness. Dried plants put behind books in enclosed bookcases will prevent any musty smell from developing.

As with so many sweet smelling plants, a tisane can be made from a handful of the flowering tops to which a pint of boiling water must be added; it is used merely as a refreshing drink. In Germany, fresh sprigs steeped in Rhine wine makes a good hock cup, *Maibowle,* traditionally imbibed on May 1; while in England it has been taken in churches on St. Barnabas' Day, June 11; but the reasons for these practices are not known. The name varies very little in provincial English from "star grass," "hay plant," "sweet grass," "sweet hair-hoof," "woodrowe," and "mugwet." The name "woodruff" was written and spelt as a rhyming couplet:

Woodde
rowffe

Obviously the name "star grass" is descriptive of the flower and leaf arrangement, and the French name *roselle,* "a wheel," describes the spoke-like whorl of the leaves. Provincial French used the name *muge-de-bois* (or Old French *muge-de-boys*) and was corrupted as the English vernacular, "mugwet."

YARROW

Achillea millefolium
COMPOSITAE

A weed native to the whole of Europe and introduced into North America, Australia, and New Zealand, yarrow contents itself with the humblest corners of the field and wasteland. Its feathery, dusty foliage is fernlike and proliferous, hence the specific name, *millefolium.* One of the commonest weeds of temperate regions its fame is as the plant of which Chiron, the centaur, taught Achilles the virtues so that he might make a salve to heal his wounds in the Siege of Troy. There it grows on the drier mountain soils up to a height of 2,500 meters. Its long flowering season and its tough creeping stems ensure its survival. The clustered daisy-like flowers are chalk-white; the entire plant thus enshrouds itself in a veil of dustiness. Usually it is ground-hugging, but in more lush environments bears ascending, somewhat wooly stalks, so tough they cannot without difficulty be plucked by hand. Certainly it is well named in French as *herbe au conpures*—it will cut your fingers but also stem the flow of blood.

Its two active alkaloids are achillein and moschatin, in conjunction with an aromatic oil which gives it its spicy, nutty scent. It has been used as a love charm, as an inducement to nose bleeding for the relief of nervous headaches, as a herb tea for fatigue, cystitus, haemorrhoids, and incontinence, and the ointment as a salve for suppurating ulcers and varicose ulcers. Culpeper recommended "it stays the shedding of the hair, the head being bathed with the decoction of it." It is a binding herb, tough of growth as is the periwinkle, and likewise, under the influence of Venus, but used medicinally to stem flows and fluxes. The dried leaves can be mixed with tobacco or used as a substitute; a tisane sweetened with honey can be made, or the tips can be added to beer, as in Sweden.

The Country name of "nosebleed," used both in Britain and North America, confirm Parkinson's words, "assuredly it will stay the bleeding of it." Conversely as as love charm, the nose was induced to bleed by yarrow if the love was truly reciprocated.

Green arrow, Green arrow, you bear a white blow.
If my love love me, my nose will bleed now,
If my love don't love it 'ont bleed a drop'
If my love do love me 't will bleed every drop

"Green arrow" was a corruption of "green yarrow."

Another vernacular name is "carpenter's grass"—or in French *herbe aux charpentier*, for "it is good to rejoyne and soundre woundes." The name "Devil's nettle" comes from the slight tingling sensation imparted by it when drawn over the skin and "stanch" or "stench grass" and "girs" recall its styptic properties. Other recorded names are "yarroway," "old man's pepper," "sanguinary," "sneezewort," and "bloodwort."

PART IV

A Chronicle of Herbs

The Beginnings

The first known work of encyclopedic proportions on medicinal herbs was written around the beginning of the second century A.D. by Pedanius Dioscorides. Born in Anazarbus (near Tarsus in Cilicia), Dioscorides joined the Roman army as a military physician, and his travels as a soldier enabled him to study the flora and fauna of a wide region. His travels probably took him to Alexandria, where he would have had access to Arab medical writings.

His work, *De Materia Medica,* consisted of five volumes and dealt with spices, oils, salves, plants and plant material, animal products, wines, and minerals. Over 600 plants, 35 animal products, and 90 minerals are studied in *De Materia Medica,* in the author's concise Greek. Dioscorides' theories concerning plant cures would appear in translations, commentaries, and manuscripts for centuries to come: he is credited, even now, with first recording the attributes of certain plants, and he added considerably to the knowledge of drugs. His procedures in setting down information also significantly influenced pharmaceutical writings.

Much of his work was translated into Arabic around the ninth century by Stephanus, son of Basilius; and a notable medieval Latin translation has been attributed to Peter of Abano. Several Anglo-Saxon versions are reputed to have been produced. Dioscorides' theories, together with those of his contemporary, Galen, were the basis of standard medical practice for fifteen centuries. In the sixteenth century, Pietrus Andreas Mattioli, who gave his name to the genus *Matthiola,* made his commentary translation of *De Materia Medica* the most celebrated of numerous variations attempted during that period.

Both Dioscorides and Galen drew on Arabic and Egyptian sources, on contemporary Greek practice, and on writings now long lost. Galen was a Greek physician who practised mainly in Rome during the second century A.D., eventually becoming court physician to Marcus Aurelius. To Hippocrates' theory that disease was caused by the imbalance of the four humors—blood, phlegm, black bile, and yellow bile—he added his own theory of "types" or temperaments that reflected these humors: the sanguine or buoyant man, the phlegmatic or sluggish, the melancholic or dejected, and the choleric or quick-tempered. General acceptance of these beliefs inhibited the investigation of the true nature of disease for a very long time.

It was not until the establishment of the medical schools of Salerno and Montpellier that "medical research", as we know it, began. Salerno rose to importance through the work of a drug-seller, Constantinus Africanus (1020–1087), a much-travelled man who was granted working facilities by the monks of Monte Cassino in Italy. He was later admitted to the abbey and spent much of his time translating Arabic works on medicine into Latin, thus widening the availability of medical knowledge and infusing fresh ideas into Western thought.

Almost simultaneously, Gerald of Cremona was working on translations in Spain. The treasures of Toledo had been opened up to the Christians when they captured the town from the Moors in 1085, and, with the tapping of this Islamic knowledge, a central core of learning in astronomy, medicine, and natural history was formed. Gerald translated the works of renowned Arab physicians such as Rhazes and Avicenna, the latter's *Canon Medicinae*

("Canon of Medicine"), written in the early eleventh century, became a standard work, which was still used in universities like Montpellier as late as 1650. The great amount of information that resulted from Gerald's work brought about a reevaluation of medical teaching, which was to exert a profound influence on the newly founded universities—particularly that of Montpellier in the south of France. By 1137, Montpellier appears to have had a fully established faculty of medicine, though early Arab methods were so much a part of its teaching, and the code of Galen was held in such blind esteem, that the search for medical learning came to a halt, stifled for a time by its own assumptions.

However, the competition that arose between these two centres eventually provided the impetus for an advancement of knowledge, as Italy with her newly arisen culture reassessed the pharmacology of the previous centuries and reconstructed Arabic doctrines, establishing Salerno as the medical centre which would provide the watershed of twelfth-century medical learning. This influence was gradual. It would be another three centuries before the invention of the printing press in Europe and the resultant spread of literacy were to highlight the need for a fresh approach.

In England, the first major work on botanical medicine was a manuscript prepared at Oxford by a man in holy orders: John of Gaddesden's *Rosa Medicinae* (or *Rosa Angelica*), compiled between 1314 and 1317. His knowledge of plants and of medical practice was great, and his long study had made him both mindful and tolerant of widely differing notions. In his preface, John of Gaddesden acknowled es his humility of purpose in preparing the book: "Therefore I have wished to write this book for the humble to read" *(Ideo humilibus optavi facere istum librum).*

The work was an acknowledged rendering of Greek, Arabic, and Jewish medical writings, a compendium of eleventh- and twelfth-century knowledge of the physician and surgeon, together with contemporary observations:

> For nothing is set down here but what has been proved by personal experience either of myself or of others, and I, John of Gaddesden, have compiled the whole in the seventh year of my "lecture".

And there is little doubt that *Rosa Medicinae* was respected by both the author's contemporaries and his immediate successors; for us, it provides a comprehensive picture of the medical practice of the period, though curiously omitting the astrological references which carried great weight at that time. There were only four printed editions of *Rosa Medicinae,* the earliest printed in Pavia in 1492, the second in Venice in 1502, a third in 1517, and finally, the Augsburg edition of 1595, which updated the arrangement of subject matter and corrected some of the Latin but, to quote Dr. Cholmeley, "destroyed the quaintness of the work by leaving out the preface and many of Gaddesden's extremely curious derivations".

Later in the fourteenth century, there appeared in England the phenomenon of vernacular texts, making the written word available to a much wider public. Prominent among these texts were numerous medical and pseudo-medical treatises, mostly in verse to facilitate their commitment to memory. Since they were usually translations of works previously available only to the learned and privileged, they propounded no new ideas as such. Even the tragedy of plagues like the Black Death, which ravaged Europe in 1348–1351, did not seem to prompt men to investigate disease afresh. Although many works dealt with combating the plagues, it was generally accepted that disease was an act of God. No theories about the cause were propounded, and men's concern was with the necessity for protection from the epidemics. Boccaccio tells how

> In the year then of our Lord 1348, there happened at Florence, the finest city in all Italy, a most terrible plague; which, whether owing to the influence of the planets, or that it was sent from God as a just punishment for our sins, had broken out some years before in the Levant: and after passing from place to place and making incredible havoc all the way, had now reached the west. . . .

In England, a proclamation was affixed to the doors of churches, giving instructions and recommendations for guarding against the plague. Diet and exercise were advised; hot baths and sleeping after meals were to be avoided, and dwellings were to be filled with the scents of violets, bay leaves, fennel, mint, roses, and aromatic herbs. The period cannot be cited, then, for its medical discoveries, but it does evince the continuing awareness—however misdirected—of the protective or healing properties of plants and the growing popularization of medical botany.

With the invention of the printing press in Germany about 1448, most standard works were to become available in printed form, sometimes in more than one edition. In botanical works, the old stylized forms of the plants were used as illustrations, and, in the early years of the sixteenth century, the Renaissance provided a new phenomenon: the herbal. The *Grand Herbier,* published in Paris, is the most notable example of this early period. The precise date is unknown but was certainly before 1526, for in that year Peter Treveris published the second edition in London—evidence that books and information traveled rapidly from one country to another. Most botanists were able to visit the whole of Europe.

Hieronymus Bock, one of the German fathers of botany, was among the first herbalists. He studied flora from life, making notes of his own observations and, in short, herborizing or botanizing. A contemporary was Otto Brunfels, who had been a Carthusian monk, converted to Protestantism, worked as a schoolmaster in Berne, and then as a physician in Strasbourg. His *Herbarum vivae eicones* ("Types of Living Plants") is generally acclaimed as the first herbal with illustrations drawn from living material. This living material was often wilted by the time it reached the artist, Hans Weiditz, who was a very literal draughtsman and thus produced some illustrations of rather limp plants. Nevertheless, the book is regarded as an important turning point in the history of the European herbal. Other books of the time were illustrated with woodcuts that had been copied time and time again, thus omitting much important detail; Weiditz, however, meticulously based his drawings on his own careful observation. His unusual approach was an essential contribution to the development of botanical study.

Another important contemporary was Leonhard Fuchs, whose noteworthy herbal, *De historia stirpium* (1542) has plant descriptions arranged alphabetically. Fresh material was used for illustration, and Fuchs identified living plants, as Bock had done. Fuchs's herbal was the first to include plants from the New World, such as Indian corn and the great pumpkin. In these early days, the development of the herbal seemed dependant on physicians and men of the church: Dodoens, l'Ecluse, and l'Obel on the Continent of Europe, and William Turner in England.

Turner, who studied at Cambridge, was the son of a Northumbrian tanner. As a man with ardent Protestant principles at a time when the climate of the English court fluctuated, Turner was forced several times to flee to the Continent when the Catholics were in favor. His wide travels during these periods of exile created the opportunity of meeting and exchanging ideas with the leading botanists of the time, and Turner was also able to study medicine in Italy. When back in England, he pursued a close observation of the native flora and published two short works quite early in his career, one of which was widely praised: *The names of herbes in Greke, Latin, Englishe, Duche and French wyth the commune names that Herbaries and Apotecaries use.*

But it is because of his work, *A New Herball,* that Turner is called "the father of English botany." It was written in three parts, the first appearing in 1551. The long delay before the appearance of the second part was due to Turner's fleeing the country yet again, when Catholicism was restored during the reign of Mary Tudor and his two close friends, Ridley and Latimer (formerly Bishop of Worcester), were burned at the stake for heresy in Oxford in 1555.

With the beginning of Elizabeth I's reign, Turner returned to England but his energies were at first directed towards fighting for his reinstatement as Dean of Wells, in Somerset.

Turner had been made Dean in 1550, but he was deprived of the post in 1553 on Mary Tudor's accession. He regained the Deanery in 1558 but was suspended finally for nonconformity in 1564. It was 1562 before the second part of *A New Herball* appeared, and, in 1568, a combined edition included the third part. The work contributed to the development of medical knowledge and was widely acclaimed as the first volume of its kind in England, describing to men in their own tongue the plants of their own land.

Dodoens, a native of Malines, in present-day Belgium, and physician at the court of Maximilian II, the Holy Roman Emperor, was working at the same time on his herbal *Crŭÿdeboeck,* which was published in 1554, written in the Dutch vernacular, and gave flowering times for the Low Countries. He grouped plants according to their properties and affinities rather than alphabetically, as Fuchs had done. The same small woodcuts were used in his book that had been used to illustrate Fuchs' editions, together with some new ones. This work was significant for inspiring a fresh school of thought on the method of classifying plants, which gave rise to a number of scholarly works, mainly originating from the printing house of Plantin at Antwerp where *Crŭÿdeboeck* and Dodoens' later collected works, *Stirpium historiae Pemptades Sex*, had been produced.

Carolus Clusius, or Charles de l'Ecluse, was a native of Arras in France, a man of prodigious learning and ability who epitomizes the "Renaissance man," having grasped to the full every opportunity of the age for study and travel in order to teach, write, and translate. He served the court of Maximilian II, where he probably knew Mattioli and Dodoens, and, while there, he was able to study the indigenous flora of the Carpathians. He had also traveled to the Iberian Peninsula, and his books on the flora of both regions were published by Christophe Plantin, who was responsible for the publication of so many important works. L'Ecluse translated Dodoens' *Crŭÿdeboeck* into French, publishing it almost simultaneously with the original under the title *Histoire des Plantes.* Dodoens and l'Ecluse appear to have been close colleagues: they spent the last years of their working lives together at Leyden, where l'Ecluse was a professor of Botany.

At the same time, Mattioli was engaged in his translations and commentaries on Dioscorides, annotating and embellishing an original edition bought in Constantinople for 100 ducats, a very high price. His work, *Commentarii in sex Libros Pedacii Dioscorides* (Venice, 1544) contained more commentary than Dioscorides' original work and was to provide something of a landmark in the spreading of knowledge. Some 30,000 copies of this early edition are believed to have been sold, and the work was soon translated into Czech, German, and Italian and published again in Venice in 1585 in an enlarged and revised edition.

In 1578 an English version of *Crŭÿdeboeck* was published. It was freely translated by Henry Lyte, an "amateur" botanist; its illustrations were made from the woodcuts originally made for Fuchs and owned by Plantin's publishing house in Antwerp. The work has come to be known as, simply, *A Niewe Herball,* but in the manner of the day, its full title was *A Niewe Herball or Historie of Plantes: wherein is contayned the whole discourse and perfect description of all sorts of Herbes and Plantes: their divers and sundry kindes: their straunge Figures, Fashions and Shapes: their Names, Natures, Operations and Vertues, and that not onely of those which are here growying in this our Countrie of Englande, but of all others also of forrayne Realmes, commonly used in Physicke; First set foorth in the Doutche or Almaigne tongue, by that learned D Rembert Dodoens, Physition to the Emperour: And nowe first translated out of French into English, by Henry Lyte Esquyer.* And, for the English edition, Lyte appended notes from his own observations and made some corrections to the original text, though he did not say so in his title!

Perhaps the most significant link between the botanical activities of the Continent and royal patronage in England was provided by Mathias de l'Obel. Born at Lille in Flanders in 1538, he was educated in medicine and became a physician at the court of William the Silent, who led the Dutch Protestant revolt against Spain. L'Obel's court appointment

opposite Tobacco plant

apparently ended when the prince was assassinated in 1584; he then went to England with Pierre Pena, a friend and fellow botanist. L'Obel was to spend the rest of his life in England: He became a friend of Lord Zouche and accompanied him to Denmark on one of his botanical expeditions in 1598. Upon their return, he was appointed superintendent of Lord Zouche's garden at Hackney—a parish now within Greater London. And in 1607, he was appointed *Botanicus Regius* ("King's Botanist") to James I of England.

The garden of Lord Zouche (or, more precisely, the 11th Baron Zouche of Harringworth) became a centre of activity for the increasing number of plant enthusiasts, and also a collecting point for the plants themselves: Zouche's continental expeditions extended even to Greece and Constantinople in the quest for plants to bring back to London. Man's tendency to collect material was thus becoming significant in England for the first time in horticulture, but the quest for the new and the curious was as much the expression of a genuine search for knowledge as it was a quirk of fashion. Economic botany, medical needs, and herbal practice on the one hand and horticulture and gardening for pleasure on the other were coming to a parting of the ways.

Apothecaries and Herbalists

Horticulture as such had come in the middle of the sixteenth century with the arrival on British soil of religious refugees from Flanders and France. They brought with them methods and skills in the cultivation of plants. In some cases, they brought the plants as well. These people settled mainly in East Anglia (now Norfolk and Suffolk) and in south-eastern England, around London.

Meanwhile, the drug merchants and the apothecaries sought to serve the increasing demands of medicine. The apothecaries formed the link between the two worlds of gardening and botany on the one hand, and medical science on the other. Many of them cultivated their own physic gardens and became leaders in medical botany as well as foremost gardeners.

Such a man was John Gerard, one of the most influential herbalists of the age. An apothecary and an ardent plantsman, Gerard was born in Cheshire in 1545. His *The Herball or Generall Historie of Plantes* was published in 1597 by John Norton, a printer and bookseller at the sign of "The Queen's Arms" in St. Paul's Churchyard, London. Much has been written about Gerard's source material, and doubts have been raised, dispelled, and reasserted as to his accuracy and qualification to write *The Herball.* That Gerard prepared his work in the manner of his predecessors—by copying, correcting in accordance with his own findings, adding and making commentary—is generally accepted. But his work is largely based on a translation of Dodoens' *Stirpium historiae Pemptades Sex* by a Dr. Robert Priest who had been commissioned by John Norton to do the translation. Priest had died in the winter of 1596, leaving the work unfinished, and Gerard was probably asked to complete it. At the same time, he incorporated some work of other botanical writers to which he had access: that of William Turner, L'Obel and his colleague Pierre Pena, and, since Norton had access to the woodcuts used in *Eicones* ("images") *of Tabernaemontanus* by Jacob Theodor Dietrich, these also appear in *The Herball.*

Yet, in spite of acknowledging much of his source material, Gerard took great pains in the preface to note that the partially prepared translation left by Dr. Priest at his death "likewise perished."

Gerard emerges, then, as an ambitious man with an enormous desire for recognition. His own garden in London was near his house on the south side of Holborn, between Fetter Lane and Chancery Lane, running southward on land he had leased. Here he formed a collection of plants from all parts of the world, which he acquired easily as gardener to the powerful statesman, William Cecil, Lord Burghley. The latter's garden was known to contain many imported species. The list Gerard published in 1596 of the plants growing in his own garden—though probably intended for private circulation—was substantiated by l'Obel, who claimed that he had seen all of them there. This list was the first of its kind and has provided the only evidence available of plants, both native and introduced, under cultivation in England at that time.

He also made some field excursions into Kent and Middlesex, recording seventy species of flora in Middlesex for the first time. Gerard was already in charge of the physic garden of the College of Physicians when he became embroiled in a battle to be allowed to control —or, indeed, to start—a physic garden for the Company of Barber-Surgeons. His wish to direct these rival establishments may have been for the good of the apothecaries' profession, but it is more likely that his reasons were those of self-advancement.

It is ironic that Gerard's claim to immortality should rest upon the painstaking work of Thomas Johnson, an apothecary by trade but a worthy botanist commonly described as "the best Herbalist of his age in England." Johnson edited and corrected *The Herball*, maintaining much of the quaintness of style and matter so characteristic of Elizabethan botany but carefully updating and correcting the text. The new version was published in

1633, twenty-one years after Gerard's death, and illustrated by more than 2,500 woodblocks that belonged to Plantin. It was reprinted, unchanged, in 1636.

On his arrival in London from his native Yorkshire, Johnson had been apprenticed to William Bell, a grocer, for at this period the trade of apothecary was not yet separate from that of grocer. He was made a Freeman of the City of London in 1618, a year after the Worshipful Society of Apothecaries received its charter and carried on business at the sign of the Red Lion in Snow Hill. (It was at Johnson's shop that bananas were seen on sale for the first time in England.) And he was to open a new chapter in the history of British botany by becoming what we know as a field botanist, studying, identifying, and recording the flora he found on his trips in search of native plants. Johnson recorded over 600 species in Kent and led the first botanical expedition to Wales, taking an interpreter with him! His party climbed Snowdon in their quest for "new" botanical species. Always of adventurous spirit, Johnson eventually joined the Royalist army, becoming a lieutenant-colonel. He was killed in the last stage of the siege of Basing House, Hampshire, in 1645.

One of the most prominent apothecaries of London in these early days was Gideon De Laune, born in Rheims, France, in 1565 and schooled in the mysteries of the apothecary's trade. His father, a Protestant pastor and physician, had studied medicine in Paris and at Montpellier and, having spent some time in England, took his family there in 1582. Gideon de Laune was appointed apothecary to Queen Anne, consort of James I, and no doubt he worked closely with the king, who determined to incorporate the apothecaries as a guild in their own right, thus separating them from the Grocers' Company with whom they had been incorporated since 1378. Drugs had been sold by the grocers (or *grossarii,* "sellers in gross"), and there had been frequent accusations—apparently justified—of fraudulent practice involving the sale of adulterated drugs, often on open-market booths. The remark that "Grocers were merchants but the Apothecary's trade was a mystery" has been attributed to James I (the word "mystery" having its older connotation of art or craft).

By the time Gideon De Laune established himself in England, many apothecaries, while seeking to disenfranchise themselves from the Grocers' Company, were resisting repeated attempts by the College of Physicians to set up their own physic garden. The apothecaries believed strongly that this was *their* prerogative. The practice at that time was for the physician to diagnose and prescribe and for the apothecary to dispense medicines and attend the patient. Nevertheless, by 1586, the decision had been made to establish a physic garden connected with the College of Physicians' building in Knightrider Street (near the site of St. Paul's Cathedral) for the purpose of studying plants at firsthand. John Gerard's appointment as curator further offended the apothecaries, for he belonged to the Company of Barber-Surgeons; the whole operation seemed to them an encroachment upon their professional territory and a rebuff in their fight for recognition. It was not until 1617 that the Worshipful Society of Apothecaries of London was finally incorporated, with 114 apothecaries, "being His Majesty's natural subjects," nominated as members, together with a few foreigners who became associates.

Gideon De Laune, generally acclaimed as the "founder" of the Society, was at that time a member of the Court of Assistants. He was elected Master of the Society in 1637, having first served in the office of Junior Warden (1624) and Senior Warden (1627). The present Apothecaries' Hall was built during the "phoenix" era of the City of London in 1672. There is a story that the portrait of Gideon De Laune in the Great Hall was one of the articles dragged to safety from the flames of the Great Fire which eventually destroyed most of the previous building. A white marble bust of De Laune, presented in 1676, also stands today in the Apothecaries' Hall, in honor of one of the Society's greatest benefactors, whose life spanned ninety-four years.

Simultaneously with the charter of the Society of Apothecaries, it was enacted that no grocer should keep an apothecary's shop and that medicines were not to be sold by surgeons. A chartered body was given the authority to search the shops of apothecaries within seven miles of London to examine drugs in stock and in use, and similar bodies were set up in provincial centres. So determined was the society to meet in full the demands of the profession and to fight fraudulent practices and oppose charlatans that, in 1623, it established a dispensary for the use of its members which standardized the more important and commonly used preparations. But the old differences with the College of Physicians festered, and, in 1697, the more affluent physicians were able to set up three dispensaries of their own in London, one at the Physicians' College in Warwick Lane, another in St. Martin's Lane, Westminster, and the third in St. Peter's Abbey, Cornhill.

Nonetheless, the apothecaries had become a recognized trade or guild in their own right, and, although most of them remain nameless, they held the responsibility for the care and cultivation of many herbs that would otherwise have appeared only in the gardens of the landed aristocracy. Many apothecaries had their own gardens, and all were botanists with the ability to recognize and identify plants accurately and to certify the wares of the drug merchants and herb gatherers. For some time, they bridged the gap that separated the world of medicine from that of the new horticulture.

They were also destined to direct the great and gradual change from medieval guilds to the national professional organizations of the nineteenth century. For 200 years following their inception, the apothecaries remained an exclusive practising body of men. Other London guilds (with the exception of the Stationers' and the Carmen's) quickly developed into charitable organizations and social clubs.

The formation of the Society of Apothecaries was timely. An ever-increasing population with unfamiliar diseases arising from more extensive travel, along with the lack of hygiene at the time, demanded much experiment on the part of both physicians and apothecaries. And so the scope of medicinal needs began to broaden; in 1588, only 14 per cent of drugs imported into Britain had come from outside Europe, yet by 1604, the number of imported drugs of plant origin had risen so rapidly that customs officials began to treat these commodities separately; and by 1669, imports of this kind from beyond Europe had increased to 70 per cent. Whereas £2,300 was spent on these commodities in 1587, £13,000 was the figure for 1630, and £60,000 for 1670. These drugs were either imported mainly by grocers or purchased wholesale from the East India Company drug merchants. The apothecaries would send carriers to fetch their requirements from wholesalers in London, Norwich, York, or Bristol. This expansion of the trade in medicinal drugs and the introduction of organized trading meant that the Society of Apothecaries expanded its membership.

John Parkinson, who was probably born in Nottingham, England, in 1567, had his garden in Long Acre (near Covent Garden in London) and was apothecary to James I. He is remembered chiefly for two books, the first entitled *Paradisi in Sole Paradisus Terrestris* ("The Earthly Park of Park-in-Sun") and published in 1629; it dealt with cultivated plants, particularly flowers. The second, *Theatrum Botanicum* ("Theatre of Plants"), was issued in 1640; it was a herbal in which close to 4,000 plants were described. Parkinson's writings are representative of his period, when newly introduced plants and knowledge were infused into the insular habits of the British Isles.

At this time the poorer classes and peasants collected their herbs from the fields or grew them around their cottages. The rural communities put every plant to some use, whether economic or symbolic. Medical services were costly, and it was Nicholas Culpeper who, in 1652, produced the first book designed to give the poor the information they needed to apply appropriate plant remedies. The full title of his book was *The English Physician or an Astrologo-physical Discourse of the Vulgar Herbs of this Nation Being a Compleat Method of Physic Whereby a man may preserve his body in health; or cure himself being sick for three pence charge with such things onely as grow in England, they being most fit for English Bodies.*

Culpeper sacrificed much in wealth and reputation to serve the common people, and while in retrospect he is often regarded as a crank for the astrological aspect of his botany, he was merely playing to the gallery, as shown by the success of his herbal. Subsequent editions appeared in 1653, 1664, 1693, 1695, 1714, 1725, 1733, 1784, 1792, 1814, and 1820.

Nicholas Culpeper was born at Ockley in Surrey, England, in October 1616. His father, the Reverend N. Culpeper, had died two weeks previously. An only child, Culpeper was brought up at Isfield in Sussex with his maternal grandparents, his mother having returned to them after her husband's death. Culpeper was a good Classics scholar at Cambridge. While still there, he got engaged, but his fiancée had the misfortune to be struck by lightning during a thunderstorm just before the wedding. The tragedy affected Culpeper deeply; he left Cambridge and refused to return and finish his studies. This angered his grandfather and resulted in the loss of financial help from his family.

Culpeper then became apprenticed to an apothecary in St. Helens, Bishopsgate, London. By 1640, his master had died, leaving him to carry on and move the practice to Red Lion Street, Spitalfields, London. The same year, he married a young girl, Anne, who was to bear him seven children. His scholarly ability and inclination to help the poor, coupled with his ardent belief in astrological botany and the Doctrine of Signatures, brought him into conflict with the medical profession of the day. Fury was roused by his translation into English of the *London Pharmacopoeia* ("London Dispensatory"—the physicians' "secret handbook" of remedies), and while Culpeper probably had more knowledge of plants than most doctors and could easily have courted the influence of his father's Royalist family, he chose independence of thought: indeed, he fought on Cromwell's side in the Civil War. He died in January 1654 of tuberculosis, before his writings had become popular. Additional manuscrips were published posthumously with the help of his wife.

What, exactly, were Culpeper's theories, which were so widely disputed in his day? Working from his belief in astrological influences, Culpeper placed herbs under the dominion of the sun, the moon, or one of the five known planets—Jupiter, Saturn, Mercury, Venus, Mars—and he listed, in his *Astrological Judgment of Diseases,* the parts of the body governed by the planets and the signs of the zodiac. Adherents to the theory have taken astrological botany further in the light of present-day knowledge: In temperate zones, no one would dispute that seasons affect radically both plant and animal life. Vegetation also is affected by phases of the moon, with increase in growth or proliferation of cells most marked towards the new moon. Throughout the thirteen lunar months of the calendar, growth is regulated or activated by the season and the moon, so that there is very little growth of plants prior to the full moon in December (in the Northern Hemisphere) but much growth before the April and May full moons.

The Doctrine of Signatures claimed adherents throughout the Middle Ages, and Culpeper, despite his academic ability, was an exponent of this theory, whereby certain plants were ascribed occult properties, parts of the plant representing that part of the body or condition for which they were intended. For example, the leaves of pulmonaria were thought to resemble the lungs in shape, and so they were used in the relief of pulmonary disorders; in consequence, the plant is commonly known as lungwort. Likewise, the color obtainable from saffron suggested its use in the treatment of biliousness, and the felted leaves of coltsfoot and mullein were suggestive of mucus and thus used in the treatment of coughs, and so on. The root tubers of the lesser celandine were used to treat haemorrhoids; the markings in the flower of eyebright suggested its use for treatment of the eyes; and the form of the walnut was likened to the brain and was recommended for headaches and madness. Sometimes, the sign was more obscure and might represent an animal, the bite of which was to be treated by the plant: the adder's tongue *(Ophioglossum vulgatum)*, for instance, was to be applied to the bite of an adder. There had been much controversy about the theory before Culpeper expounded it, although he was not without advocates. William Coles, a doctor from Adderbury, Oxfordshire, upheld him on this theory, though he was a bitter opponent of his astrological beliefs. Coles settled in Putney, in south-west London, after qualifying in medicine at Merton College, Oxford, and was to write his well-known book, *The Art of Simpling,* soon afterwards.

These early herbals were important traveling companions for the increasing number of English who were setting out for the New World. From the edited Gerard to the influential Culpeper, these handbooks of herbal remedies were regarded as indispensable in the New World, where many identical species of plants would be found, as well as genuses then unknown to the new settlers, and strange new plants they had never seen before. Mention of Culpeper's *English Physician* is even found in the inventory of a Cape Cod physician who died *c.* 1760, and it seems to have been thought of as an essential reference work by most New England physicians and other "practitioners of physick" at the time.

The latter group were frequently clergymen, who saw fit to look after both the souls and the bodies of their congregations. One such was Edward Taylor of Connecticut who wrote his own "Dispensatory," listing close to 400 plants and their attributes. And like their sixteenth- and seventeenth-century contemporaries in England, the Puritans of New England found assurances for the worth of their plant remedies in the book of Genesis and in other biblical passages which state that herbs have been placed here on earth for man's benefit.

How well, then, did these remedies work? It seems, from records of the time, that results were much as one might expect, with the "kill or cure" qualities of many doses. When a patient recovered, after being subjected to such "cures" as herbal teas which would purge "both upwards and downwards," this meant that the correct balance of his system had been restored. If he did not recover, then this was simply regarded as God's will. Disease was seen as an alien visitor to the body, or "host," and therefore any or all extremes were resorted to in order to be rid of it.

The Puritans took very few plants which were thought to have occult properties to the New World, but those plants they did import, along with the native flora, were to influence both their way of life and their gardening. We know, from surviving early documentation, that many New England gardens were planted "according to Culpeper" (or Parkinson), and it is even more fascinating to realize that many herbs which we regard today as growing wild in the New World have wandered from these early gardens.

The Collectors: Botanists and Gardeners

During the sixteenth century in Europe there was an increasing growth of interest in plants, and much knowledge was accumulated and published. Many new plants were added to the European collections, and continued to arrive during the two following centuries through connections with the Dutch East India Company, and the British East India Company, and by the developing routes to the New World. By the eighteenth century plant expeditions were undertaken in the search for new materials to satisfy the curious gardener and to provide green medicine.

Some of the earliest recorded botanic gardens were in Italy: at Pisa (1543), Padua and Florence (1545), Rome (1566), and Bologna (1567). These were designed to serve the study and investigation of plants, not only as part of the still mysterious world of nature but as physic essential to man. Padua, a seat of learning founded in 1222, established what is generally regarded as the first garden for scientific study and later initiated pharmacognosy (the biology, biochemistry, and economics of nonfood natural products of value in medicine, pharmacy, etc.). In 1545, Francisco Buonafede, who held the chair of *lectura simplicium* ("professor of *materia medica*") at the University of Padua, gained permission from the senate of the Republic of Venice to establish a garden for the cultivation of medicinal plants from which his students could learn their *materia medica.* The garden was laid out under the guidance of Andrea Moroni and led to the study of botany as a separate science.

Luca Chini held the chair of *lectura simplicium* at the University of Pisa from 1544 to 1556 and is credited with developing methods for preserving pressed and dried plant specimens —the basis of all the herbaria and *hortus siccus* (i.e., "dried plant specimens") of the world. At about the same time as Buonafede established his garden, Luca Chini founded a similar one at Pisa; it was transferred in 1595 to a site south of the Piazzo del Duomo. Tilli in *Catalogus Platarum Horti Pisani* ("Catalogue of Plants in the Pisa Garden," Florence, 1823), listed the plants cultivated at Pisa in geometrically arranged beds, grouped according to their properties and morphological characteristics—a tradition maintained since the garden was begun. Beds were allocated to prickly plants, fragrant plants, marsh-loving plants and there was a *vaparium pro plantis Americanis* (an early type of greenhouse for American plants).

John Ray, the leading British botanist of the seventeenth century, visited both gardens in 1664. He said of Padua, "Here is a publick Physic garden, well stored with samples, but more noted for its prefects, men eminent for their skills in Botanics." This must have been accurate reporting, for the men concerned in establishing and organizing these new style gardens must have been far more interesting than the simples they were growing, most of which would have been known already to a botanist of Ray's caliber. The intention was to provide a *hortus medicus* (physic garden) and a *hortus botanicus* (botanical garden), and with the rather vague approach to botany at that time, almost any plant may have found its way there.

It was half a century before Henry IV of France founded a garden at Montpellier in 1593 specifically for the scientific study of *materia medica.* Four years later, Henry of Navarre directed that Jean Robin, an apothecary of Paris, should lay out a small garden for the Faculty of Medicine of the University of Paris. Robin already had a famous private garden of his own and he was the Court Botanist to Henry III, Henry IV, and the succeeding Louis XIII. His scientific garden for the university—on the southern bank of the Seine at the eastern edge of the "city" of Paris—developed into the present Jardin des Plantes.

The example set by the University of Padua in changing the method of teaching and encouraging the use of living, drug-yielding plants was emulated by other universities outside Italy. A physic garden was laid out at Heidelberg in 1577. In the same year, the garden at Leyden was established and became famous for a wonderful collection of exotic plants from the Dutch East Indies and the Orient. Other gardens were to follow: Strasbourg in 1620, Oxford in 1621, Edinburgh in 1680, and Amsterdam in 1682. In Portugal, plans for a physic garden at the University of Coimbra were rejected on the assertion that "His Majesty does not wish to establish a garden which would be larger and more sumptuous than that at Chelsea in the City of London, the most opulent in Europe." In all probability, the riverside site and south-facing slope of the Chelsea Physic Garden, together with its extensive three and a half or four acres, gave it an air of luxury in comparison with the enclosed, geometrically contrived plots of the Italian cities.

Later gardens were not essentially for physic but frequently provided sites to display plants from the four known continents. The University of Upsala in Sweden (always to be associated with the great botanist Linnaeus) founded a garden, *Hortus Upsaliensis,* about 1655, which was subsequently destroyed by fire in 1702 and afterwards neglected until Linnaeus himself undertook its reestablishment and arranged the plants according to his own system—naming them by genus and species, in fact the basis of the modern method of classification. The Upsala garden thus became a world-famous center for botanical studies; in the master's own words, it was a "living library" of plants for public use and from which plant names might be learned. This old garden was for a time transformed into a park, but during the past fifty years, its original plan has been faithfully restored by the Swedish Linnean Society.

The first serious attempt to form a physic garden in London can probably be attributed to Gerard and the Company of Barber-Surgeons, who appear to have examined likely sites during the years 1597 to 1605. In this connection, a plot adjoining Somerset House was leased to Gerard by Queen Anne on the condition that he supply her household with herbs, flowers, and fruit. However, the Company's attempt to find a suitable site in London proved unsuccessful, and, instead, the first physic garden in Britain was established at Oxford, as part of the School of Medicine. It was founded in 1621 on five acres leased from Magdalen College by Henry Danvers, Earl of Danby, who, "being minded to become a benefactor of the University, determined to begin and finish a place whereby learning, especially the faculty of medicine, might be improved." By 1632, this meadowland outside the walls of the city had been raised above the level of the winter flood waters of the river Cherwell, which washed its southern and eastern boundaries. A fourteen-foot wall had been erected to enclose three of the five acres and a main gateway (which still stands) and two smaller ones had been built. The geometric plan within the walled garden remains today.

Jacob Brobart the elder was the first *Horti Praefectus* (gardener or supervisor) at the Oxford garden and published the first catalogue of the 1,600 plants in the garden in 1648. However, the original plans for the work of the garden had been interrupted by the Civil War, and so no steps were taken to appoint a Professor until 1669 when Dr. Robert Morison, a Scot, was put in by Charles II. Morison was botanist and physician to the King. He proceeded to give lectures in the garden where he "read in the middle of it (with a table before him) on herbs and plants thrice a week." His own special interest was in striped and variegated plants—a study for which the School of Botany at Oxford is still renowned. (Oxford also claims to have shared in the discovery of the sexuality of plants.) On Morison's death in 1683, Brobart's son, Jacob the Younger, succeeded him.

The next important appointment was that of Dr. Humphrey Sibthorp in 1735, when, according to Druce's *Flora of Oxfordshire,* he gave "one not very successful lecture . . . and every scientific object slept during the forty years he held the post." His son, John Sibthorp, Doctor of Medicine, succeeded him and is notable for his zealous pursuit of science—albeit outside the Oxford Garden. He made two journeys to Greece to study the indigenous flora there, and to establish the botanical and historical authenticity of Dioscorides' Herbal, publishing (in ten folio volumes) *Flora Graeca* ("Greek Flora"), 1806–1840.

Reports exist of the sorry state of the Oxford Garden in 1824 and in succeeding years, due largely to lack of funds, but this was to be changed by Dr. Charles Daubeny, appointed Professor in 1834. Besides being an energetic fund-raiser, he supervised the laying out of a new experimental garden, and changed the name from "Physic Garden" to "Botanic Garden". Dr. Daubeny lived to see the gardens entirely rearranged, enriched with extensive greenhouses, and generally made more attractive. The experimental work on the mineral requirements of plants inaugurated by Daubeny led eventually to the establishment, by one of his pupils, John Bennet Lawes, of Rothamstead Experimental Station at Harpenden, Hertfordshire, England.

Another great physic garden to have survived and flourished in England on its original site is that at Chelsea, founded by the Worshipful Society of Apothecaries in 1673. The plot of three acres, one rod, and thirty-five perches is first mentioned in the minutes of the society dated June 21, 1674, when it was resolved to build a wall around the existing garden. The wall was to be paid for at the society's own expense with the assistance of any subscriptions they might procure. The proposal was made and accepted that the Court of Assistants would pay £2 every year for each of six "herbarizings" conducted by the apothecaries. These "herbarizings" were walks in the country to collect or simply observe plants, under the guidance of experts. This proved a very successful scheme, and funds that were raised helped with the cost of the wall. The proprietors of the laboratory (dispensary) stock gave £50 towards the wall, in return for which they were granted a plot within the garden "for the growing of herbs." One of the fourteen members of the society responsible for the decision to build the wall was James Rand whose son Isaac, an apothecary with his practice in the Haymarket, London, is known to have been a keen herbarizer and botanist employed at the Chelsea garden. He is credited with being the first to record *Rumex palustris* (marsh dock) in Tothill Fields and *Mentha pubescens* "about some ponds near Marylebone."

The Chelsea Physic Garden, which has been maintained over the years as a centre for the study of botany and physic, borders the north bank of the River Thames, and in the seventeenth century it was near what was the village of Chelsea, about three miles to the west of London. The apothecaries had their own barge which plied its way from the City to Chelsea, where access to the garden was gained directly from the river. The land was originally leased from Charles Cheyne—afterwards Lord Cheyne—but early setbacks and financial troubles beset the Society in the establishment of their garden. Their funds at that time must have been at a low ebb, for they were also rebuilding their Livery Hall after its destruction by the Great Fire of 1666. By 1693, the garden could still not be described as flourishing and the Society considered abandoning it; however, they did not, and some years later, in 1708, ninety people subscribed additional funds. The garden was kept going until Dr. Hans Sloane, who purchased the Manor of Chelsea in 1712, becoming the apothecaries' lessor, offered a solution to their problems. In 1722, a new lease was granted in perpetuity, at a rental of £5 per annum, with the condition that the apothecaries deliver to the Royal Society 50 specimen plants each year until about 2,000 specimens had been assembled. The wealthy Dr. Sloane had been created a baronet in 1716 and, by this time, was himself President of the Royal Society (the foremost scientific society in Britain, founded in 1645).

When Philip Miller was appointed gardener at Chelsea in 1722, one of his attendant duties was to give at least two demonstrations of plants to students in each of the six summer months and in the early years, students were frequently taken on herborizing or botanizing expeditions in the fields around Chelsea. Miller, who was introduced to the Society of Apothecaries by Sir Hans Sloane, was one of the ablest of eighteenth century gardeners, and the author of the famous *Gardeners Dictionary* (1731), generally regarded as the prototype of horticultural publications. On its publication, he was named *Hortulan evum princeps* at Chelsea.

It was at Chelsea Physic Garden that Elizabeth Blackwell studied for her book, *A Curious*

Herbal (1737–39) working on both text and illustration and lodging close to the garden. Sir Hans Sloane had suggested to her that there was a need for a herbal of medicinal plants and she set about its preparation, working from plants in the apothecaries' garden, in order to meet the debts of her husband, Dr. Alexander Blackwell, who had been cast into a debtors' jail. Philip Miller is thought to have helped her in her work during his time as controller of the garden. He was succeeded by William Forsyth in 1770. William Curtis was subsequently appointed *Praefectus Horti* and Demonstrator of Plants in 1773 and it was he who established *The Botanical Magazine*, which has ever since been linked with the Chelsea garden. It became the leading botanical publication of its day and, indeed, of the next two hundred years. Wilfred Blunt, a leading botanical authority in Britain, has called the magazine "a national institution of which Englishmen may be justly proud".

When Linnaeus visited the physic garden in 1736, he recorded, "Miller of Chelsea permitted me to collect many plants in the garden." One of Linnaeus's pupils, Pehr Kalm, was to record visits there on 28th April and 8th May, 1748. Kalm was in England en route to North America where he was going in search of new seed material to improve Sweden's poor meadows, acid swamplands and dry hills. Linnaeus had convinced the Swedish Government and the Royal Swedish Academy of Science that Kalm should be the man to go on the expedition, but he and his chosen companion and assistant, Lars Jungstrom, had to wait in England from 17th February, 1748 until 5th August of the same year "for want of a vessel to cross to America."

However, he seems to have been unimpressed by the Chelsea garden for he fails to describe any of its features, although he did note about the district of Chelsea the "frightful number" of market gardens and "tree schools"—"or as they are here called, nurseries." Kalm was much more impressed by Sir Hans Sloane's natural history collections which, after his death in 1753, formed the basis of the collection of the British Museum in London, together with his library, which the nation purchased for £20,000.

On their voyage back to Sweden from America in 1751, Kalm and Jungstrom spent a further six weeks around London—their ship had run aground in the Thames! Pehr Kalm's "North American Journey" *(En resa till Norra Amerika)* was published in 1753, 1761, and 1776 in Stockholm, the last edition including the account of the visit to England. In London, Kalm was introduced by Mr. Ellicot, FRS, whom he noted was "now reckoned to be one of the best clock-makers in London," to Peter Collinson who, in turn, introduced him to Mark Catesby. Catesby had traveled in Virginia in 1712 and sent back to England numerous seeds and plant specimens that formed the basis of Collinson's tremendous enthusiasm for North American plants. Peter Collinson, a Quaker, was a draper and haberdasher by trade, and a botanist by inclination. Since his company traded with North America, it was inevitable that as a gardener he should build up a collection of plants from the New World. Kalm visited Collinson's garden in Peckham (south of London) and recorded that he had found "scarcely a garden in England in which there were so many kinds of trees and plants, especially American ones which can endure the English climate, and stand out the whole winter."

The increasing interest in plants from the New World, the exchange of knowledge, and the sponsoring of journeys of botanical observation gave a new dimension to the lives of botanists in the eighteenth century. Sir Hans Sloane and his contemporaries persuaded Mark Catesby to return to North America to investigate systematically the natural history of some of the states. He traveled through Carolina, Georgia, and Florida in 1722–1725 and visited the Bahamian Islands before returning to England in 1726. The native flora and fauna were described and illustrated by him in crowded etchings in *The Natural History of Carolina, Florida and the Bahama Islands,* first published between 1730 and 1748. Pehr Kalm had seen Mark Catesby's published work and much admired the meticulous etchings, though he remarked upon the high price of two large volumes saying "both together now cost in England twenty-two to twenty-four guineas therefore not for a poor man to buy."

Peter Collinson had helped to subsidize the publication, and he was a patron of many botanical undertakings connected with North America, though despite his interests and knowledge of North American flora, he never visited the New World.

John Bartram was born in America of emigrant parents who had come from Derbyshire in England. A keen farmer and botanist, he built himself a house near Philadelphia in 1782, laid out a garden and set about filling it with rare and beautiful plants. He engaged a manager for his farm, paid a schoolmaster to instruct him in Latin, and embarked upon a life of plant-hunting, often trekking over virgin country in Pennsylvania, Maryland, Georgia and the Carolinas to Florida. After being engaged by Peter Collinson, by letter, for they had never met, he was encouraged by contacts in England to pack plant material in an ox bladder half filled with wet moss and the plants' natural soil, in order to consign them safely to England. In this way hundreds of seedlings and plants arrived in England from 1734 until Collinson's death in 1768. Among the introductions made in this way are *Magnolia grandiflora, Kalmia latifolia, Erythronium dens-canis,* some Michaelmas daisies, some lilies, *Viburnum dentatum* and collinsonias, which commemorate the patron himself.

At first Collinson paid him in kind by exchanging plants and supplying him with the latest botanical books from Europe; but then a number of Collinson's friends, among them Lord Petrie, Philip Miller of Chelsea Physic Garden and Sir Hans Sloane, all fascinated by this new plant material, arranged together to pay Bartram a proper subsidy and thus enable him to undertake many expeditions. In 1765, through their influence Bertram was appointed as a botanist and plant collector by George III, at a salary of £50 per annum. George III was at that time amassing a large collection of plants at the newly formed garden around Kew Palace, and which garden was the basis of the present botanic garden. The correspondence between Collinson and Bartram reflects the botanical history of the time, and Bartram's herbarium of pressed specimens can be seen in the Natural History Museum, South Kensington, London.

Bartram's garden was the first botanical garden in the New World and was established for the study and scientific evaluation of plant life; he was the first American to use the Linnean system of classification. During the latter part of the eighteenth century, a few more botanical gardens were founded in America, including George Washington's at Mount Vernon, but it was not until the end of the nineteenth century that the American universities followed the example of their European counterparts and began to establish their own gardens for study.

The Missouri Botanic Garden, opened to the public in 1889, is also well known to botanists all over the world. It was begun in 1870 by Henry Shaw and, for many years, known as Shaw's Garden. Its most famous feature is probably the Climatron with its geodesic dome, which allows a magnificent display of tropical and semitropical plants to grow in a habitat which recreates their native climates.

Today, there are 117 major botanical gardens in the United States, 38 in Britain, and nearly 200 in Western Europe.

The Commercial Herb Farm

As botany turned more and more towards the cultivation of decorative plants and refined food plants, the pharmacists—modern-day apothecaries—remained the last practitioners of herbal lore, and the cultivation of herbs for cosmetic and medicinal use became a modern industry.

In the parish of Mitcham, Surrey, to the southwest of London, Thomas Potter and John Potter, probably brothers, were gardening commercially in the seventeenth century. John Potter had a large family, and at least two sons followed him in his business: Henry, born 1699, and Ephraim, born 1703. It is generally recorded that the growing of physic plants—in particular, lavender and peppermint—as a commercial venture began in Mitcham about 1768 or 1769. But it seems probable that these dates are too late; Ephraim was the first in the family to style himself a physic gardener, and he died in 1775. He was succeeded by his son, James, born 1734, who, with his sister Anne, did the most to gain for Potter and Moore their great reputation as growers of physic plants.

Anne had married Benjamin Moore, a calico printer of Mitcham, and their eldest son, James Moore (1770–1857) was taken as partner by his uncle, James Potter, hence the name "Potter and Moore." Potter lived near Figs Marsh, in the village of Upper Mitcham, and was a subscriber to James Edwards' *A Companion from London to Brighthelmston*. In this work, Potter was described by Edwards as a botanical herbalist "Whose Botanical gardens are very extensive and who has works here for extracting the essence of all his botanical herbs." His sister Anne Moore and her family probably lived at nearby Mitcham Brewer.

James Moore inherited the control of the physic garden, under his uncle's will, when James Potter died at Bath "after a severe and tedious illness in his sixty-sixth year." At that time (1799) there were 250 acres occupied by physic gardens in the parishes of Mitcham, Merton, and Carshalton in Surrey, 100 acres of which were under cultivation with peppermint. By 1850, 820 acres were cultivated by physic gardeners, Moore having the largest property. Moore was a philanthropic extrovert whose energy and wealth colored his career. Before 1809, he had bought for himself the Manor of Biggin and Tamworth in Mitcham, and, in 1813, he purchased the private chapel at Mitcham Church for £200. He never married but had several illegitimate children, one of whom, James Bridger, succeeded him both as Lord of the Manor and as principal proprietor of the business of "Potter and Moore, physic gardeners."

About 1850, the acreage under cultivation with physic plants in the Mitcham area was distributed as shown in the accompanying table.

GROWER	NUMBER OF ACRES	NUMBER OF STILLS
Moore (James)	350	5
Arthur	300	3
Martin	40	3 (not much used)
Newman	40	1
Sprules	50	2
Weston	40	0
Total	820	14

There were several smaller growers in the same area who cultivated only a few acres and others who had only half an acre and sent their supplies for sale directly to the London market of Covent Garden. One such grower was John Anderson, a physic gardener of Broad Green, Croydon, Surrey (east of Mitcham), who was associated with Dickson and

Anderson, founded in 1772 and herbalists of Covent Garden.

In 1850, the principal crops were peppermint, lavender and chamomile, though aconite, belladonna, caraway, squirting cucumber, elecampane, licorice, foxglove, lovage, angelica, hemlock, savine (juniper), poppy, roses, and marsh mallow were also grown. Mr. Arthur, on his 300 acres, is recorded as growing the greatest variety of plants in the district.

Surviving records indicate that the three mints, spearmint, peppermint, and pennyroyal, were among the first plants ever to be grown in the Mitcham district, but as the cultivation of spearmint was less profitable than that of peppermint, only a sufficient amount was grown in any year to meet the actual demands: "in the absence of orders beforehand, the ground is otherwise appropriated." A ton of peppermint yielded two and a half to three pounds of oil, a ton of spearmint only half that amount.

Fifty acres of licorice were cultivated on the Potter and Moore land in James Moore's day; the estimated yield was about twenty hundredweight per acre in 1805, and the expense of taking up the roots by fork about £10 per acre. Forty years later, James Bridger had joined the business and estimated that this price had risen to something between £14 and £16 per acre. The rising costs, the insufficient demand for home-produced physic plants, and the increase in the price of land were all contributory factors in the decline of the physic gardeners' trade at the end of the nineteenth century and during the first generation of the twentieth.

Even 100 years ago, the distillation of lavender was costing the small still owners something considerably in excess of the market price for oil of lavender. About a pound to a pound and a half of oil could be obtained from a day's distilling, using fifty gallons of water to twenty-four dozen bundles of lavender, each dozen bundle weighing about twenty pounds. In the larger stills, such as those supervised by James Moore and James Bridger, the capacity was from 700 to 1,000 gallons. Lavender was cut and bundled with stalks, called a mat, each mat weighing one hundredweight. Twenty to twenty-four of these would fill to capacity a thousand-gallon still. It would take two hours to get up steam, and two and a half hours to draw off the best quality oil; anything distilled after this stage would be of second or third quality.

Another prominent commercial grower of both lavender and peppermint was William Ransom, one of the foremost men of the pharmaceutical world in the mid-nineteenth century. A Quaker, he was a pharmacist, botanist, archaeologist, magistrate, and benefactor and, above all, a highly successful businessman. The Ransom family had settled in Hitchin, Hertfordshire (north of London) in the seventeenth century and were descendants of a family of farmers, landowners, and millers from Norfolk. William, son of John Ransom, was born on January 28, 1826. He was educated at Isaac Brown's Academy, Hitchin, a Quaker establishment where his school friend was Joseph Lister—later Lord Lister, the first surgeon to use antiseptic treatment for wounds. Ransom's apprenticeship was served with Messrs. Thomas and William Southall, manufacturing chemists of Birmingham; then, while still a minor, he opened a pharmacy in Sun Street, Hitchin. He was given the use of a 200-year-old range of buildings in nearby Bancroft, belonging to his grandfather; among the effects there, Ransom found a still that had been used by his grandmother for distilling sweet herbs. The young Ransom started the cultivation of medicinal and aromatic herbs in the 1840s, and, ten years later, he was well known as a distiller of lavender and peppermint oils. In 1856, he married Anne Mary, eldest daughter of Thomas Southall; she bore him three daughters and a son, Francis.

Ransom's farm became extensive; scattered fields in various parts of Hitchin and Mappershall were brought under cultivation for the production of medicinal herbs: belladonna, buckthorn, chamomile, cherry laurel, dandelion, elder, foxglove, hemlock, henbane, monkshood, poppy, rosemary, squirting cucumber, wild rose, and, of course, lavender and the mints were all to be found there. His ten acres of lavender included *Lavendula vera, L. stoechas,* and *L. spicata*—all cultivated for the distillation of otto of lavender, oil of lavender, and, subsequently, lavender water. Gathering wild herbs for Mr. Ransom was a seasonal occupation, for we read of "sunburnt and swarthy women and hordes of village children arriving with handcarts and wheelbarrows and aprons full of dandelion roots—as many as twelve tons of dandelions have been received at the Distillery in the course of a Saturday morning." In 1862, Ransom won a prize at the International Exhibition (an early "trade fair" held at South Kensington, London) for "pharmaceutical extracts, essential oils and dried herbs of superior quality."

His son, Francis, joined him in the business, carrying out extensive research into the plant belladonna. He became a member of the examining body of the Pharmaceutical Society and its President when the Conference was convened at Cambridge in 1910. On January 1, 1913, "William Ransom and Son" became a private limited company, the elder Ransom surviving until the winter months of 1914.

The "Damask" and the "Provins" or "Cabbage" roses were another important commercial crop. In 1805, James Moore had seven acres of Damask and three acres of Provence roses; nearby, Arthur cultivated both, but he found the Provence rose, which he identified as *R. centifolia vulgaris foliacea,* the easier. It did not suffer from "maggots," and because the flowers were used in an expanded condition, gathering had only to be done on alternate days. The whole flower was used for distillation, though the resultant oil was better if the calyces could be removed and discarded. Arthur's "Damask" rose was in fact *Rosa gallica officinalis* (the Apothecary's rose), and, since it was used in the bud stage, the blooms were collected by women and children "twice a day in order to secure the buds before they are too expanded." The buds were dried rapidly by stove heat to retain the color, but those buds required for conserves were sent to market fresh. About 2,000 flower buds "the size of a large nutmeg" made up 10 pounds of dried flowers or 100 pounds of fresh. There is evidence that *R. gallica officinalis* was cultivated also in Oxfordshire and Derbyshire.

The general assumption is that licorice *(Glycyrrhiza glabra)* was introduced into England by the Black Friars; John of Gaddesden, writing in the early fourteenth century in Oxford, mentions its use, giving a lengthy list of suggested remedies against scrofulous glands and then adding that in case of failure, an application could be made of "snails and licorice." William Turner, writing in 1548, also mentions licorice. Apothecaries knew one form of it in their physic gardens—the common licorice known as *G. vulgaris.*

A correspondent subscribing July 24, 1730, to Stephen Switzer's *The Practical Husbandman and Planter,* signs himself as "J. P.", and there seems little doubt that he was John Perfect, as Switzer called him "a Person well known in the North for his skill in Nurseries and Planting of all Kinds." John Perfect of Pomfret (later Pontefract) was a nurseryman subscriber to Switzer's book and also to Philip Miller's 1731 edition of *The Gardeners Dictionary.* J. P. describes in detail the cultivation of licorice as it was carried out in the eighteenth century and mentions particularly the commercial cultivation at Pomfret. Stephen Switzer noted that licorice had originally been brought from Spain but that the cultivated root in England reached greater perfection and that it was "much planted about Godalming in Surrey, Worksop in Nottinghamshire, and at Pomfret in Yorkshire." Batty Langley (see also page 17) had previously described in some detail the cultivation of licorice in his *New Principles of Gardening,* adding "to preserve Liquorice from drying after being taken up, You must prepare a Bed of Sand within your Greenhouse etc., and therein place all the Roots in Beds or Rows, about half an inch asunder, which will preserve them very moist throughout the whole Winter."

John Perfect, writing in 1730, indicated that commercial cultivation of licorice in Pomfret had been carried on for some years: "about seven Years ago all the Liquorice at *Pomfret* was monopolised and engrossed by a Set of Merchants, etc. But the Engrossers, by sending too great a Quantity together, found to their Cost, that it heated and smoaked like a Hay-Reek put up too green." According to J.P., two acres of land "within the tope of the castle [were] imployed in the Propogation of this noble, useful Plant" and one of those acres yielded "five hundred Stone Weight . . . in one crop: Which must be accounted a very good advantage for in three Years it amounts to eighty seven Pounds ten Shillings; which is little less than thirty Pounds *per* Acre, one Year with another." In Pomfret at that time, there were fifty acres of cultivated licorice, called Liquorice Garths, "many of them small Apartments, which entitle the Possessors to as many Votes for Members of Parliament, as they are possessed of those small Parcels of Land." The number of plants to the acre was 80,000 to 96,000. The account concludes with "P.S. Our Liquorice Garths take up so many Hands, at the Time of Year (the lifting season) that there are scarce any Labourers to be got, at any Rate, for other Works."

The making of "Spanish," or Spanish licorice, was in full progress in the town of Pomfret in the eighteenth century. The juice of the licorice root was boiled in an iron pot to a black substance, which, on cooling, was pressed into little "Liquorice Cakes" and stamped with a pattern "resembling the ancient Castle of that Town, now in ruin." These Pontefract cakes are manufactured even now as a specialty of the town and, often, still sold in Britain in the familiar black and green tin box, which was commonplace in British sweet-shops prior to the 1939–1945 war.

In 1813, Farey wrote in *General View of the Agriculture of Derbyshire* that licorice was not cultivated in that county, but that he had seen it grown commercially at Bardsey, East-Regton, East-Keswick, Collingham, and on the north side of the River Wharf in Yorkshire. He recalled: "As I rode by the Liquorice fields at Pontefract I was struck by their resemblance to a nursery of young Ash plants, when about two or three feet high." Later in the nineteenth century, the acreage under cultivation with licorice in England seems generally to have diminished, so that the Reverend V. H. Moyle (a member of the Council of Swanley Horticultural College) writing about commercial herb cultivation in 1892 says of licorice:

> the expense incurred in its cultivation renders it not a very remunerative crop . . . The crop is usually lifted in the end of the third season after planting, and the labour and expense incurred in this work are great and therefore the growers seldom lift liquorice themselves but sell it as it stands, leaving the purchaser to harvest it.

If the growing of large crops of certain herbs was at times unprofitable, what of the many herbs, like elderflower and comfrey, which were needed for the making of physic but never in quantities that would induce the commercial herb grower to cultivate them? These were gathered by the herb "simplers," who went about Britain a century or more ago, collecting many plants from the wild, in season, and selling their harvest to the herbalist who, in turn, sold the dried herbs to the druggists or to the public. These simplers were the inheritors of the former "green men" whose itinerant trade in Britain is still sometimes marked by inn signs such as "The Green Man" or "The Green Man and Still."

Of the lesser herb crops, chamomile was grown in Surrey and in Derbyshire, *Daphne mezereum* (mezereon) in Kent and Hampshire, coriander and saffron in Essex—all for the confectioners', distillers', and druggists' trades. Rhubarb was a specialized crop, but a considerable amount was cultivated in the Banbury area, in a region bordering Northamptonshire. A rhubarb merchant, William Rufus Usher, is listed in Rusher's Directories as being at Neithorp (in Oxfordshire) in 1841–1843 and from 1844–1849 at Overthorp (then in Oxfordshire, now in Northamptonshire due to a boundary change). It was to Usher that some crowns of the true official rhubarb (*R. officinalis*) were sent, about 1873, when the official rhubarb was first introduced into cultivation in Europe, but the plant that he grew commercially for medicinal purposes was *R. rhaponticum*. Apparently, "Mr Usher's rhubarb farm" was well known for many years from the 1840s to the '70s. Bentley and Trimmer, in *Medicinal Plants*, 1880, verify that "Banbury [is] the only place in England where it is cultivated for its roots and the annual yield is about ten tons." The washed roots were sliced and dried to form "fine large flats," and "fine large rounds."

Spearmint as a market crop was raised in market gardens around Fulham in London and nearby at Gunnersbury and Isleworth on dampish ground. Mr. Elliot, a market gardener of Fulham in the 1890s, had several long ranges of heated pits to force mint from autumn until the following spring, when outdoor crops became available; thus the remunerative value of the crop varied according to the severity or mildness of the winter.

Mint appears to have been grown in many areas in England for the purpose of distillation largely in very small holdings, whose siting was dependent upon accessibility to a local still. Proven wills of the eighteenth century reveal mint stills as an effect and sometimes even existing stocks of oil of peppermint. Hitchin, Hertfordshire, Long Melford, Market Deeping, Lincolnshire and Mitcham, Surrey are generally listed as having been the main commercial mint-growing acreas in England, yet by 1923 there were not more than 150 acres under cultivation at Mitcham where the acreage had once exceeded twice that amount; the average yield ranging from 20–30 lbs. of oil of peppermint per acre. In these areas, large stills were used, the crop was of comparative bulk and over as many as ten weeks distilling was carried on night and day.

Derbyshire in the north Midland of England appears to have supported several small farms or holdings cultivated physic plants; valerian in particular was grown at Milltown and Northedge in the Parish of Ashover, about five miles south east of Chesterfield.

Gradually, the economic tide began to swamp the smaller commercial enterprises. Wholesale drug companies organized their own farms and the bulk of plant material was imported into the United Kingdom; advances in science also meant that many synthetic drugs would be manufactured. One of the last physic gardens in London to distil its own medicinal preparations was that of the Clock House in Chelsea, owned by a Miss Howard, as late as 1828. The ground formed part of the ancient garden and mansion of Sir Thomas More (statesman and author of *Utopia*) whose house had become a royal residence after his death and then eventually passed into the hands of Lord Burleigh, the Earl of Beaufort, and Sir Hans Sloane. Miss Howard's distilled waters were held in very high esteem, and her patrons included many wealthy households.

Elsewhere, physic gardens still existed; crop reports, for 1913, for instance, show cultivation being carried on by the Ransoms at Hitchin, Potter and Clarke (formerly Potter and Moore) at Mitcham, Mr. Seymour at Holbeach, Norfolk, and Mr. Bing at Grove Ferry, in Kent (the two latter being exclusively cultivators of peppermint).

The decline in small holdings for the cultivation of medicinal plants must now be set against the increased cultivation of culinary herbs. The demand for parsley, sage and watercress grew to such an extent that, today, they are the three main commercially grown herb crops. Parsley and sage are produced mainly as a minor crop of market gardeners in the vicinity of good brisk markets, but watercress needs unpolluted water-beds and thrives particularly in chalk-drained water, such as that of the Lea Valley in Hertfordshire (north of London). The cultivation of watercress there began about 1860 and continues to flourish around Boxmoor, Croxley Green, and Chesham; it is sent not only to Covent Garden but to northern markets as well. In 1883, near Berkhamsted, a Mr. Bedford converted a number of ditches for the successful cultivation of watercress and used the London Midland and Scottish railway to supply northern markets.

In Hampshire, too, watercress was an important commercial crop in the latter half of the last century. It was grown in chalk-drained springs and water-beds, the oldest of which were around Andwell and Maplederwell near the sources of the river Loddon. Later, the cultivation was also established near Basing, at Ashford (near Petersfield), near the sources of the river Rother at Steep, in the valleys of the Test and Itchen at Freefolk, and in other areas where ideal conditions prevailed.

Those declining enterprises which had managed to survive up to the time of the First World War (when imports of many German and Austrian-grown drug plants ceased) experienced a short-lived resurgence of commercial interest which was fostered by E. M. Holmes, Curator of the Pharmaceutical Society of Great Britain and the Board of Agricul-

opposite Rhubarb

ture and Fisheries. Under the auspices of the Women's Farm and Garden Association, the Herb Growers' Association came into being. The cultivation of some medicinal plants was monopolized on *materia medica* farms, but both patriotism and initiative were shown by such organizations as the Evesham Smallholders' Association, which began to work along cooperative lines in 1915 and, in spite of an unfavorable growing season in 1916, earned £1,300 on eleven acres of belladonna and £150 on one and a half acres of henbane. The enthusiasm of the British Board of Agriculture for this new association appears to have fluctuated greatly, but the Herb Growers' Association soon set up its own drying sheds for herbs and began to issue monthly advisory leaflets to its members. Nevertheless, it ceased to exist in 1918.

One of the members of the Herb Growers' Association was Mrs. Maud Grieve, who had grown medicinal plants at Chalfont St. Peter in Buckinghamshire before World War I and supplied the manufacturing chemists; during the war, she issued a remarkable series of leaflets which later formed the basis of her important book, *A Modern Herbal*. Her garden at The Whins was enlarged with the assistance of Miss Ella Oswald, and much instruction about herb growing was given there, especially to women cultivators and members of the Herb Growers' Association.

The most notable British herbalists between the world wars were probably the partners, Dorothy Hewer and Margaret Brownlow, whose enterprise was called The Herb Farm, at Seal (near Sevenoaks) in Kent. Dorothy Hewer began with an acre of land in 1926 and grew lavender, peppermint, rosemary, sage, angelica, lemon balm, thyme, and marjoram; she had her own drying sheds. Her garden was to become both a commercial proposition and a teaching establishment. One of her pupils, in 1933, was Margaret Brownlow, who later returned to Seal and became Miss Hewer's partner. Miss Brownlow made a worthy name for herself as a herbalist and an authoritative writer on herbs and became managing director of The Herb Farm following Miss Hewer's death in 1948. It was only the untimely death of Margaret Brownlow herself that brought an abrupt end to the work at Seal. When her estate was being settled, the nurserymen, Laxton and Bunyard, took over the herb nursery. Some years later, in 1971, their parent company, R. J. Cuthbert of Llangollen, North Wales, sold that part of the business to Bees Nursery of Chester, and the Seal farm was included in the sale.

The cultivation of herbs in England is today carried on by capable hands on various small plots, notably at the Chiltern Herb Farm, Buckinghamshire, Stoke Lacey Herb Farm, Herefordshire, and Ashfield Herb Nursery in Shropshire. The latter was begun when Edwin and Annette Evette took over a piece of land at Hinstock near Market Drayton in 1967; it had not been farmed for a century, but curiously, the deeds, by reference to an earlier deed dated October 4, 1809, show that the land was previously owned—and no doubt cultivated—by John Nicholls, an apothecary. History repeats itself in that small hamlet, where the major part of Manor Farm, on which the herb nursery has been established, dates from the fifteenth and sixteenth centuries.

Apart from the commercial concerns of the last century which sold their produce direct to drug houses or to such markets as Covent Garden, the selling of herbs has been a part-time occupation for all but the herbalist. Gypsies and street sellers offered herbs for sale, the itinerant green man collected plants in the countryside and sold them in the towns, and street cries, especially in the cities, advertised herbs for sale. In legislation against "stalls and Nuisance" in London as early as 1631, an attempt was made to clear the streets by levying fines against street vendors such as "oyster, herb and trype women." Herb markets were organized affairs in some cities; Covent Garden was described in the eighteenth century as "a magnificent Square wherein (to its disgrace) is kept an Herb and Fruit Market, Two Charity Schools, One Meeting House, a Parish Workhouse, Two Bagnois, a Cold Bath and a Playhouse." At York, a herb market was built at the west end of the Church of All Saints Pavement about 1727. Throughout Europe, herbs have been offered for sale at fairs and in markets; they are a conveniently small commodity cheap to buy and easily carried away. Probably the last surviving herb market of fair-like proportions was that at Vilna, now Vilnyus, and at one time capital of Lithuania. It was begun by King Ladislas Jagiello in 1387, two years after his conversion to Christianity, and became an annual event, held on St. John's Day, June 24, and assembled under the ancient wall of the church of St. John. Over 125 kinds of medicinal herbs were to be found there on the day, with sellers squatting on the pavements offering wares that they might have brought from up to 100 miles away. The fair continued to be held at least until 1938.

In North America, herb growing between the seventeenth and nineteenth centuries was mainly done by the individual settler or farmer—or more specifically, by his wife. A catalog was produced in 1771 by Prince's Nurseries of Flushing, Long Island, probably the first seedsmen as such in the United States, which offered many herbs for sale.

The Quakers are important in the history of pharmaceutical development on both sides of the Atlantic. A different religious society whose members are known as Shakers emigrated to America in the eighteenth century from England. They are said to have been the first to grow medicinal plants for profit in the United States, early in the nineteenth century. Herb growing for medicinal needs became an important industry; by the 1850s, nearly 200 acres were cultivated with medicinal herbs in Quaker communities at Harvard, Massachusetts, and Mount Lebanon, New York.

Peppermint and spearmint have long been grown commercially in Michigan and New York State for flavoring chewing gum. However, the sharp changes in temperature of most areas of the North American continent have meant that herb crops were not generally an easy commercial proposition. In addition, the cost of hand labor was prohibitive in comparison with that available in Europe. It is only in recent years, when the demand for herbs has been so great and the advances in growing, harvesting, and storage techniques so rapid, that commercial herb farming has begun to expand in North America, especially in California.

Appendixes
Bibliography
Index

Appendix I

English and American Common Names

A list of the more important common names on each side of the Atlantic. For easy reference botanical names are also given. The order of the listing is based on that of Part III, "A Modern Herbal."

ENGLISH	BOTANICAL NAME	AMERICAN
aconite monkshood helmet flower old wife's hood	*Aconitum nepallus*	aconite
acorus sweet flag myrtle grass myrtle sedge cinnamon sedge sweet rush	*Acorus calamus*	sweet flag calamus root flag root
agrimony church steeples liverwort	*Agrimonia eupatoria*	tall agrimony agrimony stickweed
alecost costmary	*Tanacetum balsamita*	alecost costmary mint geranium
alexanders alexandrian parsley	*Smyrnium olusatrum*	(not known in N. America)
alkanet	*Pentaglottis sempervirens*	alkanet
allspice Californian allspice	*Calycanthus floridus* *C. occidentalis*	Carolina allspice Californian allspice
American spikenard	*Aralis racemosa*	American spikenard Indian root spignet
American sarsaparilla	*A. nudicaulis*	wild sarsaparilla false sarsaparilla
angelica	*Angelica archangelica*	angelica
arnica mountain arnica	*Arnica montana*	arnica
artemisia	*Artemisia spp.*	artemisia
wormwood waremouth absinth mongwort	*A. absinthium*	common wormwood
old man southernwood lad's love maiden's ruin	*A. abrotanum*	southernwood lad's love
mugwort	*A. vulgaris*	mugwort

ENGLISH	BOTANICAL NAME	AMERICAN
balm lemon balm	*Melissa officinalis*	lemon balm
basil sweet basil	*Ocimum basilicum*	sweet basil
bush basil	*O. minimum*	bush basil
bay sweet bay	*Laurus nobilis*	sweet bay
belladonna banewort death's herb dwale deadly dwale sleeping nightshade	*Atropa belladonna*	belladonna
bergamot monarda bee balm	*Monarda didyma*	Oswego tea bee balm indian plume fragrant balm
betony herb St Fraiid betayne wood betony bidney bishopswort wild hop	*Stachys officinalis*	betony woundwort
bistort Easter giant Easter mangiant passions snakeroot English serpent	*Polygonum bistorta*	bistort
borage bee-bread coll tankard herb of gladness	*Borago officinalis*	borage
bryony cowbind cow's lick felon berry hedge grape snake berry tetter berry wild wood vine	*Brionia diocia*	bryony
burdock, great	*Arctium lappa*	cockle-bur beggar's buttons cuckoo button clot-bur
burnet	*Sanguisorba officinalis*	burnet
American burnet	*Sanguisorba canadensis*	American great burnet
calamintha	*Calamintha ascendens* *(C. officinalis)*	
caper spurge milk weed	*Euphorbia lathyris*	caper spurge

ENGLISH	BOTANICAL NAME	AMERICAN
caraway	*Carum carvi*	caraway
carnation	*Dianthus caryophyllus*	carnation
catmint catnep	*Nepeta cataria*	catnip
celandine, lesser pilewort	*Ranunculus ficaria*	
celandine, greater swallow-wort killwart wartflower wartweed wretweed	*Chelidonium majus*	greater celandine swallow-wort
centaury banwort bloodwort bitter herb hurd-reve sanctuary	*Centaurium minus*	
chamomile	*Anthemis nobilis*	chamomile bowman
cherry wild cherry gean	*Prunus* spp.	cherry
chervil	*Anthriscus cerefolium*	chervil
chicory bunk monk's beard	*Cicorium intybus*	chicory blue daisy coffee weed
chives	*Allium schoenoprasum*	chives
cinquefoil	*Potentilla reptans*	
clary	*Salvia horminium*	(no common name)
clary sage Christ's eye clear eye	*Salvia sclarea*	clary sage
clematis	*Clematis vitalba*	clematis
coltsfoot hoofs tushy lucky gowan dummy weed coughwort	*Tussilago farfara*	coltsfoot
comfrey knitbone boneset consound	*Symphytum officinale*	common comfrey knitbone
coriander Chinese parsley	*Coriandrum sativum*	coriander
corn salad lamb's lettuce	*Valerianella locusta*	corn salad

ENGLISH	BOTANICAL NAME	AMERICAN
cotton lavender lavender cotton	*Santolina chamaecyparissus*	lavender cotton grey santolina
cow parsley	*Anthriscus sylvestris*	
cowslip Our Lady's bunch of keys St Peter's keys culverkeys galligaskins herb paraysy paigle palsywort St Peterwort	*Primula veris*	cowslip
cumin	*Cumium cyminum*	cumin
curry plant	*Helichrysum angustifolium*	curry plant
dandelion blowball peasant's clock cankerwort crow parsnip Irish daisy doon-head-clock fortune teller one o'clocks swine's snout	*Taraxacum officinale*	common dandelion blowball lion's tooth peasant's clock
Daphne mezereon	*Daphne mezereum*	Daphne
Spurge laurel wood laurel dwarf bay fox poison	*D. laureola*	spurge laurel
dill	*Anethum graveolens*	dill
elder elderberry eldern ellan elnorne ellen tree bour tree boretice bore husselwood	*Sambucus nigra*	(known as European elder but does not occur in U.S.A.)
elecampane scabwort horse heal	*Inula helenium*	elecampane horse heal yellow starwort
erygium eryngio sea holly	*Eryngium maritimum*	eryngo sea holly
fennel	*Foeniculum officinale*	fennel
fenugreek	*Trigonella foenum-graecum*	fenugreek
feverfew	*Chrysanthemum parthenium*	feverfew

ENGLISH	BOTANICAL NAME	AMERICAN
foxglove fox fingers lady's thimble pop glove witches' fingers witches' bells bluidy man's fingers foxes gleow	*Digitalis purpurea*	foxglove
fritillary snake's head fritillary chequered daffodil chequered lily guinea-hen flower	*Fritillaria meleagris*	fritillaria
garlic	*Allium sativum*	garlic
gentian yellow gentian bitterwort baldmoney	*Gentiana lutea*	yellow gentian
geranium	*Geranium* spp.	
goat's rue	*Galega officinalis*	goat's rue
good King Henry Lincolnshire spinach Lincolnshire asparagus	*Chenopodium bonus-henricus*	good King Henry
ground ivy alehoof hayhoof tun hoof gill ale Gill-by-the-ground Gill hen hedge maids Lizzie-by-the-hedge	*Glechoma hederacea*	ground ivy Gill-over-the-ground field balm creeping Charlie
hellebore Christmas rose	*Hellebore niger*	Christmas rose
hemlock herba benedicta herb bennet St Bennet's herb bad man's oatmeal bunk heck-how hummock cambuck kricksies	*Conium maculatum*	poison hemlock
hemp agrimony	*Eupatorium cannabinum* *E. purpureum*	hemp agrimony Jose-pye weed purple boneset trumpet weed purple throughwort gravel root kidney root
henbane loaves of bread chenile henbell stinking Roger belene bruisewort	*Hyoscyamus niger*	henbane

ENGLISH	BOTANICAL NAME	AMERICAN
horehound, black	*Ballota nigra*	black horehound
horehound, white	*Marrubium vulgare*	common horehound
horse radish	*Armoracia rusticana*	horse radish
hound's tongue gipsy flower rose noble dog's tongue	*Cynoglossum officinale*	hound's tongue gipsy flower
houseleek hen-and-chickens huslock Jupiter's beard sungreen jubarb jobarbe imbreke	*Sempervivum tectorum*	houseleek hen-and-chickens
hyssop	*Hyssopus officinalis*	hyssop
indigo	*Indegofera tinctoria*	indigo
iris, yellow flag flagons Jacob's sword laister	*Iris pseudacorus*	yellow flag
jasmine	*Jasminum officinale*	jasmine
jewel weed	*Impatiens capensis*	spotted touch-me-not snapweed silver cap
balsam	*Impatiens glandulifera* syn *I. roylei*	(does not occur in the U.S.A.)
juniper	*Juniperus communis*	juniper hack matack horse savin
lady's mantle	*Alchemilla vulgaris*	lady's mantle
lavender	*Lavendula officinalis*	lavender
licorice liquorice	*Glycyrrhiza glabra*	licorice
lily-of-the-valley	*Convallaria majalis*	lily-of-the-valley
lime lime tree	*Tilea* spp.	lime lime tree
lovage	*Ligusticum officinale*	lovage
lungwort Jerusalem cowslip soldiers and sailors Adam and Eve Mary's milk drops	*Pulmonaria officinalis*	lungwort
madder dyer's madder	*Rubia tinctorum*	madder
mallow	*Malva sylvestris*	mallow

ENGLISH	BOTANICAL NAME	AMERICAN
mallow, marsh	*Althaea officinalis*	English mallow
musk mallow	*Malva moschata*	musk mallow
marigold pot marigold Mary buds gold of ruddes	*Calendula officinalis*	pot marigold
marjoram	*Origanum majorana*	sweet marjoram
meadowsweet	*Filipendula ulmaria*	meadowsweet Queen of the meadow my lady's Bett
Queen of the prairie	*F. rubra*	Queen of the prairie
melilot	*Melilotus officinalis*	melilot
mignonette	*Reseda odorata*	common mignonette
dyers' rocket weld	*R. luteola*	dyers' rocket yellow weed weld
mint water mint	*Mentha aquatica*	water mint fish mint apple mint
corn mint	*Mentha arvensis*	corn mint
Japanese mint	*M. arvensis piperascens*	Japanese mint
horse mint	*Mentha longifolia*	horse mint
peppermint	*Mentha* X *piperita*	peppermint
eau de cologne mint bergamot mint pineapple mint lemon mint	*M.* X *piperita citrata*	orange mint bergamot mint
white peppermint	*M.* X *piperita officinalis*	
black peppermint	*M.* X *piperita vulgaris*	black peppermint
pennyroyal	*Mentha pulegium*	English pennyroyal
spearmint spiremint green lamb mint Our Lady's mint	*Mentha spicata*	spear mint
round-leaved mint apple mint woolly mint monks herb	*Mentha suaveolens* and hybrids	pineapple mint (when variegated)
Bowles' mint	*M. spicata* x *suaveolens*	Bowles' mint
mullein Jacob's staff Jupiter's staff Peter's staff shepherd's staff candelwick plant blanket weed beggar's blanket felwort fluffweed old man's flannel	*Verbascum thapsus*	great mullein velvet plant flannel plant mullein dock common mullein Aaron's rod

ENGLISH	BOTANICAL NAME	AMERICAN
Aaron's rod	*V. nigrum*	garden mullein
Myrtle	*Myrtus communis*	Myrtle
nasturtium	*Tropaeolum majus*	nasturtium
nettle stinging nettle	*Urtica dioica*	stinging nettle
nipplewort	*Lapsana communis*	nipplewort
onion	*Allium cepa*	onion
Welsh onion	*A. fistulosum*	Welsh onion
ramsons hog's garlick stink plant	*A. ursinum*	(does not occur in U.S.A.)
parsley	*Petroselinum crispum*	parsley
pasque flower	*Pulsatilla vulgaris*	
pelargonium	*Pelargonium* spp.	pelargonium
pellitory of the wall wallwort parietary paletin Billie beatie lichwort	*Parietaria diffusa* (syn *P. officinalis*)	
periwinkle scorcerer's violet	*Vinca* spp.	common periwinkle running Myrtle
poppy cock rose redweed headache corn poppy	*Papaver rhoeas*	poppy corn poppy
opium poppy	*P. somniferum*	opium poppy poppy seed poppy
purslane	*Portulaca oleracea*	purslane
pyrethrum	*Pyrethrum coccineum*	pyrethrum
rhubarb	*Rheum officinale*	rhubarb
rose	*Rosa gallica officinalis*	rose
Rosemary	*Rosmarinus officinalis*	Rosemary
rue	*Ruta graveolens*	rue
saffron	*Crocus sativus*	saffron
sage	*Salvia officinalis*	sage
samphire crestmarine sea fennel pierce stone rock samphire	*Crithmum maritimum*	samphire
savory	*Satureia* spp.	savory

ENGLISH	BOTANICAL NAME	AMERICAN
self-heal all-heal hook heal brunella herb carpenter London bottles brown wort	*Prunella vulgaris*	all-heal self-heal heart of the earth brunella (rarely) blue curls
soapwort bouncing Bet fuller's herb crow soap latherwort bruisewort	*Saponaria officinalis*	soapwort bouncing Bet fuller's herb wild sweet William hedge pink old man's pink
Solomon's seal	*Polygonatum multiflorum*	Solomon's seal
sorrel French sorrel cuckoo meat cuckoo sorrow sour sud	*Rumex acetosa*	French sorrel
sometimes as French sorrel	*R. scutatus*	garden sorrel
St John's wort	*Hypericum perforatum*	St John's wort
sunflower	*Helianthus annuus*	sunflower
sweet Cicely sweet fern British myrrh	*Myrrhis odorata*	
tansy buttons bitter buttons	*Tanacetum vulgare*	tansy
tarragon estragon French tarragon dragon's herb dragon's mugwort	*Artemisia dracunculus*	French tarragon
Russian tarragon	*A. dracunculoides*	Russian tarragon
thistle	*Carduus benedictus*	thistle
holy thistle St Benedict's thistle	*Silybum marianum*	
thorn apple stramonium devil's apple devil's trumpet	*Datura stramonium*	thorn apple stramonium Jamestown weed jimson weed
thyme lemon thyme German thyme winter thyme	*Thymus* X *citriodorus*	thyme lemon thyme golden-edged thyme
English thyme wild thyme mother's thyme	*Thymus serpyllum*	creeping thyme mother of thyme
common thyme black thyme garden thyme	*Thymyus vulgaris*	French thyme English thyme

ENGLISH	BOTANICAL NAME	AMERICAN
tobacco	*Nicotiana tabacum*	tobacco
valerian phu phew phew plant	*Valeriana officinalis*	garden heliotrope valerian
veratrum American white hellebore false hellebore green hellebore	*Veratrum viride*	American white hellebore itch weed green hellebore false hellebore
verbena lemon verbena	*Lippia citriodora*	lemon verbena
vervain herb of the cross holy vervain pigeon's meat	*Verbena officinalis*	European vervain simpler's joy herb of the cross pigeon grass berbine
violet sweet violet apple leaf bairn wort blaver banwort Bessy blanwood vilip	*Viola odorata*	English violet sweet violet March violet
wall germander wood germander wood sage	*Teucrium chamaedrys*	germander
	T. canadense	American germander
watercress well cress water grass broffin cress water crashes teng-tongue	*Nasturtium officinale*	watercress
willow herb rosebay fireweed	*Chamaenerion angustifolium*	great willow herb spiked willow herb fireweed
wintergreen partridge berry Canada tea tea berry	*Gaultheria procumbens*	wintergreen mountain tea ground tea tea berry spice berry checker-berry
witch hazel	*Hammamelis virginiana*	witch hazel
woodruff sweet woodruff	*Asperula odorata*	sweet woodruff
yarrow nosebleed devil's nettle sneezewort old man's pepper	*Achillea millefolium*	yarrow nosebleed milfoil

Appendix II

Common Names in Five Languages

As in Appendix I, botanical names are also given for ease of reference, and the order of the listing is based on that of Part III, "A Modern Herbal."

ENGLISH	BOTANICAL NAME	FRENCH
aconite	*Aconitum napellus*	aconite napel
acorus	*Acorus calamus*	acore
agrimony	*Agrimonia eupatoria*	agrimoine soubeirette
alecost	*Tanecetum balsamita* (syn. *Chrysanthemum balsamita*)	herbe Sainte-Marie tanaisie balsamite
alexanders	*Smyrnium olusatrum*	maceron
alkanet	*Pentaglottis sempervirens* (syn. *Anchusa sempervirens*)	orcanète bugloss
allspice	*Calycanthus floridus*	arbre Pompadour
American spikenard	*Aralia racemosa*	
angelica	*Angelica archangelica*	angélique
arnica	*Arnica montana*	aronique tabac des Vosges
artemisia	*Artemisia* spp.	absinthe armoise
balm	*Melissa officinalis*	mélisse
basil	*Ocimum basilicum*	basilic
bay	*Laurus nobilis*	baie
belladonna	*Atropa belladonna*	belladone
bergamot	*Monarda didyma*	bergamote
betony	*Stachys officinalis*	épiaire bétoine
bistort	*Polygonum bistorta*	bistorte
borage	*Borago officinalis*	bourrache
bryony, white	*Bryonia dioica*	bryone blanche
burdock, great	*Arctium lappa*	
burnet	*Sanguisorba* spp.	pimprenelle
calamint, common	*Calamintha ascendens*	
caper spurge	*Euphorbia lathyris*	catapuce
caraway	*Carum carvi*	carvi
carnation	*Dianthus caryophyllus*	oeillet
catmint	*Nepeta cataria*	herbe aux chats cataire
celandine	*chelidonium majus*	le grand éclaire

GERMAN	SPANISH	ITALIAN
Eisenhut	aconito	aconito
Kalmus	calamo	acoro aromatico
kleiner Odermennig	agrimonia	agrimonia
Alecost		tanaceto balsamatico
Smyrnerkraut	esmirnio	macerone
Ochsensunge	alcama lengua	alcanna
Gewürzstrauch	calicanto	calicanto
Angelika Engelwurz	angélica	angelica
Bergwohlverleih Arnika	árnica tabaco de montana	arnica tabacco di montagna
Absinth	alcachofa arcacil	carciofo
Melisse	balsamita	balsamo
Basilienkraut	albahaca alabega	basilico
Lorbeer	laurel	lauro
Belladonna Tollkirsche	belladonna belladama	belladonna
Bergamottenbaum	bergamota bergamoto	bergamotta
Betonika	betónica	bettonica
Wiesenknöterich	bistorta dragúnculo	bistorta
Borretsch	borraja	borragina borrana
Zaunrübe		brionia bianca
Pimpernell	pimpinella	pimpinella
	calamento	calaminta
Springwolfsmilch	tartago	catapuzia
Kümmel	alcaravea carvi	carvi
Nelke	claveles	garofano
Katzenminze	menta de gato	nepeta erba dei gatti
Schellkraut	celidonia	celidonia

ENGLISH	BOTANICAL NAME	FRENCH
celandine, lesser	*Ranunculus ficaria*	ficaire éclairette
centaury	*Centaurium minus*	centaurée
chamomile	*Anthemis nobilis*	camomille romaine
cherry	*Prunus* spp.	cerise
chervil	*Anthriscus cerefolium*	cerfeuil
chicory	*Cichorium intybus*	chicorée
chives	*Allium schoenoprasum*	ciboulette
cinquefoil	*Potentilla reptans*	quintefeuille
clary	*Salvia horminum* *Salvia sclarea*	vigne blanche toute-bonne sauge sclarée
clematis	*Clematis vitalba*	
coltsfoot	*Tussilago farfara*	tussilage
comfrey	*Symphytum officinale*	consoude
coriander	*Coriandrum sativum*	coriandre
corn salad	*Valerianella locusta*	mâche
cotton lavender	*Santolina chamaecyparissus*	santoline
cow parsley	*Anthriscus sylvestris*	cerfeuil sauvage
cowslip	*Primula veris*	primevère commune fleur de coucou primerolle brayette
cumin	*Cumium cyminum*	cumin
curry plant	*Helychrysum angustifolium*	
dandelion, common	*Taraxacum officinale*	pissenlit
Daphne	*Daphne mezereum*	Daphné
dill	*Anethum graveolens*	aneth fenouil bâtard fenouil puant
elder	*Sambucus nigra*	sureau
elecampane	*Inula helenium*	aunée
eryngium	*Eryngium maritimum*	panicant marin
fennel	*Foeniculum officinale*	fenouil
fenugreek	*Trigonella foenum-graecum*	fénugrec
feverfew	*Chrysanthemum parthenium*	matricaire pyrexie pyrèthe
foxglove	*Digitalis purpurea*	digitale
fritillary	*Fritillaria meleagris*	damier fritillaire
garlic	*Allium sativum*	ails
gentian	*Gentiana lutea*	gentiane

GERMAN	SPANISH	ITALIAN
Feigwurz		ranunculo ficario
Flockenblume	centaura	centaurea
Kamille	manzanilla camomila	camomila
Kirsche	cereza	ciliegia
Kerbel	perifollo	cerfoglio
Zichorie	achicoris	cicoria
Schnittlauch	cebollino cebolleta	cipollina
Fünf-fingerkraut Fingerkraut	quinquefolio cincoenflama	cinquefoglio pentafillo
Muskatsalvee Schlarlachkraut	salvia chiarella maggiore	salvia scearea erba scanderone
Waldrebe	clemátide	clemàtide
Huflattich	fárfara	farfaro
Schwarzurz	consuelda	consolida
Koriander	cilantro	coriandolo
Ackersalat	macha valerianella	valerianella
Buschzypress	santolina	santolina
Weisenkerbel		cerfoglio salvatico
Petersblume Schlusselprimel	primula vellorita	primaverina
Kreuzkümmel	comino	cumino
Löwenzahn	diente de león amargón	dente di leone radicciella radicchièlla
Seidelbast	Dafne	Dafne
Dill	eneldo	anito
Holunderbeer	saúco	sambuco
Alant Alantwurzel	énula	enula campana
Krausdistel Maerwortel		eringo marino
Fenchel Schwarzkümmel	hinojo	finocchio
Bockshornklee	alhoula	fieno greco
chrysanthème	matricaria piretro	camomilla matricaria
Fingerhut	digitalis dedalera	digitale
Schachbrettblume	fritilaria	fritillaria
Knoblauch	ajo	aglio
Enzian	genciana	genziana

ENGLISH	BOTANICAL NAME	FRENCH
geranium	*Geranium* spp.	géranium
goat's rue	*Galega officinalis*	faux indigo sanfoin d'Espagne
good King Henry	*Chenopodium bonus-henricus*	chénopode bon-Henri
ground ivy	*Glechoma hederacea*	lierre terrestre
Hellebore	*Helleborus niger*	ellébore
hemlock	*Conium maculatum*	cigue
hemp agrimony	*Eupatorium cannabinum*	chanvrine
henbane	*Hyoscyamus niger*	jusquiame
horehound, black	*Ballota nigra*	marrube noir
horehound, white	*marrubium vulgare*	marrube blanc
horse-radish	*Cochlearia rusticana*	raifort
hound's-tongue	*Cynoglossum officinale*	langue de chien
houseleek	*Sempervivum tectorum*	joubarbe
hyssop	*Hyssopus officinalis*	hysope
indigo	*Indigofera tinctoria*	indigotier
iris faux-acore	*Iris* spp.	iris
jasmin	*Jasminum officinale*	jasmine
impatiente n'y touchez pas	*Impatiens* spp.	jewel-weed
genièvre	*Juniperus communis*	juniper
alchemille	*Alchemilla vulgaris*	lady's-mantle
lavender	*Lavendula officinalis*	lavande spic
licorice	*Glycyrrhiza glabra*	réglisse
lily-of-the-valley	*Convallaria majalis*	muguet
lime	*Tilia* spp.	tilleul
lovage	*Ligusticum officinale*	livèche
lung-wort	*Pulmonaria officinalis*	pulmonaire
madder	*Rubia tinctorum*	garance
mallow	*Malva* spp.	mauve sauvage
mallow, marsh	*Althea officinalis*	guimauve officinale
marigold	*Calendula officinalis*	souci
marjoram	*Origanum* spp.	marjolaine
meadowsweet	*Filipendula ulmaria*	reine des prés
melilot	*Melilotus officinalis*	mélilot
mignonette	*Reseda odorata*	réséda
milkwort	*Polygala* spp.	polygala laitier

GERMAN	SPANISH	ITALIAN
Storchschnabel	geranio	geranio
Geisklee	ruda cabruna	capraria
armer Heinrich		bono Enrico
Gundermann	hiedra terrestre	edera terrestre
Nieswurz	eléboro	elleboro
Schierling	cicuta	cicuta
Abkraut		eupatorio
Bilsenkraut		jusquiamo nero
schwarze Bulte		marrubio nero
weisse Andorn	marrubio	marrubio comune
Meerettich	rábano picante o rústico	rafano
Hundeszunge	cinoglosa langua de perro	cinoglossa
Hauswurz Dachwurz	sempreviva hierba puntera	barba di giove
Ysop	hisopo	issopo
Indigo	indigo	indaco indigofera
Schwertlilie	flor de lis	iride
Jasmin	jazmin	gelsomino
Camellienbalsamine		
Wacholder	enebro	ginepro
Mantelsinan	alquímila pie de león	alchemilla comune
Lavendel	lavándula espliego	lavanda spiganardo
Lakritze	ozozura	liquirizia
Lilienconvallen Maiglöckchen	muguete lirio de los valles	mughetto lacrima della madonna
Linde	lima	tiglio
Liebstöckel	ligústico	ligustico
Lungenkraut	pulmonaria	polmonaria
Krapp	rubia	robbia
Malve Apothekersstockmalve	malva	malva malvavisco
Dotterblume Ringelblume	cálendula flamenquilla	calendula fiorrancia
Marjoran	megorana orégano	maggiorana
Spiräe	ulmaria barbe de cabra	spirea
Meliloten	melilot trébol dulce	melilito
Resede	reseda	reseda
Milchkraut		erba da latte

ENGLISH	BOTANICAL NAME	FRENCH
mint	*Mentha* spp.	menthe
mullein	*Verbascum thapsus*	molène bouillon blanc
myrtle	*Myrtus communis*	myrte
nasturtium	*Tropaeolum majus*	capucine
nettle, stinging	*Urtica dioica*	ortie
nipplewort	*Lapsana communis*	lampsane
onion	*Allium* spp.	oignon
parsley	*Petroselinum crispum*	persil
pasque flower	*Pulsatilla vulgaris*	fleur de pâques pulsatille
pelargonium	*Pelargonium* spp.	pelargonium
pellitory	*Parietaria diffusa* (syn. *P. officinalis*)	épinard de murailles
periwinkle	*Vinca* spp.	pervenche
poppy	*Papaver* spp.	pavot coquelicot
purslane	*Portulaca oleracea*	pourpier
pyrethrum	*Pyrethrum coccineum*	pyrèthre
rhubarb	*Rheum officinale*	rhubarbe
rose	*Rosa* spp.	rose églantier odorant
Rosemary	*Rosmarinus officinalis*	romarin
rue	*Ruta graveolens*	rue
saffron	*Crocus sativus*	safran
sage	*Salvia officinalis*	sauge
samphire, rock	*Crithmum maritimum*	chrête marine herbe de St. Pierre
thistle	*Silybum marianum* *Carduus benedictus*	chardon
thorn apple	*Datura stramonium*	pomme épineuse stramonie
thyme	*Thymus* spp.	thym serpolet
tobacco plant	*Nicotiana tabacum*	tabac
valerian	*Valeriana officinalis*	valériane
veratrum	*Veratrum viride*	hellébore blanc
verbena, lemon	*Lippia citriodora*	citronnelle
vervain	*Verbena officinalis*	verveine
violet	*Viola odorata*	violette
wall germander	*Teucrium chamaedrys*	chêneau
watercress	*Nasturtium officinale*	cresson de fontaine

GERMAN	SPANISH	ITALIAN
Minze	menta	menta
Wollkraut	verbasco gordolobo	verbasco
Myrtle	mirto	mirra
Kapuzinerkresse	capuchina nasturcia	nasturzio
Nessel	ortiga	ortica
Niplewurz		lampsano
Zwiebel	cebolla	cipolla
Petersilie	perejil	prezzemolo
Osterblume Küchenschelle	anémone	anemone
Pelargonie	pelargonio	pelargonio
Glaswurz		
Immergrün Singrün	pervancha pervinca	pervinca
Mohn Schlafmohn	adormidera amapola	papavero
Burgelkraut	verdolaga	portulaca porcellana
Pyrethrum	piretro	piretro
Rhabarber		rubarbaro
Rose wilde Rose	rosa escarmujo olorosso agavanzo	rosa rosa selvatica
Rosmarin	Rosmarino Romero	Rosmarino
Raute	ruda trago amargo	ruta
Safrangewürz	azafrando	zafferano
Salbei	salvia	salvia
Meerfenchel	hinojo marino	finocchio marino
Distel	cardo	cardo
Stechapfel	estramonio	stramonio pomo spinosa
Thymian	serpoleto tomillo	serpillo timo
Tobakpflanze	tabaco	tabacco
Baldrian	valeriana	valeriana
grüne Nieswurz		veladro
Eisenkraut	verbena	verbena
Eisenkraut	verbena	verbena
Veilchen	violeta	violetta mammola
Batenikel Berggamander	pinillo maro	germandria
Brunnenkresse	berro	crescione di fonte

ENGLISH	BOTANICAL NAME	FRENCH
willow herb	*Chamaenerion angustifolium*	épilobe saulaie
wintergreen	*Gaultheria procumbens*	gauthérie couchée
savory	*Satureja* spp.	sarriette
seaweed	*various*	algue
self-heal	*Prunella vulgaris*	brunelle
soapwort	*Saponaria officinalis*	saponaire
Solomon's seal	*Polygonatum* spp.	sceau de Salomon
sorrel	*Rumex acetosa*	oseille
St. John's wort	*Hypericum* spp.	mille-pertuis perforé
sunflower	*Helianthus annuus*	soleil tournesol
sweet Cicely	*Myrrhis odorata*	cerfeuil musqué
tansy	*Tanacetum vulgare*	tanaisie herbe aux vers
tarragon	*Artemisia dracunculus*	estragon
witch hazel	*Hammamelis virginiana*	hamamélide
woodruff, sweet	*Asperula odorata*	aspérule odorante
yarrow	*Achillea millefolium*	millefeuilles herbe aux charpentiers

GERMAN	SPANISH	ITALIAN
Weiderich		lauro roseo
Wintergrün		tè di montagne
Bohnenkraut	ajedrea	savore
Algen	alga	alga
Brunellen	sanícula	brunella
Seifenkraut	saponaria jabonera	saponaria
Salomonssiegel	sello de Salomón	sigillo di Salomone
Sauerampfer	acedera	acetosa
Johanneskraut	hipérico	erba di san Giovanni
Sonnenblume Sonnenkraut	helianto	girasole
spanische Süssdolde	perifollo	seseli
Rainfarn Gänserich	tanaceto balsamita minor	tanaceto
Estragon	tarragon estragón	tarragone dragoncello
Zaubernuss	hamamelis	hamamelis
Waldmeier		raspello odoroso
Schafgarbe	milenrama	millefoglie

Bibliography

ARBER, Agnes	*Herbals, their Origin and Evolution*	1912
ANESTY, Esther B.	*The Delectable Past*	1965
AVAY et FONDIN	*Santé et Beauté par les Plantes*	1968
BLANCHAN, Neltje	*Nature's Garden*	1927
BLUNT, W.	*The Art of Botanical Illustration*	1950
BOCKÉE FLINT, Martha	*A Garden of Simples*	1900
Botanical Magazine		
BRITTEN & TRIMMER	*Medicinal Plants*	1880
BROTHWELL, D. and P.	*Food in Antiquity*	1969
BROWNLOW, Margaret E.	*Herbs and the Fragrant Garden*	1957
CAMPBELL, R.	*The London Tradesman*	1747
Chemist & Druggist		
CHURCHILL, W. S.	*A History of the English Speaking Peoples*	1956
CLAPHAM, TUTIN & WARBURG	*Flora of the British Isles*	1952
COATS, Alice M.	*Flowers and their Histories*	1956
COLES, W.	*The Art of Simpling*	1656
CROW, W. B.	*The Occult Properties of Herbs*	1969
CULPEPER, N.	*The English Physician*	numerous editions
DAVID, Elizabeth	*Spices, Salt & Aromatics in the English Kitchen*	1970
DOWSETT, C. F. (Ed.)	*Land, its Attractions and Riches*	1892
EVELYN, J.	*Acetaria, a Discourse on Sallets*	1699
GERARD, J.	*Herball*	1597
GEUTER, Maria	*Herbs in Nutrition*	1962
GRIEVE, Mrs. M.	*A Modern Herbal*	1932
GRIEVE, M.	*Culinary Herbs and Condiments* (Dover Edition)	1961
HADFIELD, M.	*A History of British Gardening*	1969
HENRY, S.	*American Medical Family Herbal*	1814
HEWER and SANECKI	*Practical Herb Growing*	1969
HILL, J.	*Family Herbal*	*c.* 1770
HORWOOD, A. R.	*British Wild Flowers in their Natural Haunts*	1919
JEFFERS, R. H.	*The Friends of John Gerard*	1967
Journal of the Agricultural Society		
Journal of the Pharmaceutical Society		
Journal of the Royal Horticultural Society		
KALM, P.	*Account of a Visit to England*	1748
KREIG, Margaret B.	*Green Medicine*	1965
LAW, D.	*Herb Growing for Health*	1969

LANGLEY, B.	*New Principles of Gardening*	1727
LEIGHTON, Anne	*Early English Gardens in New England*	1970
LEYEL, Mrs. C. F.	arrangement of Culpeper's *English Physician and Complete Herbal*	1961
	The Culpeper's House Herbals:	
	The Truth about Herbs	
	Compassionate Herbs	
	Hearts Ease	
	Herbal Delights	
	Cinquefoil	
	Elixirs of Life	
	Picture Cook Book	1958
MACLEOD, Dawn	*A Book of Herbs*	1968
McDONALD, D.	*Sweet Scented Flowers and Fragrant Leaves*	1895
Marshall Cavendish Encyclopedia of Gardening		1968–9
MEAD, W. R.	*Pehr Kalm in the Chilterns*	1962
MEADE FAULKNER, J.	*History of Oxfordshire*	1899
PETULENGRO, L.	*The Roots of Health*	1968
PRATT, Anne	*Haunts of Wild Flowers*	1892
ROHDE, Eleanor Sinclair	*Herbs and Herb Gardening*	
	A Garden of Herbs	
RIMMEL, E.	*Book of Perfumes*	1864
Sanders Encyclopaedia of Gardening (ed. A. G. L. Hellyer)		1964 edition
SANECKI, Kay N.	*Wild and Garden Herbs*	1956
	Discovering Herbs	1970
STOBART, T.	*Herbs, Spices and Flavourings*	1971
SUZANNE, A.	*A Book of Salads; the Art of Salad Dressing*	1914
TEETGEN, Ada B.	*Profitable Herb Growing*	1919
UPHOF, J. C. Th.	*Dictionary of Economic Plants*	1968
Victoria County Histories		
WHITTLE, T.	*Plant Hunters*	1970

Index

Sweet Sultan

Scullcap

Orache

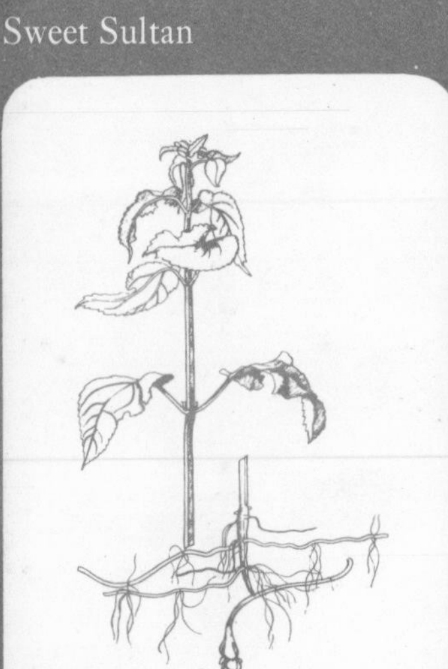

Artichoke

Thistle

Woad

Caper Spurge

ASTRONOMY TODAY

QUEEN MARY
AND WESTFIELD COLLEGE
UNIVERSITY OF LONDON